In Memory Of

Fiona Brown

1958 -2018

Who made books work

Please take heed

UNDER no circumstances should medical advice from the 1950s be followed today. It could well be dangerous. The world of medicine has changed immeasurably, with new research, new drugs, more learning, and old ideas disproved. The information doctors give in the 21st Century will be at odds with the older advice — as is proved several times by the comments from our modern doctor.

You cannot rely on opinions that are more than 60 years old. Do not follow any of the old remedies in this book. If you are ill, or suspect you are ill, see your own doctor and take heed of what he or she tells you.

Some of the 1950s ideas wouldn't work anyway. You won't get much benefit from tying a sock round your throat, or turning sideways-on to an electric fire (instead of facing it).

However

THERE is also good advice in these pages. There is common sense, if a little old-fashioned, and words of genuine wisdom that would remain true no matter what era they are from. It will pay you to look after your feet, to not get stressed, and to make sure you look after your wife (or husband). And "warm feet, cool head" is a pretty good recipe for being comfortable in bed.

Of course you will have to exercise judgment and common sense of your own to pick and choose between the bizarre, the dangerous, and the useful.

And

SOCIAL attitudes, levels of equality, and virtually all the world in all its various ways, have changed since the 1950s. Research into the effects of smoking was in its infancy. We knew much less about strokes and cancer. Understanding of mental illness was far behind what it is today.

Things were different. People were different.

It is unfair to judge patients or doctors, men or women, attitudes or ideas, through the long lens of history. We don't own time machines to go back and inform our parents and grandparents of what is, and is not, acceptable today. Please extend a little tolerance and a little understanding to the 1950s ideas, language and degree of medical knowledge on these pages.

No doubt, in 70 years' time, people will look back and marvel at how quaintly old-fashioned and ignorant we were.

Steve Finan

The Doc Replies

Medical wisdom from the 1950s Sunday Post

ISBN 978-1-84535-733-7

Published by DC Thomson Media 2019

Edited & Internal Design by Steve Finan
Cover Design by Chris Hudson.

For any further info, contact Steve Finan

sfinan@dctmedia.co.uk

This book was first published in Great Britain in 2019 by DC Thomson Media, Meadowside, Dundee, Scotland, DD1 9QJ.

Thanks to . . .

Maggie Anderson, Craig Houston, Richard Prest, David Powell, Barry Sullivan, Raymond Barr, Chris Hudson, Deirdre Vincent, Nikki Fleming, Jacqui Hunter, Sylwia Jackowska, Gill Martin, Susan Heron, Dawn Donaghey, Denise West, James Kirk, Kirsten Morrison, Kay Burness, Bill & Chris Nicoll, Fraser T. Ogilvie.

And heartfelt thanks and sympathies for the suffering, curiosity, and ability to contract interesting ailments of Sunday Post readers.

Special thanks to . . .
Dr Lynda Morton, MBChB.

In compiling a book of 1950s medical articles, it was imperative to seek a modern expert's view to explain, balance and (in many cases) refute some of the advice from the 1950s. It needed a 21st Century GP to cast an eye over the material.

But then, if modern advice was needed, why not get some that came with wit, personality and character?

Which led me to Doctor Lynda Morton.

Lynda is a hockey-playing, Vespa-riding, sailing enthusiast, and also a highly-respected, opinionated, and engaging working GP. She is revered by her patients. She has personality, says what she thinks and, all in all . . . is something of a force of nature!

And she brought her understanding, wisdom and enthusiasm to this project. Her contributions give this book a huge lift. She provides funny, insightful and incisive modern comment on every chapter.

I am thankful that she agreed to work on this book, it would have been a much less successful venture without her.

My special thanks for: **THE MODERN VIEW, BY DR LYNDA**

Steve Finan

Contents

Contents

— Chapter 1 —

Only In The 1950s

THIS is a good place to start. When reading the articles in this chapter, you will realise that the 1950s were very different to today.

Very different indeed, and in several ways.

For a start, the Doc of those days didn't have the benefit of the years of scientific research between then and now, and he didn't care if he sounded just a trifle sexist, and he wasn't at all squeamish about telling you how quickly you'd die — depending on the job you had.

The article describing jobs a husband shouldn't let his wife do is a good example of how gender roles and attitudes have changed. Indeed, you wouldn't be able to fully understand just how much, and in what ways, things have changed if you didn't know what the world used to be like.

The smoking article, which lists the many and varied benefits of the habit, is a good example of the strides that have been made in medicine.

The warning over the dangers of getting too enthusiastic about the end of sugar rationing is social history.

The world is a different place now.

So, as you'll have to recognise throughout this book, it would be unfair to make judgments on 1950s attitudes with 21st-Century standards of behaviour in mind. The past is a foreign country, its standards and customs are not ours.

Please read carefully, please be tolerant, please allow for the passage of time.

Jobs A Husband Should Never Let His Wife Do

December 17, 1950

TWO of my women patients are the same age (in their early fifties) and in similar circumstances. But you wouldn't think so to look at them.

One has a worn-out appearance. The other is always fresh and young-like.

What's the secret of No 2's youthfulness?

A good part of it, I'm sure, is due to her husband.

If he can help it, he never allows her to do jobs in the house that a man should do.

It's the heavy jobs that wear out a woman more than anything. They certainly cause most of the chronic backaches and tiredness I see in my waiting room, because a woman's frame isn't made to cope with them.

A man's is.

For example, it's the man who should lift the sofa nearer to the fire.

His lower back is straighter and that makes him better fitted to make a straight lift.

At the worst, he may pull a muscle, but a woman can easily suffer a serious internal injury.

A man, too, has the knack of setting his feet for a lift. Women are more often flat-footed, and don't have the same balance or spring.

For these same two reasons – a more curved back and flatter feet – a woman is handicapped if carrying something heavy upstairs.

Let hubby do it.

He has the further advantage of being more able to transfer his weight from one step to another.

The man should wash the outside of windows.

It's not only a strain on the back, but the job usually needs a head for heights – and the average woman hasn't got that.

The man should also work the wringer. Nothing tires a woman so much.

But the man has stronger back muscles and much broader shoulders, so that when one shoulder goes forward he has a lot more purchase and can apply a lot more power.

Breadth of shoulder combined with longer arms is a useful combination, too, when the mattress has to be turned. One swing from a man and the job's done. Most women have to do it in several panting stages.

Many women struggle and strain to open jars with screw-tops or stoppers. They shouldn't. They don't have the necessary strength in fingers and wrists.

A man's hands are bigger and his grip is half as strong again. That also makes him handier with a tin opener. So pass over such jobs to the man of the house.

One job I'd like to see men tackle is – beating a cake mixture in a bowl.

Women may smile, but a man can do this better and quicker. He has a stronger grip and stronger wrists and back muscles. He can even grip the bowl better between his knees, because he's less likely to be knock-kneed than his wife!

Other daily jobs a wife should leave to her husband include carrying buckets of coal and beating rugs.

He has the chest muscles to lift the bucket without strain, and the shoulder-swing that beating requires.

Even such a small thing as winding the clock should be the man's job. His stronger fingers give him a better "feel" of the winding, and he's less likely to overwind.

I never like to see a woman manhandling a pram down a flight of stairs.

As the wheels roll down from step to step, the strain is on the small of the back. And better a man's back than a woman's.

In addition, mothers with young babies risk giving themselves a serious internal injury.

Finally, if little Tommy requires a licking, then it's his father's job to do it.

If Tommy struggles, his mother isn't physically or even emotionally fit to deal with him. In fact, when corporal punishment is needed, mother should leave the room altogether.

Some of this advice may surprise some husbands.

But if they take it in, then they'll find their wives will benefit in two ways.

Their physical health will be better, and the feeling of partnership will make all the difference in the world to their morale.

Even the best washing machine can only do part of the job!

look for the name ACME on the wringer

THE MODERN VIEW, BY DR LYNDA

OH my goodness! This made the hairs on the back of my neck stand on end. There is absolutely no medical basis for any of this article!

Apart from men being bigger, physically, than women and good at lifting heavy things, this is hilarious. I'd love to see my other half fighting with a wringer or turning a mattress. It's funny enough to see the pair of us changing the king-sized duvet cover together!

He does indeed move the sofa closer to the TV, but only because he won't admit he needs glasses to see the puck on the ice hockey game. And, thanks to rubber jar-opener grippers, I'm sure I'll continue to manage bottle tops myself.

Fortunately, buckets of coal and rug-beating are things of the past, and clock winding has also been phased out in the digital age. So if technology continues to advance then perhaps we will be able to do away with men altogether... especially if they're caught giving little Tommy a licking.

Seriously, though, modern society and technology have seen the traditional male/female roles changing. A woman's experience of life has changed greatly from the traditional role of mother and housekeeper. Women have moved into every area of modern life, from business to the social sphere and beyond.

Female evolution, from a repressed, dominated housewife to confident managerial professional in today's society, started in World War 1, when they had to fill traditional men's roles and continued to do so after the men returned.

When this was repeated in World War 2, women had been given a taste for freedom and power and things would never be the same again. The Suffragette movement, which had begun a hundred years ago, had eventually prevailed.

In the 1950s, as you have just read, there was still an air of conservatism and dominance in the male world. But things were changing and although they still embraced the traditional roles, more and more women infiltrated the traditional male bastions of business and society in general.

Men's roles have changed too. Traditionally they went out to work, taking responsibility for providing for the family, while the wife kept the home and nurtured the children.

Nowadays, the stay-at-home dad and working mum is common, and often both parents have to work to meet the desire to own a house and maintain the standard of living they desire.

Society is still changing. Same-sex relationships and marriages, and children brought up in homes with complex relationships are not uncommon — all of which creates different stresses and pressures. Who knows what the next 70 years will bring.

I wonder what the 1950s Doc would have made of it all? I'm pretty certain he would have disapproved.

There's a Lot Of Bunkum Talked About Smoking

February 22, 1953

SEVENTEEN million people in Britain are cigarette smokers. Three million are pipe smokers. Every day the average smoker gets through 12 cigarettes or 4 oz. of pipe tobacco. The big question is, then, "are we smoking too much for the good of our health?"

I'd say this. Cigarette smokers — no. Pipe smokers — Yes!

There's a lot of nonsense talked about the evils of smoking. Moderate smoking does NOT cause T.B. It doesn't even spoil our wind for the ordinary calls of everyday life.

What about cancer of the lung? Well, every one of us has the risk of it, and smokers increase the risk by one-tenth!

It's true smoking may take the keener edge off our fitness. And it's true there's enough nicotine in one cigar to kill two people, and enough in five cigarettes to kill one person—if it were taken in its pure form.

But the amount of nicotine a moderate smoker takes in does little harm! If it's at all possible, doctors never ask a patient to cut out tobacco — only to cut it down.

Nicotine is a queer kind of poison. The amount we actually take into our system from five cigarettes is so minute the "poison" does us good!

First to benefit is the circulation. A cigarette improves the heart action. After the smoke the heartbeat drops back with no ill-effect.

But too much tobacco and the heart action falls below its normal rate. That's the danger!

If the heart is inclined to race away when you're excited, a cigarette has a steadying effect. It also induces deeper breathing.

Tobacco also helps the digestion. It increases the flow of juices. For this reason a man who smokes after a meal gets a definite benefit.

He's getting the juices to work, and he's sitting still. That extra ten minutes of sitting down is one of the most valuable helps to a good stomach there is! Not only that. You're less likely to be constipated with a cigarette after a meal.

But it's unwise to smoke in place of a meal or on an empty stomach. The digestive juices have nothing to work on and eat into the stomach lining.

In cold weather, smoking actually warms the body by improving the surface circulation.

Smokers don't get colds or flu so often — because they get rid of phlegm more easily.

A cigarette or pipe at the right time can be extremely good for the nerves. It's a godsend in calming emotion or quieting nerves after an accident. For this reason it's good for shy folk.

Even watching smoke has a soothing effect. Smoke in the dark and you lose half the benefit!

Excessive smoking — more than 15 cigarettes a day — goes for the nerves, lungs, and heart.

We all want to get the best out of tobacco. It's easy — one hour's interval between cigarettes. Three or four hours between pipe-fills.

Smoke slowly — that's important. You get less nicotine into the system.

What if you want to cut out tobacco altogether? Best way is to try just after a cold or flu.

Don't be disheartened if you fail. Eighty per cent of givers-up start again after a week. Ten per cent after a month.

For the remaining ten per cent, the craving is still there after a year — however slight!

Your health will not, on the whole, be remarkably different if you cut out smoking.

But there's one danger. You may eat too much because your sense of taste and smell does improve!

**Whatever the pleasure
Player's complete it**

Dos And Don'ts If You're Ever In A Motor Car Smash

June 1, 1958

HAVE you ever asked yourself this question? How would I behave if I was ever in a nasty motor accident?

Would I panic and do all the wrong things?

From my experience, the chances are you might.

First of all, nobody gets off scot-free in an accident. Everybody, no matter how strong or tough, suffers from shock.

The brain gets a jarring against the skull. The nervous system is to some degree out of order through sheer fright. Even if the shock is only slight, it dulls our judgment.

So, seconds after an accident, you're just not yourself.

Even so, it's well worth knowing the answers to these questions that are bound to flash through your mind:—

There's Mr Smith lying at the roadside.

Should I try to bring him round with a drink?

You daren't give an unconscious person anything to drink. The tea is liable to go down the wrong way— into the lungs. Even a quarter cupful of tea could literally drown him.

But if Mr Smith is able to sit up and swallow, then hot, sweet tea is excellent.

How about brandy or whisky?

When the victim looks as if he needs whisky to put the colour back into his cheeks — that's just the time you mustn't give it.

After any accident, there's always the risk of a haemorrhage. Of course, Mr Smith may have no cuts showing, but there could be bleeding inside.

And your whisky could increase the bleeding — and may even kill him.

Should I prop up the badly injured?

Definitely—NO. Leave them lying flat. Loosen round the neck, throw a coat round their legs. That's all.

The danger is that the neck—or even the spine — may be partially broken. If you move the injured man, you may complete the break.

What if someone is only dazed?

It depends on the colour of their face. Being dazed and pale isn't a good sign, even if they're apparently uninjured.

Get them to sit by the roadside, or, better still, to lie flat.

The chances are one in five there's concussion. The skull could be fractured. Being kept still may well save a life.

Should I get a lift for the injured?

By all means stop a passing car. But don't ask the driver to take the injured to hospital.

Instead, ask him to go and bring a doctor. You can do untold harm by rushing anybody to hospital.

A car can be awkward for a fit person to get into — let alone someone who may be badly injured.

Is there a right way to pull an accident victim clear of a crash?

If you must move the injured, look carefully at the legs and arms. If one appears to be twisted, it's possibly broken.

So concentrate on keeping that limb extended. The idea is to prevent the broken edges overlapping and perhaps piercing the flesh.

How do I deal with a passenger who's hysterical?

Get her away from the scene of the accident. Slapping the face isn't the answer. Set her to do something—look after a child, for instance.

What if someone's bleeding badly?

You don't need to be an expert to stop bleeding. Press firmly on the spot.

This'll give you an idea of how hard. Put a finger on your own pulse. Increase the pressure until the pulse beat is almost stopped. That's the right pressure to put on the wound.

If the wound is big, tie a scarf or soft belt above it.

Don't tie too tight. You don't even need to stop the bleeding. Just enough to slow it down.

Keep the tourniquet on for five minutes at a time—but no longer. You can do untold damage unless you let the tourniquet off for 30 seconds every five minutes.

What if one of the passengers has pain when he breathes?

You can take it his ribs are cracked or bruised. Don't strap up the ribs. Instead, put his arm in a sling.

In that way his own arm eases the strain on the ribs with 100 per cent safety.

It's Worse Than Any Bite Or Sting

July 20, 1958

OUCH! You're stung in the arm by a wasp. Your arm swells up. It throbs. And you start thinking the worst, don't you?

You remember reading somewhere of a holidaymaker who died after a sting.

Well, forget it. You've more chance of winning £200,000 in the football pool than dying from that sting.

A sting can harm you in two ways.

No. 1 — from the actual poison injected into you. One in 10,000 people is very sensitive to that poison. If there's a weakness in your family to hay fever, asthma, nettle rash or strawberry rash, a sting will upset you more than is usual.

The effect of the sting also depends on how the wasp was feeling at the time!

A wasp lands on your arm and you brush it off. It stings instinctively. But that's not half so bad as the sting of a very angry wasp.

If, for example, you try to swat a wasp in the kitchen, up goes its dander. Its poison is far stronger.

It's the same with bees. A sting from a bee on a flower is nothing compared to a sting from a bee disturbed near a hive. This bee has a stronger poison. And gives a bigger dose, too!

So make it a rule on holiday — never swat a wasp, or bee.

If you are the kind of person who reacts badly to a sting, you can get tablets from the doctor to take with you on holiday. They're wonderfully effective.

You hear tales of people stung on the throat, or tongue, and then they choke to death by the swelling. That's extremely rare. All the same, keep your mouth closed when wasps are around.

There's little else you can do about a sting.

The puncture is tiny and self-sealing. You can't get at the poison. A hankie wrung out in cold water and fixed over the sting is as good a remedy as anything.

But, for goodness sake, keep your fingernail off the sting mark. That's danger No. 2.

It's scratching that brings on the alarming symptoms of blood poisoning.

It's bad enough to scratch a sting, but ten times worse to scratch a bite — particularly a cleg bite.

The cleg (horse-fly or gadfly) is the lad to watch. He feeds around cattle and horses. He's not particular where he goes.

So if you scratch a cleg bite, you risk blood poisoning. The scratch drives germs (not poison) into the tissues.

If a germ gets into the blood stream it can be serious, particularly when you're run down.

If yellow fluid starts oozing from the bite (say on the arm) it's local poisoning. Swelling, throbbing, redness are alarming, yet they're telling you the local defences are doing their job.

But here are the symptoms you can't ignore: Red streaks going up the arm. A tired, dull ache all over. Headache. Phone the doctor right away. It looks like blood poisoning.

But even a cleg bite isn't nearly so dangerous as a prick from a thorn. Roses, bramble bushes, spiny hedges — thorn pricks from these cause far more blood poisoning, and even death.

You see, a thorn point is coarse compared to a sting. It goes 20 times deeper into the tissues.

It's far thicker than a sting. The point is liable to break off and remain under the flesh. And the "wound" is kept open.

There's also more chance of the thorn stabbing into a vein. Then any germ getting in simply runs round the system, multiplying as it goes.

So don't treat thorn pricks lightly. Dab the area with methylated spirits. Sterilise a needle (over a match flame) and get out the point of the thorn at all costs. Don't worry if the needle becomes black with carbon from the flame. That's a good sign.

A thorn prick needs bathing with hot water. And keep an eye on it for at least two days.

Above all, remember — no scratching.

Please Be Sensible With The Sugar
September 6, 1953

NOW, right away, don't think I'm a killjoy. But when sugar comes off the ration at the end of the month please don't overdo it!

Always keep in mind this fact. The body could do without sugar.

Taken in moderation, sugar can give you extra energy within ten minutes. It can also give you warmth. One sugared drink can keep you warm on a cold night for over an hour.

But take too much and you're liable to land yourself eventually with "sugar poisoning".

You'll feel wabbit and mentally dulled. You'll lose your appetite and have a blown-up feeling. And you'll probably put on a lot of fat!

Sugar goes directly to the bloodstream for use as energy and for heat.

What can't be used is stored in the liver. Too much in the "sugar bank" is a strain on the liver.

Eventually the liver gets rid of it, and it goes into fat. That's why a sweet-tooth person is so often liverish and overweight.

One warning that you're overdoing the sugar is a sudden horrible sour taste in the mouth.

Cane or beet sugar, the kind that comes in the ration, is very quick to ferment.

So too much can definitely harm the digestion. It can cause chronic flatulence. Folk who should be particularly careful about "sugar poisoning" are over-sixties who are fat, and people who are bothered with flatulence. Also those with a pimply skin.

I can see an awful lot of us taking sugar in our porridge now. That isn't good for us. As I've said, sugar goes straight into use in the body. So if the body gets too much, it thinks it's quite satisfied, and has less interest in the food that follows.

How much is too much?

Well, it's often not so much the amount eaten, as the time at which it's taken.

If you're about to do a big job, you can take a lot of sugar. A housewife on washday will get a lot of benefit out of a sweet drink before she gets over the washtub.

Then another sweet drink in about an hour, in fact, every hour! But in the afternoon, while sitting reading a book, these two drinks would be too much!

It might take the edge off her vitality for the rest of the day.

Coffee in the morning? If you're working you can take two, or even three teaspoonfuls of sugar. But at night one is enough.

Coffee after a mid-day meal is a good idea. And make it fairly sweet. The sugar helps tremendously in the digestion of the fat that's "gone" before!

We all complain sometimes that fish and chips are hard on the tummy, especially at night.

Well, here's a tip: after a supper like that, eat a sweet cake or take a sugared drink. It helps digest the fat you've taken.

Mothers often worry about children taking too many sweet things.

Well, mum, you can't give children too much sugar. They need it for energy.

Next to children, probably the folk who benefit most from sugar are elderly persons who are thin. They get the energy and heat they need so much.

Best Jobs For A Grand Old Age
July 30, 1950

HAVE a look at the following list. It shows 20 of the longest-lived jobs and professions – in order of longest life.

1. **Gamekeepers**	11. **Engineers**
2. **Draughtsmen**	12. **Plumbers**
3. **Costing clerks**	13. **Engine drivers**
4. **Teachers**	14. **Postmen**
5. **Bank and insurance workers**	15. **Architects**
6. **Clergymen**	16. **Commercial travellers**
7. **Foremen**	17. **Lawyers**
8. **Farmers**	18. **Dentists**
9. **Bakers**	19. **Fishermen**
10. **Carpenters**	20. **Doctors**

Is there anything we can learn from the list – things that will help us to live a long and healthy life? Definitely yes!

Notice how the gamekeeper heads the list. He has many advantages that mean long life.

One big reason, of course, is that he comes from country stock. Most of us born of country stock live longer than a townie. It's inborn in us – due to generations of plain, wholesome food and active life without undue strain.

But another big reason is that the gamekeeper lives a natural life in the fresh air. If he has a fatiguing day, he can arrange for his next day to be a bit easier.

You rarely see a keeper rushing about. His walk is slow and steady, his temperament placid. Both these traits are among the best assets for ensuring a long life.

The gamey has another advantage. He's the master of his work – work isn't his master. He's content.

Selfish ambitions can gobble you up as quickly as anything. The drive to "get on", often at other people's expense, hardens the arteries as well as the heart.

That's one reason why you see some rapidly-successful business men die in their fifties.

This links with another secret of long life – "no matter what your income is, live within it". Half the nervous strain I meet is due to people spending that little more than they can afford.

A keeper escapes that. He isn't in the high-income group, but his needs are simple.

He's also helped by the variety of his work. He works with brain as well as muscle. He's usually a keen reader, interested in current affairs, and with plenty of opportunity to think about them. His leisure hours in his home are a fine offset to his outdoor life.

Draughtsmen, I think, are well up in the list of long-livers because they do creative work, yet are free from the worry of final responsibility.

In addition, any difficulties they meet in their work are left on the desk.

Costing clerks don't have the same advantage of creation, but their work is light, they have good conditions and can enjoy manual hobbies.

Teachers live long because they constantly associate with young people. Pupils may be trying, but there's always the stimulus of youthful interests.

From the health point of view, teachers usually come from good homes and enjoy good food when young. In their adult life they don't come into contact with the common adult infections and they enjoy long, health-giving holidays.

The clergyman's greatest asset is his faith in the future. His whole upbringing and teaching give him tolerance and sociability. He mixes with all kinds of people. He's seldom ruffled, and can usually adjust his timetable to avoid harmful rushing about.

A happy balance between brain and muscle always helps longevity. That's why engineers are high on the list.

It's also partly why foremen live longer than their men. To be a foreman, a man has usually to be outstanding mentally as well as physically. He also has to be adaptable in dealing with people.

Commercial travellers have an ideal job for health, provided they're in a reasonably good line. They're a lot in the open, and enjoy variety and freedom of movement. And they have to cultivate cheerfulness, one of the greatest assets for long life.

You may be surprised to see doctors among the long livers.

They have late hours, frequent spells of overwork and run all kinds of risks. The reason why they survive so long is that they're trained to fight infection.

Every job has something to it that tends to prolong or shorten life. If our job has more debits than credits it's no use moaning. It's up to us to cultivate the assets as much as we can.

In general, here's my formula – as much fresh air as possible. Good food as a child. Live within your means. Seek contentment. Be gracious and cheerful. Be moderate in alcohol and tobacco.

And, very important – never allow yourself to be embittered by thinking that other people are doing you down. Think well of your fellow men.

So here's a long and happy life to you!

Now Here Are The Women Who Live Longest

August 6, 1950

Why widows top the list.

I STARTED something last week when I told how a man's job affects the length of his life. I made an awful mistake – I left out the women!

My apologies, ladies. In the list below, you'll see what YOUR chances are of a long life.

1. **Widow**
2. **Housewife**
3. **Teacher**
4. **Nurse**
5. **Buyer**
6. **Heads of store departments**
7. **Parlourmaids**
8. **Tablemaids**
9. **Dressmakers**
10. **Two-job women**
11. **Spinsters**
12. **Shop assistants**
13. **Clerkesses**
14. **Typists**
15. **Cooks**
16. **Charwomen**
17. **Factory workers**

At the top of the list are widows. Why? To begin with, they're ten times more sensible about old age than men or spinsters.

Offer an old lady an arm, and she'll accept it as homage. Offer the same arm to an old man or spinster, and you'll probably get a round of the guns.

Widows stay at home more – and escape risk of accident and weather.

Unmarried women have often to go out for company. But not so the widow – folk come to her.

Widows are keenly interested in children and young people. Old age doesn't deprive them of "getting a kick out of life".

Now, what about housewives?

They, too, live longer than their unmarried sisters, especially if they have a family. To be a wife and mother is a natural fulfilment in life.

The woman who is both a wife and mother is trained to think of others. And she has less chance of getting soured in later life because of the cheery and loving company round her.

Of unmarried women, teachers are easily first as long livers. All their lives they closely associate with young people, and so are better qualified than most women to enjoy old age.

They usually have cultural interests, like books and music, and have no time to feel lonely. They have little financial worry, their hours are good and they have long holidays.

In addition, they're always boss. That gives them confidence in facing anything, even old age.

Why do nurses, whose job is very often so exacting, come so far up the list? Mainly, I think, because they're intensely interested in other people, and are trained to look after their own health.

Often they marry later in life and make ideal wives. Thus they gain a happy home life – a great asset to longevity.

In the case of heads of store departments and buyers, the main reason they live long is the feeling they've achieved something worthwhile. They exercise authority. They meet lots of people and learn how to handle them. They travel.

Result – they acquire poise and have many friends in later life.

Parlour-maids, table-maids, and women in the better domestic service jobs, such as housekeepers, are lucky too. They live a sheltered life, have few worries and aren't tempted to think too much about their own ills.

Now we come to the second half of the list.

First, two-job women – those who have to work as well as keep house. Such women are never free from worry, and it tends to increase as they grow older. They're open to hazards of outside life. They're apt to skimp meals.

And, anyway, too much rush and bustle isn't healthy for a woman after the age of 50.

Why are clerkesses and typists so far down the list? Mainly because they're forced to go on working, and they lose the comparative peace in old age which a married woman enjoys.

In addition, many working women as they grow older, become less efficient at their jobs, yet tend to domineer because of their length of service. Tempers are ruffled and they suffer. This colours their attitude to life and people, and so they're apt to suffer from too few friends and too much loneliness.

In fact, ladies, whether you're married or single, I'd say your own mental attitude is all-important. Be gracious, as a woman was meant to be. Keep young in spirit and in the company you keep.

And never be ashamed of going a burst on a new hat or a snappy frock. Anything that makes you feel good will also help you to have a long and happy life.

Simple Things We Do Wrong When We See Blood

January 9, 1955

"OH, doctor, could you come at once? Johnny's nose has started to bleed and I simply can't get it stopped." I get a phone message like this once a week.

Nose bleeding is so common. It's alarming, yes. But serious? Well, let me say right away that in 999 cases out of 1000 it's nothing to worry about.

And it's so easy to stop — if you know how.

By all means try the cold key or the cold sponge down the back. But the best way is to get two tufts of cotton wool and stick them up the nostrils.

The whole idea is not to stop the blood, but to stop the breathing through the nose. Every intake of breath through the nostrils tends to break off the blood clots which are trying to form.

Sit with the head tilted slightly back. Don't move unnecessarily.

Breathe gently through the mouth. You'll be amazed how quickly this works.

One more word — for goodness sake don't get excited. That makes the blood gush out stronger than ever.

Excitement is the worst thing for all bleeding. Fear increases the force of the heartbeat and the rush of the blood.

Folk over fifty are particularly alarmed over a bout of nose bleeding. But unless it goes on longer than 15 minutes (or unless you have artery trouble) think of it as a safety valve.

What about bleeding from cuts?

Here again, most of us make a big mistake. With small cuts we run a cold tap on the cut. Did you know that keeps the bleeding going?

The clot isn't getting a chance to form.

This, too, will surprise you. A clean cut should NOT be washed. If you do, you're likely to wash the germs lying on the skin into the wound.

Here's the safe way. One dab of iodine, and no more. That's important, or you'll burn the wound. Cover the cut with a clean, laundered hankie if you haven't a new bandage.

A hankie is better than cotton wool that's been lying in a drawer.

Another tip — do the job yourself. You're used to your own germs. Someone else's germs are five times more vicious for your system.

In the same way, getting one of the family to tend to you will be better than if a stranger does it. You've developed some immunity from the family germs.

A cut on the head nearly always looks worse than it really is. There's more bleeding because of the fine network of muscles on the scalp.

Where there are muscles, the cut tends to gape.

If the cut is at right angles to a muscle then you'll get a lot of spilled blood. That's why it's so annoying to cut yourself shaving. The face muscles hinder natural clotting.

It's silly to keep dab-dab-dabbing at a face cut.

Simply put your finger on the cut and keep the finger pressing there for one full minute. Time yourself with a watch, because it will seem a long, long time.

No woman should ignore a cut on the face. Only on Monday a woman bumped her head on a gate and cut her brow. She thought I was fussing when I said it would need stitched.

She thought I was more than fussy still when I said I wouldn't do the stitching myself, but a surgeon should do it.

It wasn't that I couldn't do the stitching. But a surgeon can do it so well that no marks show. He has about 24 different kinds of needles to choose from, for all the different kinds of skins, shapes of cut, &c.

He uses horse hair (the finest thread) for face cuts, as well as silk, nylon, &c. And he has four separate kinds of stitching. He's an artist, and when he's finished, all trace of the cut is gone.

A cut that's much more dangerous than it looks is one across the back of the fingers. A workman was most surprised when I ordered stitching. "But doctor, it's not a big cut," he said.

"It's the tendons I'm worried about," I told him.

A small tendon had been severed and would not have grown together. The two ends of the tendon had to be stitched.

If I hadn't done this the finger would have healed on the surface, but not the tendons underneath.

Most dangerous to life are cuts in the front of the wrist and groin. Important arteries are very near the surface there.

Any time the blood comes from a cut in short spurts, then get the doctor quick. Keep pressing on the wound.

Many folk are scared of a cut between thumb and forefinger, but it isn't true that such a cut is likely to cause tetanus.

Here are two points about ordinary cuts to comfort you.

If you bleed well, your heart is in good order. And if you "clot " in two minutes and stop bleeding completely in four minutes, your blood is first-class.

Yes, Let The Potatoes Grow
March 14, 1954

THIS will make a million boys and girls cheer, I'm sure. But what I have to say is true. Its far wiser not to wash your ears — the inside of the ear, I mean.

This might surprise you but the less you wash it, the less you're likely to be afflicted with deafness in old age.

You see, every ear has a tunnel running from the "outside ear" to the all-important drum. This tunnel is only one inch to an inch and a half long.

Now, one secret of good hearing is to have the walls of the tunnel as smooth as possible.

That's why washing isn't good for the tunnel.

The drying by towel afterwards roughens the walls of the tunnel and prevents easy exit for the wax.

A famous Scots ear specialist in London always told his patients — "The only thing you should poke into your ears is the tip of your elbow." And he was right.

Mothers in particular should remember this.

In a child, this tunnel is only a third of an inch long — so there's absolutely no safety margin for poking. Better for potatoes to grow than poke your ear!

It's wax in the ear that starts folk poking. Well, you shouldn't even poke with the corner of the towel, let alone with a match!

Another silly mistake is to put in drops of peroxide. That doesn't soften the wax. It makes it as hard as a brick.

Remember, too, never blow the nose violently. You can so easily bring on temporary deafness. You can even infect the ears.

If you're bothered with wax, it's a good idea to get your ears syringed by the doc twice a year.

Before you go to the doctor, you can soften the wax yourself.

For three nights before going to bed, drop in a little fine oil — almond, olive, or castor. But the oil must be cold. You can use a warm spoon, but on no account heat the oil — that's really dangerous.

Measles, mumps, and flu — these are the danger illnesses to the ear. Children, in particular, are affected.

The complications can be not only deafness, but a dangerous illness.

And it's a shame if children are allowed to struggle on with enlarged tonsils or adenoids. These affect the ears.

Some parents are stubborn about this. Yet it can mean partial deafness all the time — and trouble with the ears will often explain why some children are backward at school. They can't learn simply because they can't hear properly.

You can test your family's hearing very simply. Hold a wrist watch of good make near the ear. If the tick can be heard at arms' length, the hearing is very good. One foot away, normal. And we all should hear the tick two inches away.

Another test is even simpler. Without eating anything take a swallow. Your ear muscles are in good shape if you "hear" or "feel" a sort of plop at either ear.

When you have a pain in the ear you must use nothing but glycerine. And be sure to put it in cold.

None of this cotton wool stuffed into the ears. A clean, folded hankie laid over the whole ear, then a hot bag. That's best and safest.

Lots of folk blame swimming baths for "bad" ears. And do you know why? Jumping into the water!

This is bad. It drives the water up the nostrils. If you must jump in, then hold the nose when you do it.

Tell wee Johnnie about this right now.

Some people get along with no apparent harm, although they have a chronic running ear.

But this can be dangerous. Anybody with a running ear is below par.

I had a patient at the beginning of the year who'd tholed such an ear for twenty years. And yet I cured the trouble in a fortnight.

The credit wasn't mine. We now have a comparatively new drug that works wonders!

What about noises in the ear?

In most cases there's no need to worry. They do no harm. And, really, doctors can do nothing about "noises," like singing, whistling, blowing, or even throb!

Such noises are common when we get into our early sixties.

A last word — never hit anybody, even your worst enemy, on the ear. Even a moderate blow can split the delicate eardrum at the end of the tunnel.

No, There's No Need To Undergo An Operation Now

August 27, 1950

A WOMAN in my surgery last week had ear trouble. She dreaded the thought of going into hospital.

Then I gave her the good news that she didn't need an operation. She could hardly believe me.

That woman is one of the lucky ones. Ten years ago she'd have had to go through a painful mastoid operation.

Now injections through the opening in the ear will clear up the trouble.

Of five people who'd have had to have operations for all kinds of ailments in the 1930s, only one need face the knife today. New drugs, new treatments, have made all the difference.

We can thank the last war for that. It brought great developments in medicine.

People who benefit most are the aged, those with weak hearts, those who are bloodless or highly strung. They're spared the ordeal of the operation and long convalescence.

Treatment can often be done at home. That's a big advantage, because a strange bed and strange surroundings can have a bad effect on morale.

Many of the new cures are also ideal for children. They don't have to carry disfiguring scars for the rest of their lives.

What are the ailments we can tackle by these new methods?

Varicose veins used to require a biggish operation. The patient was "bedded" for at least a fortnight. Now the doctor gives an injection and the patient can walk about the next day.

Cysts and piles are in the same category. Only in stubborn cases is a small operation, plus the new treatment, needed.

Gland operations used to be responsible for many people going about with scarred necks. M. & B.* has changed all that, and with our modern knowledge of artificial sunlight and drugs, injections and vitamins, only one patient in ten with disobedient glands need have an operation.

Tonsils often start gland trouble. That's one reason 50 per cent of children used to have their tonsils out.

Now only about 15 per cent need have the operation. "Dirty" tonsils can be cleaned up and kept healthy for all time.

Pneumonia and pleurisy are a fairly common combination. It's apt to cause an abscess round the lung.

The 1930 way was to take a piece of rib out to get at the abscess. The lung took a year to expand again. Dressings were painful. The patient was ill for about three months.

Today, the cure may take only six to eight weeks. M. & B. and penicillin clear up the lung, or it can be drained through a tiny hole.

Not long ago a laddie came to me with a bone disease in the leg. Ten years ago he'd have needed an operation to save his leg.

Fortunately I got at the trouble early, and the new drugs worked wonders. He won't even have the limp that often followed an operation.

Slight deformities in babies, such as knock-knees or bandy legs, and even club feet, can be put right by massage, plaster, electrical treatment – one of them or a combination.

One of the trickiest operations was for a squint. Even if the squint was very slight, a complete cure couldn't be guaranteed. Yet it used to be the only hope.

Not now. By giving the child glasses when he's still tiny, and making him do recently-developed eye exercises, the squint can be overcome.

Once, every case of appendicitis meant an operation. Now, unless very acute, an appendix can be quietened so that there's no fear of major trouble developing.

Even in minor ailments, like small abscesses, boils, carbuncles, quinsy, whitlows, &c., the lance is no longer the only cure. Sulpha drugs control the inflammation before the pus forms. There's no waiting in misery for an abscess to "get right".

Some people think doctors are only too ready to suggest an operation.

Don't believe it. With so many new cures to help us, we never call in the surgeon unless it's absolutely necessary.

*M. & B. (often referred to as M&B 693) was an early antibacterial drug, produced by British chemical firm May & Baker. It is no longer used to treat humans, but still has a use in veterinary medicine.

Here's One Thing We Should All Do Ten Times A Day

May 30, 1954

WE should all be on top of the world in this good weather. But already there are folk complaining of what I call summer fatigue.

It's rather like the symptoms of low blood pressure. Tired, sluggish yet restless, and a bit depressed. The pity is that, in certain circumstances, it can last all summer.

Well, this may shock Mrs Housewife — but in three-quarters of the cases she's the one to blame.

For often, summer fatigue is nothing more than mild chronic food poisoning brought on by an unsuspected lack of cleanliness.

Food poisoning is the biggest danger we've to fight in summer. And it's the housewife who has to do the fighting. The germ centre is in the kitchen. That's where they multiply. You've simply got to "spring clean" that kitchen once a day! The shelves, the sink, the drain.

You see, the sun and hot weather kill most germs. But this is one group that simply thrives on heat — the germs that are swallowed.

And for some reason they're able to live in the tummy.

Here's a test. Are you bothered with flies?

If you are, the fault is yours. Your kitchen, your sink, even your dustbin aren't as clean as they should be. Or there's debris of old food lying in some corner.

For let me tell you, flies do not travel long distances. These are your own flies — or possibly your neighbours'.

Don't keep milk more than a day. It's the most-easily contaminated food there is.

The germs I've mentioned are harmless in small numbers — but they thrive and multiply in milk.

Milk that's gone "off" can so easily cause gastritis and enteritis. It used to be thought sour milk was good for you. That's NOT true! The only safe way to use sour milk is in scone making, where the germs are killed.

Before you do any baking or food preparing, one wipe of the table with a damp, clean cloth is no bother and very wise.

Next, every one of us should wash our hands ten times a day.

And, listen to me well, the housewife should always do this before she starts to make a meal.

When mother goes to the jam shelf and discovers grey mould on top, she blames the covers or possibly the lack of ventilation. But this often isn't the whole story. Mouldy jam is proof that there is uncleanliness somewhere.

Either the fruit wasn't washed enough, the pan wasn't clean — or mother's hands weren't quite clean at jam-making time.

In fact, jam is sometimes the reason for indigestion — all caused by uncleanliness at the time of making

So this season, ladies, make a really clean job of it!

Now we all dread polio. We don't know what starts it. But this we do know:

(1) It's passed on by dirty hands.

(2) It's carried on the feet of flies.

If we all washed our hands ten times a day, and carried on a war against flies, polio could be cut down.

Altogether there are three musts in washing—

(1) Your hands.

(2) Your feet.

(3) The back of your neck.

In nearly every case of ingrowing toenails and aching and swollen feet the cause is not enough soap and water.

Ingrowing toenails are often caused by dirt which has been allowed to accumulate under the centre of the nail, so curving it upwards and the edges inwards.

The back of the neck is an easily chafed area. Pimples and boils can start here. A clean neck all the time will save you this.

And why not brush the neck of your jacket or costume? Don't have dirt round there.

Yes, cleanliness will definitely make a big difference to everyone's summer.

10 cigarettes a day might be good for your nerves

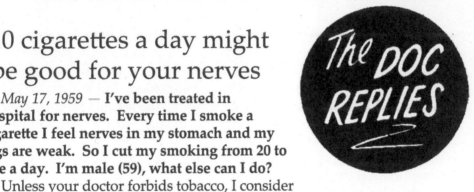

May 17, 1959 — **I've been treated in hospital for nerves. Every time I smoke a cigarette I feel nerves in my stomach and my legs are weak. So I cut my smoking from 20 to five a day. I'm male (59), what else can I do?**

Unless your doctor forbids tobacco, I consider under 10 a day might be good for your nerves. Try to arrange a quiet holiday in the country or on the moors with a pleasant companion.

January 11, 1953 — **I've been smoking for about a month. But lately it makes me feel dizzy. What's the cause? I'm 15.**

Nicotine poisoning. Cut it out entirely for at least three years.

October 18, 1953 — **Can excessive cigarette smoking cause flatulence and dizziness?**

Yes. It produces chronic gastritis, resulting in (among other things) flatulence and occasional vertigo.

May 24, 1959 — **Can a person who started to take epileptic fits at 48 go on till they are 60? Does smoking do harm?**

Such fits can be controlled by suitable medicines taken regularly. But they cannot be cured, in the strict sense of the word. In moderation, smoking is unlikely to affect them one way or the other.

April 9, 1950 — **Is smoking dangerous to a person who has a heart condition caused by rheumatic fever?**

Yes, smoking tends to speed up the heart. The extra strain isn't good for a damaged heart.

June 19, 1957 — **For years I've tried to stop smoking as it makes me extremely nervous. My hands shake when I lift anything. I've tried every "stop smoking" method I've read of, but I get fits of depression after about three days and am forced to smoke. What do you suggest?**

Keep trying and with determination you'll succeed. Some people find it easier to cut down by one cigarette every second day, until none at all is smoked. Personally, I think this is prolonging the agony. Chewing gum will help you to keep your resolution if you make a clean break.

June 21, 1953 — **I'm a heavy smoker, but never inhale. Is this type of smoking harmful?**

To a lesser degree than if you did inhale. How harmful depends on many factors – age, time of smoking, type of smoking, &c.

July 12, 1953 — **Although I recently stopped smoking, my phlegm is almost black. Could this indicate chest trouble?**

No. It's due to the amount of soot and smoke in the atmosphere you breathe.

March 9, 1952 — **I'm 16 and started smoking. My mother says it's a hindrance to health. How does it affect health when you've just started?**

Some of the commoner results can be a cough, acid indigestion and rapid heart. Don't start for another year at least.

March 11, 1951 — **I have been told over-smoking shortens a man's life. Is this the case?**

Yes. Over-smoking has a long-term effect in poisoning the system. It also quickens the action of the heart, and over a long period this can be harmful. For an office worker, even 10 cigarettes a day might be too many. But a man who is outdoors most of the day may be able to smoke 20 with no ill effects.

May 14, 1950 — **Children seem to be growing more quickly than ever these days. Boys are bigger than their fathers at age 14 or 15. Is this altogether a good thing? Are they not taking too much out of themselves?**

So long as they realise they aren't quite men, despite their long trousers at 14 and 15, it's OK. But they must realise they need a lot of strength just for growing, and shouldn't start smoking, drinking, or late hours. No boy should smoke before 18 — if he must smoke at all.

December 24, 1950 — **I am very fond of sweet things — cakes, sweets &c. Will smoking help me to cut these out?**

I certainly don't advise you to smoke for that reason. Sweet things will normally do you a lot more good than smoking. If you've to cut down sweet things for some special reason, try to do it by exercising self-control.

May 6, 1956 — **I had thrombosis a year ago. Can smoking or taking a little spirits do me any harm? I'm 67.**

I don't think that either (in strict moderation) would harm you, but you must get the permission of your doctor before trying.

April 20, 1952 — **I've been troubled for three years with tightness in the centre of my chest, causing palpitation and irregular heart-beat. I'm 52, rather a heavy smoker. Could smoking be a contributory cause?**

Yes. Give up smoking for two months. There should be a marked improvement. If not, see your doc.

November 27, 1955 — **Is smoking injurious to the eyes from within?**

Yes, in certain cases it can produce a patchy sort of blindness.

— Chapter 2 —

How To Live Longer

SO long as your smoking is moderate — 15 a day, or so, is the recommendation here — you will come to no harm ... or so they thought in the 1950s.

This, alone, is an indicator of how much research has been done and the scale of improvement healthcare has undergone.

But the medical profession in the 1950s wasn't wrong about everything.

They well knew that being overweight and being stressed wasn't good for you. They had dire warnings on the effects of pneumonia. They gave good advice on the beneficial effects of proper rest and relaxation.

There were also sage words on the intake of vitamin tablets. The best source for vitamins, we were told, was fresh fruit and greens, milk, eggs and wholemeal products.

Maybe they weren't so daft, these 1950s folk.

And they knew that everyone, throughout history, has wanted to live longer. It is a universal desire for the most important health issue of them all.

It All Depends On How You've Been Brought Up

January 22, 1950

IT depends a great deal on how you're brought up whether –

You live to be 80; you're 5 ft. 8 in. or 6 ft. tall; you're bandy or knock-kneed; you have indigestion at 30; you have glasses at 20; you get bored stiff easily; you're a success or failure.

Yes, and dozens of other things as well.

A man of nearly 90 has just come through a rather serious illness.

He's good for some years yet. A relative of his said: "Of course he's looked after himself well all his life."

I disagreed. "It's his parents he has to thank," I said.

They brought him up properly. And that's true for all of us.

General physique, for instance.

It depends, to some extent, on inheritance – how big your father was, and so on.

But it depends mainly on foundations laid in childhood.

If you're trained in regular habits, get plenty of sleep at the proper time, fresh air, exercise, good food, and especially plenty of milk, you'll be a bigger man than your father.

Lack of sunshine and fresh air, lack of fresh vegetables, fresh food and milk, living in cramped conditions and wearing tight clothes – these are the things that lead to curved bones, bandy legs, knock knees, pigeon chests.

Later on, they mean chronic catarrh – not just in the nose, but in the stomach and bowels as well.

How's your eyesight? Not so good?

Then you almost certainly started your reading career badly.

As a child you were probably allowed to lie flat on your tummy when reading. The weight of your eyeballs dragged down the muscles of your eyes and weakened them.

You may have had a habit of writing on your knee instead of going to the table, or lying curled into an armchair to read your favourite stories.

But if you were trained to read with your head up, back supported, book 18 inches away, with natural light coming from behind, then your eyesight should still be good at 50.

Some people have chronic indigestion at 30 and 40.

It's probably due to the fact that they were allowed to gobble when they were wee.

Or they ate too much of one food – it will have been the stuff they liked, not the foods that were good for them. Their diet became unbalanced.

Many folk well on in life complain of constipation and ask for a laxative. It's likely they weren't trained in regular habits when young.

Next – high blood pressure.

Everybody knows the child who screams with rage and then sulks. When he grows up, it's an even chance he'll be depressed, nervy, excitable, irritable, jumpy, and worried. That's what causes high blood pressure.

I know men whose wives describe them as "handless" in the house. They weren't properly trained when young.

Every child should be encouraged to do things. Now is the time to start your children's good habits. They'll be thankful to you for all of their long lives.

Tidying up, washing dishes, cleaning shoes, untying knots, mending, fretwork, cooking. In later life they can turn their hands to anything – and, what's more important, with ease.

How many people nowadays are easily bored!

Often they're the children who weren't taught to make their own amusements. They had toys and games thrust on them. They were picked up and played with too often.

The happiest man today is the man who was taught discipline in his childhood, and given certain principles and beliefs as a guide to live by.

That man learned things that will last him all his life – and it'll be a long one!

THE MODERN VIEW, BY DR LYNDA

IS it nature or nurture which determines who and what you are?

Nature is mainly a genetic pre-wiring, which does influence many things, such as eye and hair colour, and the passing on of some diseases such as Huntingtons or chorea down through families. Nurture is the way our upbringing, learning and environment affects the expression of our genetic make-up.

Some genetic conditions are simple and straightforward. But others, like height and physical size, are complex. Height, for example, involves multiple gene patterns and environmental factors, which is why most people grow to be as tall as their parents.

Inheritance has about 60% influence, but height also depends on lots of other environmental factors, such as how well the mother was during pregnancy (did she smoke or drink and eat well?), poor diet in childhood, disease and poverty. That's why our average height has varied over the centuries and why, generally, those of us born in the last 100 years are about 10 cms taller, on average, than those born in the medieval years.

So the 1950s Doc wasn't too far out with his opinions on the effects of a lack of sunshine, or the benefits of fresh air, fresh food and milk and cramped conditions, and their part in determining our general physique.

However the "bandy" legs and knock knees are due to Vitamin D deficiency in the main. And pigeon chests are genetic, not due to tight-fitting clothing!

Posture during reading has nothing to do with poor eyesight (the description of the weight of the eyeballs weakening the muscles made me smile). But poor eyesight might conceivably affect your posture by squinting and the tilting of your head and leaning forward to see.

Indigestion and bowel problems are very much diet-related, but I can't see that "gobbling" as a child could give you indigestion in your 30s. But dietary habits might be moulded in youth and obesity will certainly play a part.

Blood pressure is multifactorial and not caused by sulky tantrums as a child. There are plenty mild-mannered people on anti-hypertensive treatments.

But there is a lot to be said for "training" when young. There is no doubt that habits and development in childhood gives a positive sense of self, and in turn helps to make a confident happy person who respects others. It should also allow children to discover the importance of regular exercise and activity, and learn to make healthy food choices which will last into adulthood.

These factors will have an impact on how long we live.

Positive mental attitude is well known to have a huge effect on illness and life in general.

So, in (almost) the words of William Thatcher in the movie A Knight's Tale — *"Can we change our stars and live a better life?"*

I believe we can...sometimes.

Why Women Stay Young Longer Than Men
September 10, 1950

I HAD a little smile to myself last Wednesday. A friend mentioned a woman we both know. He added, "She's about forty, I think". Now, that woman is a patient of mine – and I know she's in the middle fifties.

She's typical of many women. They've a knack of not showing their age..

Under forty a woman looks a few years younger than her age. Over forty she looks as much as ten years younger. The reverse is too often the case with men. So why are women so much better at it?

Number one reason is a gift from nature. Every woman, whether she's plump or slim, has a thin layer of fat under the skin.

This acts as a cushion which holds off wrinkles and later prevents wrinkles deepening. A man doesn't have this cushion. His face becomes lined, and these lines get far deeper than they do with women.

Women have another great natural asset – freshness. Whether she's twenty or sixty, a woman does have bloom.

And, in addition to all this, most women know how to protect the skin against the elements. No man would consider using creams and lotions.

But here's a point where men certainly do slip up. Women wash and bathe oftener, and their skin is in far better condition as a result.

Often I can tell to a few years a man's age by his hands. Not so with a woman. Her hands may be as smooth and fine at sixty as at twenty. She's taken better care of them. Oh, yes, women wash even their hands far oftener than men!

They take much better care of their hair, too. A man brushes his hair with only one purpose – to get a parting. A woman brushes to improve the sheen. She brushes it at night. How many men do?

The result is women don't lose their hair as men do. And nothing ages a man as much as baldness.

Next, women have the art of doing young things. An older woman can dress as "young" as she likes, and if skilful she gets away with it. She's a joy to behold. There's much more to it than just dress. It's this instinctive desire in a woman to look young. It gives her a young outlook – and so a young look. It's her privilege to chatter and giggle like a 19-year-old.

But a man gets all dignified after 30. Giving vent to emotions isn't done.

Men bottle up their feelings, women release them! Tears and smiles – they come quite naturally, just like a bairn's.

In many ways, women never grow up. They look forward to a dance, age irrespective. A man loses is zest for such things quite early.

Of course, it can be pleaded that men have the heavy end of the stick. They have most of the worries and hazards in life. A married woman's life is pretty much the same at 50 as at 25. If anything, life is a bit easier for her at 50.

Not so her husband. His responsibilities tend to grow. But the trouble is he often lets them get on top of him. And worry – even though he's not conscious of it – ages him, while his wife stays serene and young.

THE MODERN VIEW, BY DR LYNDA

BESIDES being the fodder for every comedian who's ever lived, there are many differences between men and women, and many reasons for this.

There are all sorts of theories, but there are genuine differences in the way the sexes have evolved and the way they employ their bodies to fulfil different roles.

But do women age at a different rate? Women have a thinner skin than men and a lower collagen density which, combined with more of a hormone called oestrogen, makes them less likely to develop wrinkles. They are also generally more "sun savvy" and more likely to use sunscreens and moisturisers in general.

After the menopause, the oestrogen levels and hormone profile change fairly dramatically and women then age at a normal rate, so it may seem they look younger than they are before this. Men, however, tend to "age" at a steady rate.

There are cultural reasons why women pay more attention to their appearance, too, though in today's society boys are definitely catching up!

Baldness is a genetic issue, so nothing to do with brushing!

There are differences in the way the brain is wired too. Men and women process info differently. Men tend to use the left side of the brain to develop language, whereas women use verbal centres in both sides of the brain and have more connections between the right and left side — which some think helps explain why women are better than men at expressing emotions.

Contrary to the 1950s Doc's assertions that men have the heavy end of the stick, being a woman, I would argue against the point that our life is pretty much the same at 50 as at 25. And it's certainly not easier!

Perhaps it's cultural. In the 1950s women tended to be stay-at-home mums and by the age of 50 their children were independent and, as often as not, elderly parents had died. Jobs were more secure and there was less financial insecurity than today.

Nowadays, women combine work and parenting just to meet the mortgage payments, and children are still likely to be at home as we have them later in life.

Elderly parents live longer and need help. And job insecurity and the threat of redundancy all have an impact. And then there is the menopause!

Life is certainly not easier for today's 50-year-old woman.

It's documented that women are the chronic "worrywarts", not men, which is probably related to hormone fluctuations. But worrying gives them an advantage when foreseeing and handling problems.

Most Of Us Can Add Five Years To Our Prime

July 29, 1951

ONE thing annoys me more than anything as I go on my rounds. It's the way I see men throwing away their most valuable asset – the prime of life.

Nowadays, with modern medical aids and conditions, a man's prime begins at 32 and should last until he's 50 at least.

Even after that there should be only a slow mellowing.

But all too often I find men beginning to lose their prime qualities at 42 – ten years too soon.

A woman's prime of life is earlier than a man's. It's normally from 25 to the early forties.

And there are dashed few women you'll find losing any years for their prime of life.

Their efforts are all concentrated to prolong it as long as possible. I've known some women to hover round forty for ten years – and get away with it!

Well, there's no reason nowadays why men shouldn't hover around fifty for the same length of time. It's up to you, fellows!

By following a few simple rules, most of us can add five years to our prime.

Not only that. After our prime definitely goes, we can slow down the process of failing faculties to an amazing degree.

The thing that makes your prime of life pass most quickly is self-poisoning.

This weakens the muscles, affects the blood, strains the organs and speeds up old age.

You'd think that when you're in your prime you need more food than ever to maintain your full powers. Not so. You've stopped growing and developing. You're at your peak.

Before that you needed food for growth AND energy. Now you need it only for energy. So don't eat big meals.

In your forties eat only three-quarters of what you ate in your thirties.

If you don't your bowels, kidneys and liver will go sluggish. The waste matter isn't disposed of as it should be. You slip away from your prime.

Next, we must remember that when we reach the middle of our prime of life – say, about 40 – we've reached the peak of our abilities.

The nearer we get to fifty the more we should change our ideas as to work, sport, income and social position.

By all means hold your position. But it's wiser not to attempt to improve it, if that demands constant intensive effort.

Be content with your abilities at 50 and you're likely to have them at 55 – and later.

That goes for your golf handicap as well as your pace of work.

But more than half the secret of a long prime is the mental attitude.

Never for one moment get it into your head that the world has passed you by.

Never say "I'm getting on, you know". Keep up with the news. Have friends of all ages. Be tolerant of younger opinion and especially new ideas.

I find that a great tendency in the mid-forties is to narrow our circle of friends. That's bad. Keep up with your friends.

And never lose pride in your appearance. Be as particular about your teeth, haircuts, polished shoes, as you were in your courting days.

Now here's a most important point.

Be as smart as you can in your walk. Keep the shoulders back. Don't allow the stride to shorten.

If you give way, your abdomen muscles get flabby. The stomach becomes less efficient in extracting the good from food. And the quality of your blood falls.

These are the real signs of a departing prime of life. Grey hairs, baldness and wrinkles don't matter a hoot.

How does worry affect your prime of life?

Now, a lot of nonsense is talked about worry. In small doses it never did anyone any harm – in fact, it sometimes does a bit of good by keeping us up to scratch.

It's when it goes on over a long period that the harm's done.

And that's a common weakness in the early fifties.

It's just a habit – and it can be broken. If it isn't, the heart is apt to suffer.

And one thing that's absolutely essential to a long prime of life is a strong heart.

How To Keep Your Face Looking Young

December 27, 1959

WE can't all be pretty or handsome. But there's something even more important that you and I can have. A face that stays young for a long time – until well into the 60s.

And here are some ways to do that. Above all, avoid chronic indigestion.

Indigestion more than anything else ages a face. The nose turns peaky or red. The eyes take on an old look.

The muscles lose their tone – and premature sagging shows up.

Number two. Don't have gaps in your teeth.

If you lose a front tooth, get it seen to right away. One or two missing back teeth can also age you far more than you'd think.

It's even worse with side teeth. Gaps there can age your face in two years.

The cheeks can't help being sucked into the gaps.

And what happens? Your face gradually becomes haggard and hollowed, as well as lined.

There are two dozen-odd muscles in the face. These gaps upset the balance of muscle power. So your face takes on an old look.

Have you dandruff?

Then you've got to be reconciled to it. Dandruff can't be cured, but it can be checked and minimised almost to nil.

And that's what you must do to keep a young face. Find a good, safe soap for you. Wash your hair every two days. Then dandruff won't be constantly irritating the skin, bringing pimples and, in the long run, thickening the skin.

A coarse skin is what we have to avoid.

Now for something I feel strongly about – the toothpaste smile.

You know the kind – where only the teeth are bared. I believe that, in time, ages a face.

When you smile, let the whole face, even the eyes, smile. To smile only with the lips upsets the face muscles.

Again, in time, the face collapses a bit. So be a natural smiler, and it'll help to keep your face young.

Water is one of your best friends, too.

Wash your face at least three times a day with hot water and a soap that's kind to your skin.

Once you've found a soap that's suitable, don't ever change it.

Always dry yourself thoroughly with a roughish towel. The face muscles go in different directions – so rub in all directions.

Your skin may not take kindly to the rough treatment at first. But watch the tone of the skin improve as you persevere.

Use water in another way. Drink two pints of it a day if you can. This helps the stomach lining and kidneys. The digestion is better. Poisons in the blood are more quickly flushed out.

So in two ways the tone of the skin benefits.

A woman who uses cosmetics sparingly will look young for far longer than the woman who "piles" it on.

Excessive cosmetics stifle the skin. Your face can't "breathe" – and the ageing look is bound to come much quicker than it need.

A patient of mine – a young woman – was most attractive in appearance about five years ago. Today she looks quite old.

The reason behind that was eyestrain. She was too vain to wear glasses. In time she developed the habit of peering – and it's made her look about ten years older.

Please don't make her mistake. Glasses don't age your looks. On the contrary, if you need glasses they'll do much to preserve your appearance as well as your eyes.

What about food?

There's no doubt about which is the best single one. It's fruit – every day – either fresh or stewed. The vitamin C contained in fruit is bound to improve your looks.

Fruit and vegetables mean you'll have fewer skin infections, eat them up and it's a plateful of youth and good looks.

If your skin tends to be oily, don't worry. Just wash oftener.

A dry skin needs more attention. To my mind, a little olive oil or lanolin at night is as good as anything. Never mind these expensive preparations.

But if you are paying out for them, what you mustn't do is to try a new preparation every other week.

Chopping and changing can ruin your looks – and bang goes your chance of keeping a young face.

Do You Get All The Good You Should Out Of The Weekend?

September 11, 1955

WE can all expect to live 20 years longer than we would have done 100 years ago.

And do you know why? Because we've more leisure. It's the best safety valve we have.

If you want to get that extra 20 years – then, believe me, a tremendous lot depends on your weekends.

Most of you have Saturday and Sunday off. Well, right away, here's the secret in a single sentence: you've got to vary the weekend.

If your Saturday has been strenuous, then your Sunday has to be a lazy day – or vice versa.

On one day take two hours' rest in bed. No longer!

No matter how many hours' sleep you've lost during the week – I don't care how much – it's a medical fact that two hours extra will make good any loss.

And the best time for these two hours is in the morning.

One point – none of this ham and egg breakfast at 8am, then sleeping it off until 11. That's no good at all.

If the stomach is working, the brain is working too, and so is the system. Not only that, but there's a bigger strain on the digestion than usual, because you're not working it off.

The ideal weekend programme is this: -

Saturday morning – lazy.
Afternoon and night – pleasure.
Sunday morning – active.
Afternoon and evening – quiet.

And it's true to say that you're only ever as young as your arteries. Unhealthy arteries are the second most common cause of premature death.

A few years ago it was thought that the causes of hardened arteries were alcohol or work, plus worry.

We've now discovered that a sluggish liver is just as harmful. And a sluggish liver is what you risk with the lazy weekend habit.

But if you MUST have a lazy weekend, the best advice I can give you is – "For goodness sake eat less at the weekend".

If you're doing less and eating more, the liver is overloaded. It can't pass on the food because the body doesn't need it for energy. And the things that suffer eventually are the arteries.

Here's another point.

If your weekends are pretty hectic, your nerves are getting no rest. Constant tension like this is a factor in developing high blood pressure.

It's a funny thing, but an all-pleasure weekend brings worry and bad temper.

It's also the reason why so many folk hate Monday, and start the week hating or fearing their work.

You'll recognise the signs quite easily.

Strange aches, buzzing in the ears and sometimes passing bouts of light-headedness.

In your 40s this brings on worry. In your 60s it can kill!

So, if you have any say in the matter, don't let the young ones over-develop the busy weekend.

One splendid way to have a long life and good health is to exercise the "other half" of the brain.

You see, depending on our job, most of us use one half more than the other. The office worker uses the top half of the brain. The labourer uses the bottom half.

The top half deals with pure thinking. The lower half with automatic or semi-automatic action.

Let's look at Mr A.

He's a business executive with plenty of worry through the week. At the weekend, however, he potters about the garden. He's toning up the lower part of his brain.

At the same time, the upper half is resting. And rest allows the poisons in the muscles and cells to be washed away.

Now think of Mr B.

He's a labourer. At the weekend he does crosswords, plays cards, listens to debates on the wireless.

That's perfect. He's pepping up the top half of the brain and resting the lower half.

It's as simple as that – and both Mr A. and Mr B. are really fit to start Monday's work.

Lastly, a word for the housewife.

Do try to get yourself away from the four walls of the kitchen at the weekend. It will make all the difference to YOUR week.

This Is Most Important For Anyone Over Forty

July 18, 1954

DO you know the most important piece of advice a doctor can give the average person over 40? It's simply this:- for goodness sake, use your muscles.

The four troubles most common as we get on in years all come from lack of exercise.

Here they are in order of importance:

1) **Poor circulation**.

2) **Constipation**.

3) **Creaky joints.**

4) And the most common nowadays – **poor sleep**.

Yet we can help to dodge them all right up to the late 60s – by movement.

That's the secret – keep moving. No, not fancy exercises. But just by making sure, every day, that we give our muscles something to do.

A lot of us cut down our activities far too much after 40. And this can be more harmful than you realise – especially to the heart.

In fact, many more folk develop heart trouble through lack of exercise than over-exercise! You see, if we go lazy after 40, the blood-flow slows down. The blood deteriorates in quality because the lungs don't purify it as well as they should. So the heart becomes lazy, too, and fat gathers round it.

That's where the danger lies.

Believe it or not, lack of exercise can also bring on rheumatics.

The body has an oiling system for every joint – but it only works if the joints are moving. If the joints aren't moving, the oiling system becomes less efficient – and that's how rheumatics can start.

It's the same with constipation. To avoid it you've got to make the tummy muscles work.

And there's nothing better for this than a good, regular walk. Evening walks are doubly helpful. They're also the remedy for many forms of sleeplessness, especially if you come in slightly tired.

Apart from walking, what other exercises can we take? Well, from 50 onwards, forget about touching the toes, or any bending exercises.

These increase the strain on the arteries round the head and the risk of high blood pressure.

But swing the arms, swing the legs. Movement, lots of it, not straining effort – that's the key.

Games like family ping-pong are miles better than tossing the caber, if you get the idea.

Avoid exercises where the muscles have to stay tense for more than 60 seconds. When a muscle is hardened, the flow of blood is stopped. Overdo this – and it's easy to strain the heart.

Now here's an important point. Never exercise solely to bring down your weight.

It's a waste of time.

Did you know it takes one and a quarter hours of brisk walking to exercise off one pint of beer? And even longer to offset the food value of one egg.

Invalids, too, can help themselves to a surprising extent by exercise, whether they're in bed or in a chair.

A patient of mine helped herself to recover from serious illness just because she waggled her toes, ankles and wrists in bed.

All this helped the circulation just that little bit that was needed.

Even plucking the bedclothes, or squeezing a ball of wool, is often as good as medicine.

Why, the first thing an invalid should do – if it's sanctioned by the doctor – is to try to breathe deeply. This alone exercises 70-odd muscles.

And you know, a weak heart does NOT mean "no exercise". Sometimes gentle exercise is one way to get better, or at least prevent the heart weakening still further.

Is there any fear of a healthy person overdoing exercise? Not really, for there are three distinct warnings.

One is a blueness of the lips. That's a sure sign you're horsing yourself.

The second is if you're uncomfortably breathless.

The third is a gripping sensation at the throat. If this happens, for goodness sake, stop at once.

Of course, even sensible exercise won't give us back the years. We can't recover what we've lost. But it'll improve your health. All sorts of little troubles will disappear. And you'll hold on to muscle-tone much longer.

In fact, you may add 15 to 20 years to your active life.

Too Much Medicine ~ A Most Alarming Sign   *May 4, 1952*

IF there's one thing that alarms me nowadays, it's the amount of medicine that's going down people's throats.

Don't think for a moment this is harmless. Far from it! The more medicine we take, the less effect it has.

If you have a cold or headache, never forget it's possible to let the cold work its way out of the system, or the headache die away naturally.

This helps to increase resistance to the next bout. But too much medicine decreases resistance to the next attack. And so we get progressively worse off.

Why this cry for medicine – and more medicine – today?

The biggest reason is the deficiency of other things. Some of these deficiencies we can't do much about. But with others we can definitely help ourselves.

Worst deficiency of all is good red meat. It means deficiency in the strength of the blood and so in resistance and staying power.

There's no doubt about it, we don't have the stamina of our fathers. Whether we're bank clerks or ditch-diggers, we're apt to be played out hours before we should.

Meat gives good blood. It also helps us to work longer without another meal. With enough meat, we can go on for four of five hours without a break.

When we lack meat, we often make do with starchy foods. These "disappear" quickly in the stomach.

That's half the reason for the modern fashion of having tea breaks at work every day.

What can we do about this shortage of red meat?

There's no real substitute. But some things do help. Among them are cheese, nuts, spinach and green vegetables. It's all about the iron they contain.

And – most important – porridge for body-building powers.

Besides being deficient in the quality of our blood – and so more open to minor illnesses – many of us are deficient, too, in the way our blood circulates.

To some extent, a good circulation makes up for a lack of quality of blood. And one of the best ways to ensure you have a good circulation is – walking.

But there's a definite tendency to avoid walking today. People take a bus for half a mile or less.

As a result, the circulation gets slowed up. This has a bad effect on the whole system.

Next shortage I'd like to mention is in our vitamin intake. I know a lot of folk think talk of vitamins is faddy. But believe me, lack of them – especially today – leads to bloodlessness, rheumatism, nerves, colds, infections, flu and sore throats.

If you're bothered with any of these troubles, you may need extra vitamins.

But that doesn't necessarily mean you'll have to take vitamin tablets. The best sources are milk, eggs and wholemeal bread.

Old folk – especially those who live alone – should note that particularly. Many of them develop skin troubles, colds, rheumatism, because of vitamin deficiency.

Finally, there's the shortage that leads to so much addiction to sedatives and nerve tonics today.

It's the shortage of quietness.

Without quiet, real rest is impossible. The muscles don't get to slacken off as they should. Then there's no rest for the heart, and no respite for the nerves.

And, because of this, we're all in real danger of burning ourselves out before our time.

In fact, I'd go as far as to say that 45 minutes each day of rest AND QUIET may well add 10 years to our lives.

Without that regular quietness, we're like a piece of elastic at full stretch all the time, and liable to go "twang" in our early fifties.

With it, we have far fewer headaches, less indigestion, and less high blood pressure.

And therefore our chances of living healthily well into our seventies are greatly increased.

The Danger To Life Of Hidden Fat
April 22, 1956

YOU'D like to live to a ripe old age, wouldn't you?

Well, there's one thing above all that'll give you a darned good chance. Keep your weight down.

Perhaps you're a stone and a half above the average. Not too bad, you imagine. You're wrong. That much overweight can reduce your chances of long life by 18 per cent.

That's official! Even if you carry around only 10 lb. surplus, the odds against you living to a good age are increased by eight per cent.

And that applies to women as well as men.

Has it ever struck you that when you're fat on the outside, that can be seen, there's hidden fat inside, too?

It creeps round the heart, liver, tummy. And as you get older, the strain becomes serious, even dangerous.

Up to the age of 40, the death rate is lower among short people. But afterwards, tall folk have a better chance of getting into their seventies and eighties.

That's because men and women under 5 ft. 6 in. tend to get tubby. It's that culprit overweight again!

Another point about eating. After forty, we should all cut down our intake. What's more, we should be careful about fats. Not butter or marge, but animal fats like fatty meats.

Experts have studied this point and figures indicate that fats aren't a good bet for the old age "stakes".

What about smoking?

Cut out your 15 cigarettes a day if you like. But that in itself won't add years to your life.

So long as smoking is moderate, all's well.

It's the same with alcohol. Moderate drinkers are just as long-livers as anybody.

Next, this question of retirement. If you're a man, think twice about retiring. It's on record that many who give up their work don't live on for more than two or three years.

And research shows that, in this respect, men are tender souls compared with women! As men get on in years, they can't face up so well to any change of routine. Their health suffers. They're much more likely to go down the hill than women.

Working spinsters, for instance, live on for an average of 12 years after retirement – as against a man's two or three.

Now here's a very important factor for long life. Don't worry over your own troubles.

All other things being equal, the folk who will live the longest are those who worry over other folk's problems.

There are three jobs that top the poll for long life – clergymen, doctors, lawyers – in that order. You'll notice all three are professions that deal with other people's troubles.

It's "looking out" on the world and taking an interest in others that counts. "Looking in" at yourself and worrying about yourself are bad for the heart in the long run.

When you do get on in years, there may come a time when your son or daughter will say to you "come and live with us". Postpone saying "yes" as long as possible.

It may seem harsh, but you're more likely to live longer on your own.

Even though you may not realise it, there's a shock to the system when elderly people give up their home.

If there's no alternative, ask your hosts if they can give you not just a bedroom, but a bed-sitting-room. A room where you can make a cup of tea on your own and have your friends in.

If you're a woman, don't insist on helping the younger ones with the housework. Two women in a kitchen make for nervous tension.

Now, here's an encouraging point.

I've discovered time and again that the older my patient the more immune he is to killing diseases.

A patient in the seventies can have several different troubles, each of which could kill off younger folk. Yet the old man often keeps on without apparent ill-effects.

There's one important exception – pneumonia. It carries off half (yes, half) of our old folk.

When you're old, try to "spot" pneumonia on the first day. That's not so difficult. A sudden cough, plus breathlessness.

These are two warnings to get to bed – and to call the doctor.

The luckiest folk are perhaps those born with a slow pulse. This is practically a guarantee of long life.

Even so, you and I are pretty sure to live to seventy at least. That's today's average expectation.*

But by taking care of ourselves in the critical period (between 45 and 55) we may well live into the middle eighties, and in the future this may rise even more.

*Current UK life expectancy is 82.9 years for women, 79.2 for men (UK Office for National Statistics).

They won't stop eating and reading at the same time

January 13, 1957 — **My family, aged from 10 to 22, won't stop trying to eat and read at the same time. I'm only laughed at when I tell them they'll be sorry for this one day. Am I right?**

Provided they neither rush their meals nor overeat (both habits are encouraged by reading at table), this rather unsociable behaviour will do them no harm.

January 26, 1958 — **Is it possible for an adult to get shingles from a child who is suffering from chickenpox?**

Yes, this occurs fairly frequently – and vice versa, too, occasionally.

March 22, 1959 —**I had my baby in hospital. The name, weight and length were put on his cot – also the initials S.V.D. What do they mean?**

"Spontaneous vertex delivery" — in other words, normal, natural birth.

November 18, 1951 — **What's the best way to stop a wee laddie's nose bleeding after he's had a difference of opinion with a pal? This happened the other day, and we had an awful job.**

Lay him flat, with head propped slightly. Calm him and make him breathe through his mouth. Apply cloths wrung out in cold water to the root of the nose and back of the neck.

March 10, 1957 — **My little girl (4) has very little hair. Can you suggest treatment to promote the growth?**

Local treatment is no good. If she's as fit as possible, with a good mixed diet containing plenty of milk and fresh fruit, the likelihood is that her hair will come all right. If she's slow and has no appetite, and feels the cold badly, see your doc now.

February 12, 1956 — **Is chocolate useful as a laxative for children?**

No. If a "dose" is needed, try the good old syrup of figs.

January 13, 1957 — **Is it possible for a baby to die of cancer?**

Possible, but very rare.

July 10, 1955 — **What causes worms in an adult?**

Generally, infection from a child. The eggs (invisible) get accidentally swallowed due to careless hygiene and hatch in the bowel.

September 18, 1955 — **Can ice-lollies cause worms in children?**

It's unlikely. The complaint is usually caught by contact with other children.

March 5, 1950 — **My son is nine months old. Since he was five months he has been standing on his feet. Friends say he'll suffer later, as the strain is too much. He is healthy, sturdy, and walks about the house kicking a ball, and will not sit down until he is tired. What do you think?**

It's quite all right, as long as the child walks of his own free will, and not at the urging of a parent.

March 4, 1956 — **I'm worried about my little boy (two years four months), who isn't making much attempt to talk. "Mummy" and "Daddy" are about the only words he says yet.**

If he's otherwise normal, you shouldn't worry. I've known perfectly healthy and intelligent children who were much older before speaking.

February 9, 1958 — **My baby boy was born with a fairly big red mark on his forehead, and on one eyelid. The hospital staff told me it would wear away. He's now four months old and there's no difference. Is there anything I can do about it?**

Not at present. Leave it alone unless it begins to spread or get thicker. Later on, if he wants to, he can use "cover" paint to hide it.

September 16, 1956 — **How can I encourage my son (one year) to swallow solids? His food has to be sloppy and put through a sieve.**

Give him something hard (but inedible) to chew on. As his teeth strengthen he'll learn to eat solids. A whole apple (peeled) to nibble or scrape at often encourages children, but keep an eye on him to prevent a chunk being bitten off and choked on.

March 17, 1957 — **Is there anything we can give a baby (five months) who refuses to sleep? Mild aspirin and a "dummy" are of no avail. Two hours is the longest he sleeps at a time. My husband and I are becoming irritable through lack of sleep.**

Approach your doctor about this, for fear there's some reason for his sleeplessness not obvious to you. The doctor will examine him and prescribe what's required.

April 7, 1957 — **Is a woman of 41 too old to have a first baby?**
No.

September 7, 1958 — **Can a child (15 or under) have a tumour in the brain? If so, what causes it?**
Yes he can, but the cause is usually obscure or unknown.

October 23, 1955 — **Can you catch or pass any ailment through kissing?**
Yes. Quite a variety, and particularly colds and throat infections. Kissing should never be indulged in indiscriminately. Nor should babies be kissed by anyone except mothers.

— Chapter 3 —

It's All About Your Feet

SIT down for a moment, stretch out your legs and take a good look at a vitally important part of your body. Your feet.

The Doc of the 1950s was rather interested in feet. There were continual references to looking after them, problems they might suffer, and the dangers and diseases that might spring from them.

Smelly feet sap your vitality. Don't walk on wet sand. Your arches might not be as arched as you thought. And hell mend you if you leave more than a week between trimming your toenails.

Whatever you do, don't stand still!

Some of the warnings given here are good advice. A few of the ideas sound a little odd. Other bits are, frankly, baffling.

The November 14, 1954, article about the best way to choose shoes, however, is very useful even today

But be sure to remember to be very careful when undertaking what used to be one of life's more demanding physical challenges that, strangely, has become a much less daunting task in the modern world — the feat of endurance and stamina that was breaking in a new pair of shoes.

How Often Do You Cut Your Toenails?

July 12, 1953

THAT'S a number one question in summer. For, believe me, a third of all summer tiredness comes from the feet!

On a hot day, once your feet "give up", your whole body becomes tired before another fifteen minutes have passed.

So, you see, we've simply got to look after our feet.

And the first thing to remember is – cut your toenails once every five days. Certainly never let them grow longer than a week. If you do, you'll land for "buckled" nails.

Buckled nails are the kind you have on your hands. Have a look at them. See the nice curve dipping in at the sides. That's fine for the hands, but it's bad for the toes.

The nails of the feet should be flat. The less they curve, the less the feet ache, the less tiredness there is. For it's the ache that really pulls us down.

When a toenail curves upwards in the centre, the sides are driven into the flesh by the pressure of the shoes.

Few men cut their toenails properly. And the painful problems of ingrowing toenails are much more common among men than among women.

To get flat toenails use straight-edged scissors and cut straight across. Never use a knife or razor. A knife tends to cut deep at the sides, and so starts ingrowing.

It's surprising the amount of folk who have smelly feet.

What's more surprising is that most of them are reconciled to it. "Oh, I'm just made that way", they'll say. That's nonsense.

Smelly feet are more than embarrassing. They sap the vitality. They're a sure sign the pores are unable to breathe. The nerves in the skin are irritated. The skin is lifeless.

What's worse, the circulation is affected.

At the feet, the blood has the longest journey back to the heart. If the feet are not in good trim, the blood flow is slowed down – and the feet swell!

The cure is to wash the feet every night. Do it once with warm water and soap, then with cold water. The warm water cleans the pores. The cold water reduces the swelling.

Then, in the morning, rub your feet all over with a little methylated spirit. Then dust the inside of the socks with talcum powder.

Another idea. Have you ever thought of washing your shoes?

Try it sometimes. Wash the insides with a sponge and soapy water – then air them well.

Dry shoes, dry socks – that's the plan.

And, by the way, never wear thick socks that have shrunk with perspiration. That only makes the trouble worse. Instead, wear thinner socks.

Now, how should you rest tired feet?

There's only one way. Get them up to the level of the head. Sitting is no good. Take off your shoes and your socks, too, if it's possible.

Suppose you're out walking. You feel like resting on a gentle, grassy bank.

Then lie with the head downhill and feet uphill!

Last Thursday a woman came to me complaining of bad feet.

"S'funny thing, doctor, because I've got sensible shoes with a good support for the arch," she told me.

That was her trouble. Too much support for the arch is not good. There should always be a little space between the sole of a shoe and the arch of the foot.

Otherwise you don't get the natural spring of the foot – and the whole art of walking is spoiled.

Remember, you can't be happy or comfortable in summer if your feet aren't right.

And nothing is more important than the nightly wash.

THE MODERN VIEW, BY DR LYNDA

I HAVE to say, my number one question of patients in summer is NOT usually, "How often do you cut your toenails?" It takes about nine months for a new toenail to come in if one falls off, so they are incredibly slow growing. I'd be hard pushed to cut mine every week.

And you would not be running the risk of "buckled nails". Horizontal lines and buckling of the nails are called Beau's lines, and are due to periods of interrupted growth due to illness or deficiency of some sort, commonly iron or zinc. I think the 1950s Doc might have had sunstroke while writing this one!

The shape of the nail is of no great importance. It is ill-fitting shoes and trauma that cause ingrowing toenails — which in no way cause tiredness!

True, cutting the nail straight across sometimes with a wedge or V-cut in it does help prevent ingrowing to some extent. But who would use a knife or razor?

As for smelly feet (bromodosis), an all-year-round problem in any case, sapping your summer vitality? I can see no logic in this.

Causes of smelly feet range from a condition called hyperhidrosis (general sweating) to changing hormones, e.g. puberty and pregnancy and damp, inappropriate footwear.

I struggled to find much truth in this section, apart from the advice about washing feet in warm soapy water. Hygiene is certainly important.

Keeping the feet clean and drying between the toes properly, along with changing socks once or twice a day (preferably woollen or cotton to wick away the sweat) will help. Not wearing the same shoes every day gives them a chance to dry out, and wearing socks with closed-toe shoes is a must.

Nowadays, we have antiperspirants, medicated insoles and antifungal creams and powders which help, too.

There is a treatment still used in severe cases called iontophoresis which involves passing a small electrical current through water while bathing the feet. How it works, I'm not sure. If future doctors read this in 50 years' time, I'm sure they'll be chuckling at this one!

I did find a curious thing on an NHS website which sounded like the 1950s Doc himself wrote it — it advised that you should buy shoes in the afternoon. As the day progresses, your feet naturally swell and if your shoes fit later in the day they will be comfy all day.

And finally, resting tired feet. Elevation is exactly right, but I think it's a bit excessive to get them above your head on a hill!

What Are Your Feet Worth To You?

November 14, 1954

YOU'RE as old (or young) as your feet.

There's an awful lot of truth in the old saying. It's really sad to see a man in his fifties, who is healthy and fit, going "down the hill" because he's off his feet.

For goodness sake be kind to your feet! It may make all the difference to a healthy and active life from 50 onwards. There's no excuse, really.

For about £4 you can now get a pair of shoes with five different kinds of fittings – for each half-size! So, you see, it's pretty well certain you can get a perfect fit.

Here's another tip. Get your shoes always from the same shop. Or at least from the same firm.

And if your purse can stand it, buy two pairs at the one time. I've been doing that myself for 18 years – and it's kept me clear of any foot troubles. It's cruelty to your feet to ask them to change their shape or their points of pressure by changing brands of shoes.

And always keep this in mind when choosing a shoe. See that its point at the toe is nearer the inside edge. I think this is very important.

Now, maybe the ladies won't like this – but it's got to be said. Don't go in for excessively high heels.

It may look smart, but it's not fair to your spinal column. Many women suffer from a chronic sore back when they reach their forties and fifties. They blame housework or rheumatism, but the cause is often years of high heels.

A point about fitting that's not well known is that the instep must fit snugly. Otherwise your feet slide forward at every step, and you get the same kind of troubles that go with shoes that are too short.

Ignore the tendency to high arches unless your own arches are high. It's a mistake to think that good feet must have high arches. Some of us have naturally low arches – and an equally good spring to the step.

So don't ruin the bone structure by getting high-arched shoes.

Next time you go for shoes – here's another test of a comfortable fit. Can you wriggle your toes slightly?

I'm all for the ladies' "peep-toe" fashion, too. These big toes sticking out may not be to everybody's taste, but they're to everybody's foot comfort!

If your feet perspire more than average – it's a waste of money to buy dear shoes.

Perspiration rots shoes in no time – whether they're good quality or not. And the strange thing is that perspiring feet can be an indication of your character.

If you're highly strung, touchy, introspective or have an inferiority complex, then these traits can show in perspiration.

All you can do is – bathe the feet every day. There's nothing to beat hot water and good soap. Afterwards dry well and rub on methylated spirits.

Don't use the same shoes two days running. Allow one pair 24 hours to dry. It's surprising the moisture that comes from a pair of shoes that may seem quite dry to you.

You can prove it by this test. Lay your shoes on a dry stone step in the evening. No matter how dry these shoes appear to be, you'll find in the morning they've left a moist mark on the stone.

That proves you've got sweaty feet. Your shoes will last twice as long with a 24-hour rest. And you'll get much greater foot comfort.

Few folk realise that although badly-fitting shoes are often not painful, the damage is still going on.

A bad fit means the muscle tone of the feet deteriorates. In time, this can affect the legs. It's really the reason why so many middle-aged folk are such poor walkers.

Have you a tendency to cold feet? Well, it needn't be poor circulation. Your shoes are probably to blame.

And anybody who complains of tired feet can be nearly sure the shoes are partly to blame. But if the feet and legs are tired, it's an early indication you're run down.

Silly Risks We Are Apt To Take In Winter

October 11, 1953

WHY is it that some folk get through the winter pretty well scot-free yet others land for everything that's going?

In nine cases out of ten, the unlucky folk have themselves to blame. Many winter troubles lay us low because we do something silly. Often we don't realise we're taking a needless risk.

A common complaint I have to deal with in winter is cystitis (bladder trouble). It makes the victims pretty miserable for a long time.

Already one victim has come to me with it. He got it the same way as dozens of other folk will get it. He got out of bed one morning and planted his bare feet on the cold lino. He couldn't find his slippers, he said.

That's a very silly thing to do at any time, and the danger is doubled in winter.

Some people complain they've always got cold hands. A probable reason is that they've stopped the circulation by coming in on a cold night and warming their hands at a blazing fire.

We're all inclined to take risks "warming up". There are only three safe ways – 1. Exertion. 2. Rubbing. 3. Gradual warmth.

Numbers 2 and 3 are musts for older people. But quick heat is bad for all of us. I've heard it recommended that a good way to heat up is to plunge the hands into hot water. That's very risky. You should also resist the temptation to put your cold feet on the hot-water bottle. You run the risk of harming your feet for the rest of the winter. They'll always feel cold, and you'll probably land yourself with colds.

About 80 per cent of colds come from the feet.

Seems strange, doesn't it? For some reason, cold feet affect the lining of the nose.

We're all most vulnerable, too, when we're warm from the waist up and cold at the feet. That's why we get a chill and can't understand how it happened. For a common place to catch cold is in your own warm kitchen or living-room.

Let there be a draught round your feet when you're warm "upstairs" – and you're wide open to a cold.

Many of us fall to what I call "delayed flu".

Every time we do, the fault is entirely ours. If we'd been sensible we'd have dodged the flu.

Here's what happens. Every one of us, about once a month in winter, feels a wee bit miserable. Sometimes it's called a touch of the flu. If we insist on going out to a function, or golf, or country dancing – then, a week or fortnight later, down we go with flu or a bad chill.

When you feel miserable like this, don't do anything strenuous. The body is fighting something, and needs rest and warmth. If the body has to devote its energy to fighting cold and over-tire at the same time, the defences against the germs are weakened.

Where do we pick up rheumatism?

Well, the easiest place is on our own doorstep. It's silly to have a gossip at the door in winter. You're warm, the pores are open. The blood is flowing in a certain way. The body's burning system is set for a warm temperature.

And all that's upset at the open door. Don't do it, ladies! It's perhaps the silliest risk of all.

Another thing. After a bath, never allow the hair to be damp. The top of the head is very vulnerable to chill because it takes so much heat from the body.

Many of us believe in eating more in winter. It's a good idea, providing we do the same work and exercise as in summer. The extra food adds heat. But if we cut out any exercise in cold weather there's less need for food.

To old folk I give this warning – never risk fog outdoors. Every one of you has a chest weakness. Given the slightest chance, fog always catches old people.

Try Doing This Every Day At Dinner Time

May 13, 1956

FROM now until the end of August I'd like you all to do something simple every day at dinner-time.

Loosen the laces of your shoes quarter of an inch.

Nothing much in that, is there? Yet it can save you a great deal of bad temper, fatigue and that general fed-up feeling.

In summer it's been found that 70 per cent of us are irritated because of aching feet.

It's like this. When we put on our shoes in the morning they're quite comfortable. But by twelve o'clock the feet have swollen.

So you must give them more room. And only a quarter of an inch can make a world of difference to your stamina – and your temper – for the rest of the day.

Remember, when you're tired all over, it usually starts from the feet.

Did you know that a housewife walks about 8½ miles a day (about 17,000 steps) doing housework, answering the door, &c.?

That'll give you some idea of the strain on the arches of her feet. If she weighs about 9 stone, her arches have held up 930 tons of dead weight in a single day!

Her greatest strain is when she's standing at the sink. The muscles are then in one position, and get no relief.

So ladies, don't wear slippers when you're standing. Wear shoes with a comfortable heel. You'll feel a tremendous difference.

When your feet do ache, don't just soak them in hot water. Dip them alternately in hot and cold. It's the quickest refresher there is.

It's round about the age of 50 that trouble with our feet begins to tell.

Often I notice that patients with poor feet suffer ill-health in the second half of their life.

It's easy to understand. As we get on in years, about the only exercise we can take is walking. Walking is the best health-giver, and one of the most important factors for long life.

But if we're off our feet, the prospect is far from bright.

So let's start now to tone up our feet.

First and foremost, wash them every day. There's nothing better. Scrub them with a softish brush.

This hardens them up, cuts down swelling and prevents corns, bunions and chilblains. It'll even prevent some kinds of headaches.

Next, try half an hour in your bare feet in a room with a carpet. This gives them a chance of exercise.

Many a bunion and corn can be blamed on too long nails. The nail not only overgrows. It gets thick and horny. The toes tend to go rigid and all sorts of troubles are likely to begin.

It's easier to cut them on bath night when the nails are softer.

Have a look tonight at your big toes.

Are they turned off the straight and in towards the other toes? If they're more than 20 degrees off the straight, you're almost certain to get bunions in the long run.

What can you do about it? Change your shoes. Buy a pair that gives you toe room. (You should be able to wiggle your toes inside your shoes – that's half the secret).

When you're choosing a pair of shoes, always stand up in them and walk round the shop. The pressure of our weight spreads our feet. The heavier we are the greater the spread.

That's why fat folk should have particularly roomy footwear.

Now, are you troubled by hot feet?

A patient of mine who complained about hot feet was quite insulted when I told him the trouble was dirt!

Oh, his feet looked clean enough, and he'd put on fresh socks that morning. But fine grit had got into his socks and was sandpapering the skin.

So the simple cure is – wash your feet.

Woollen socks should be changed at least every other day, cotton and rayon socks every day.

Lastly, when you take a rest – particularly in hot weather – rest your feet above the level of your knees. Take off your socks, wiggle your toes and rotate the feet round the ankles.

It's a grand exercise, and a sure way to healthy feet.

Careful, It Takes More Out Of You Than You Think

May 4, 1958

HAVE you ever run into a spell like this? Day after day, you feel utterly washed out. You think you're run down and need a tonic. Or you think old age is getting on top of you.

There could well be another reason for this unaccountable tiredness. You're doing something that takes more out of you than you think.

At the top of the list is – believe it or not – **STANDING STILL!**

It's surprising how even the strongest and toughest of us is worn out – just by standing.

It's hard on the heart. It swells the blood vessels. It strains the joints of the spine. It pulls at the muscles of the back as well as the legs.

A day's window-gazing round the shops tells on the system more than you'd imagine. So does anything where you hold the position for any length of time.

Second on the list is **CLIMBING STAIRS OR A HILL**.

Only the under 30s can take this in their stride. Don't kid yourself that YOU are the exception.

I don't need to make you run a mile to test your heart. A dozen step-ups on to an ordinary kitchen chair is a stiffish test.

So never rush a hill or stairs. And always take a breather at the top.

As for old folk, even if you don't realise it, hills or stairs are bad for you – unless you tackle them this way.

Do it in "half-strides". That means each foot only comes level with the other. Then the other foot goes forward.

Third on the list – **DIRT**.

Dirty feet, especially, take an awful lot out of you. Not only do they make you tired physically, but they lower the morale and tire out the brain.

There's a close nerve link between the feet and head.

It's a case of the irritated feet flashing continual messages to the brain for relief.

It's almost as bad all over the skin. Once it gets clogged your whole system has to work at a higher temperature. Every pore and tiny piece of skin is under strain.

The warmer the weather, the more you feel it, too.

Energy-drainer No. 4 is **NOISE**.

Unless you're really accustomed to it, noise tires you out far more than you'd think.

If you're in a room where everybody's chattering – and it's going to be a night of it – don't compete with all the other voices. It's bad enough listening, but worse still to shout down the conversations going on elsewhere.

This is a particularly good tip on a bus journey. If it's a noisy crowd, sit back in silence, you'll save your energy.

Now for No. 5 – **A LONG SPELL OF EXCITEMENT**.

The danger here is you're not aware of its effects at the time. That's why some folk collapse at a football match. Excitement races the heart.

For folk over 65, or anybody with a dicky heart, five minutes of intense excitement is the biggest ration they can take with safety.

But even the fittest man or woman can be made limp with a long, exciting game or film.

BREAKING IN A NEW PAIR OF SHOES tires you for a week or two. That's obvious.

But did you know it's just as tiring to break in a new pair of spectacles? In this case you may have three weeks of unexplained tiredness before you're used to the specs.

Now for tiredness you should never ignore – **THE TIREDNESS THAT COMES AFTER ILLNESS**.

If the doctor sends you to bed for more than two days, you need three weeks before the old oomph comes back.

Until then, never put yourself to excessive strain. Time and a little extra rest are essential for the system to clear away poisons and rebuild dead tissues.

Here's where the other danger lies. If you take silly risks, that tissue repair may never be done. And you may never have quite the same amount of energy again.

Just one last word – when you've a stiff job to do – start slowly. And give yourself plenty of time to work up to a higher gear.

One Thing We Should All Do Before The Holidays

June 16, 1957

"DOCTOR, what's the best piece of advice you can give me to get the best out of my holiday?"

I looked at my patient for a moment.

She was fiftyish, well upholstered and there was no doubt about the answer. "Go to a chiropodist", I said, "And get your feet seen to before you set off".

We could all do the same and benefit from it. But I'd advise you not to delay. Chiropodists are already booked up for days ahead for holiday foot treatment.

It'll save you hours of pain even to have your corns pared by an expert.

He can help in another way you've never realised. Down the sides of the nail – especially the big toenail – are often unsuspected callouses.

In hot weather these growths make you wince at every step. Only the chiropodist can cut them away.

Folk with bunions aren't so easily helped. Still, he can pad up the toes to ease all the extra walking you'll be doing.

You can do a lot yourself to help your feet.

And there's nothing better than this. From now until the holidays make a point of washing your feet at least once a day. Use good soap. Wash with warm water, rinse the soap off then do the same again. Don't forget to get in between the toes. That's where trouble can develop.

Finish off by rinsing with cold water. Now rub vigorously – between the toes, too. Careful drying is as important as thorough washing.

Half the trouble with aching feet is caused by dead skin. It swells the feet and clogs the pores. The soft part between the toes is liable to become soggy.

Some folk call this soft corns – and it's the cause of about 25 per cent of aching feet.

On no account "steep" the feet. It only makes them softer.

Nails are important, too. Give them a good going over with a brush, particularly down the sides of the big toenails.

Old skin, dirt, &c., down the sides swell the toes. And the extra pressure gives you gyp on a hot day.

Use foot powder by all means. You can buy a good powder which you "puff" on the feet. This has a drying effect, and at the same time cuts down friction from the shoes. Any good talcum helps to cut down aches to zero.

When you do set out, don't harass yourself with one big suitcase. Carrying such weight for a while is cruel on your arches.

Fat people are liable to trouble that can ruin their holiday – before they arrive. So take your stuff in two small cases. At least the weight is halved.

Better still, send on your baggage.

Never travel in new shoes.

You can walk with high heels, but you can't stand comfortably. The whole weight falls forward towards the toes. There's painful pressure and strain on the legs and back. The blood flow slows down and the feet-swelling starts.

Do your travelling in comfortable, medium-heeled shoes.

Now, no matter what we do, there are times when the feet will start to ache. What's to be done?

The one thing every woman longs to do is take her shoes off for a minute or two. Don't. The swelling has "overflowed" up to the ankles, or through the straps.

Once the shoes are off, the overflow slips back to the feet. So when the shoes go on again, the pressure is worse than ever.

All you can really do is rest. Set the feet up level with the heart. This helps the blood flow round the feet and reduces the swelling a little.

If your shoes do come off, keep them off for an hour. Wriggle the toes, rub the soles, get the blood flowing. Better still, wash with cold water and dry vigorously.

Don't walk on wet sand with bare feet.

The suction is like a schoolboy's sucker. It pulls down the arches, strains the tendons and can knock your feet up.

Sandals are cool, but make sure the strap doesn't press on a joint.

Even the strongest of us can be laid limp by aching feet. But old folk and people with heart trouble, blood pressure, &c., are particularly advised to be good to their feet.

Tickly feet and leg jerks keep me awake all night

February 3, 1952 — **My tickly feet have been keeping me awake all night. Despite concentration, my leg involuntarily jerks. Now I'm taking sleeping tablets. What's the cure?**

This doesn't sound at all serious. Try taking a three-mile walk before bedtime and determining not to think about your feet after you get to bed. If this fails, see your doc.

December 24, 1950 — **A friend tells me the thaw is more dangerous to health than frost. Is this true?**

There are more colds and other minor ailments as a result of the thaw. This is because people get wet, cold feet in the slush. And cold feet cause more troubles than any other single factor I know. Galoshes and two pairs of socks are a sensible precaution.

October 2, 1955 — **My daughter has a painful bunion. Any remedy?**

Roomy shoes and kaolin poultices till the inflammation subsides. Operation if necessary.

June 14, 1959 — **I'm a transport inspector (63) and suffer from rheumatism and haemorrhoids. I'm on my feet all day. The calves of my legs ache. I've awful pains in the feet when I go to bed and my buttocks itch. Am I doing myself harm working on for another 12 months?**

Both conditions are made much worse by the tiring and exposed nature of your work. You should try to get an easier job, preferably indoors, till you reach the proper age for retiring.

May 9, 1954 — **Any danger of infection from wearing shoes of a person who had athlete's foot?**

There most certainly is, unless they're thoroughly disinfected — an almost impossible task.

September 11, 1955 — **What can I do to get rid of painful hard skin on my heels? After washing, I pumice-stone them, but next day they crack.**

Rub nightly with olive oil instead of pumice-stone, which is making the skin harder.

October 16, 1955 — **My son (10, and tall for his age) tends to walk on the ball of his foot, lifting his heels off the ground. He says his heels feel numb and suddenly little pains attack them.**

Take him to see your doc. (and perhaps an orthopaedic specialist) before he gets into bad habits of walking.

April 6, 1958 — **I've heard it said that one should never wear boots or shoes belonging to someone else, as there's nothing worse than leather for infection. Is there any truth in this?**

Yes, it's quite true, so far as fungus infections are concerned. Other diseases aren't transmitted in this way.

January 10, 1954 — **My son (7) always has cold feet and takes one cold after another. What's the remedy?**

Perhaps too little outdoor exercise. It would be well to have your doc check up on his general health, however.

January 13, 1952 — **I'm bothered with cold feet. Sometimes they're painful. My legs seem to be giving out, as they tire very quickly. I am 75, 5 feet 6 inches tall, and weigh 13 stones.**

You're far too heavy for your height and age. Your heart has to pump blood to keep your extremities warm, but too much of its effort is taken up carrying your weight. Get your weight down by a stone and a half.

February 28, 1954 — **My wife and I both have varicose veins. We sit with our feet near the fire. Can that make the veins worse?**

No, but it increases the skin congestion and may produce varicose eczema.

October 9, 1955 — **Is there a remedy for an enlarged joint in my big toe? The trouble isn't yet far advanced but is causing considerable pain.**

Protection from pressure and friction, plus bathing each night, will help a lot; but the only cure is an operation on the deformed joint.

May 20, 1951 — **What's the best way to keep your feet cool in summer?**

Light, roomy shoes. Loosely-fitting socks. Wash the feet every night. Powder them with borated talc in the morning.

September 28, 1952 — **My feet are often cold and numb and the soles sore. What's the remedy?**

Try daily washing with soap and warm water. Rinse with tepid water, and dry briskly. Use a little methylated spirit and talcum to harden the skin.

October 23, 1955 — **What can I do for a small lump under the sole of my foot? It's very painful at times.**

This is a plantar wart, I imagine. Treatment is best got at the skin department of your hospital.

August 18, 1957 — **When I sit for a short time with my legs crossed, my feet sleep. I'm also beginning to suffer from very cold feet. I'm 50.**

Avoid sitting like this and you may not be troubled in future. Take care that your footwear is roomy and clean, and don't wear suspenders or tight-topped socks.

— Chapter 4 —

Your Health And The Weather

IN the days when many more people walked than drove cars, when you waited in queues for buses or trams twice a day — the weather had more chance to "get" to you.

And it wasn't much better indoors. Coal fires were great sources of heat, but they also drew vast amounts of oxygen and air from a room and jetstreamed it up the chimney. That air had to be replaced, so icy-fingered draughts worked their way into and around the house, despite the best efforts of draught screens.

In the 1950s, the ordinary person's world was often a colder place than it is nowadays.

There were ways to cope, of course.

According to the 1950s Doc, woollen gloves (not leather ones) helped, as did washing your face often, not slouching and knitting your way through the cold evenings. Oh, and it was always best to say goodbye to friends quickly!

However, summer wasn't much healthier.

You could get "sun indigestion", and dancing the night away while on holiday wasn't recommended if you'd been sunbathing earlier. You should eat half as much as usual — but drink twice as much. And watch out when shaving!

You could be forgiven for thinking that no matter what the weather was doing — it wasn't good for you!

An Hour In The Sun Takes More Out Of You Than An Hour's Hard Work

June 11, 1950

DURING this past fortnight an awful lot of folk have begun to suffer from sun indigestion. They get it in the form of tiredness, catarrh, asthma, heart trouble, headaches, or eye strain.

Instead of the good weather pepping them up, it lays them low.

The sun is like food to us. It creates life and vigour. But the body can't take too much of it too quickly. That's why, if you're determined to get a good tan, you should start by sunbathing in the shade.

Two days in the shade will tan the skin gently, and set up a resistance to the full glare later.

After that, try half an hour lying in the sun for a day or two. And at no time exceed an hour.

Tanning should take a fortnight, not a day. What's more, ladies, too quick a tanning will ruin your looks! The skin coarsens, and gets thick. By autumn it's a dirty colour.

Now, here are a few dos and don'ts:

Don't lie on the sand face downwards. The back of the neck and head are most susceptible to heat-stroke.

Do your exercises before and not after a sunbathe.

This is because, believe it or not, if you spend an hour lying in the sun, even if you stay perfectly still, it takes as much out of you as an hour's hard tennis.

If you are dancing at night or having a strenuous programme, cut out sunbathing earlier in the day.

If you've a tendency to a weak chest, asthma, or heart trouble, take it easy with sunbathing.

Stay in the open and catch any breeze that's going.

In hot weather the heart gets extra work in regulating the body's heat. Sunbathing increases that work.

And in people liable to catarrh, sunbathing can bring on a cold. The heat irritates the membrane of the nostrils, and this causes nasal catarrh.

Don't use cheap sun glasses. They're apt to cause the very trouble you want to avoid – headaches and eye strain.

NEVER read with them.

Now, a tip for all of us – when the temperature is in the seventies eat a third less food, and drink twice as much liquid.

And, remember, hot weather can bring on tummy trouble due to food poisoning. Food decomposes quicker, and there are more dust and flies about.

If we get sand in our sandwich on the beach we throw it away, but town dust is much more harmful. Tinned food should be eaten within

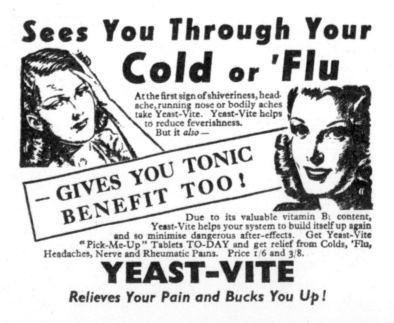

an hour of opening. Milk should be covered, and the larder and pantry always kept closed.

The housewife is well advised to buy "only for the day." Left-overs should be cut to a minimum.

Men should be extra careful when shaving. The lather dries very quickly and the shave is rougher. In addition to the hairs, the surface skin may be scraped off.

Then the sun irritates the tender surface, and this may set up a mild form of dermatitis. That's why some of my male patients are complaining of an itchy face.

A good idea is to lather half the face at a time.

Use an after-shave lotion too – or try your wife's cold cream, if she'll let you!

THE MODERN VIEW, BY DR LYNDA

"SUN indigestion" is something of a Docism, though he does explain it in the rest of the paragraph. He's talking about too much sun — not that we get that very often!

Exposure to sun has its good and bad points. It's a fantastic source of Vitamin D for your bones and it raises endorphin levels, which make you feel good, and reduces the risk of seasonal affective disorder.

UV light is associated with melatonin synthesis in the eyes which helps normal sleep patterns and is possibly implicated in the successful management of multiple sclerosis.

On the down side, long-term exposure is associated with skin cancer and skin aging, immunosuppression, cataracts and macular degeneration. So there needs to be a balance between enough and too much.

So the 1950s Doc wasn't far wrong!

Take too much sun too quick and sunstroke occurs, which can be pretty severe with burning blistering skin, headache, fatigue and (in severe cases) death from dehydration and overheating.

I'm not sure about his dos and dont's, though.

Shade and sensible exposure is good, and drinking more is very important in the heat.

Food decomposes quicker, but these days most houses have fridges — even if it is just for the beer — so unlikely to be a problem now.

But the 1950s Doc certainly speaks with a convincing voice of authority, doesn't he! I'll be wearing my sunglasses more often in the sun!

People Who Stand Up Best To Winter

September 17, 1950

"HOW I dread the winter", said a patient the other day. That patient was making a mistake which many of us do. Her attitude to winter was defeatist. She was inviting trouble.

The folk who stand up best to winter are those who brave it. And the best way for the normal person to brave winter is to pay particular attention to skin tone between now and March.

The skin is like a safety valve for body temperature. If it's stifled, it starts to go lazy on the job. How can we tone it up and keep it toned?

First, by not being cowardly about baths in winter. If you're in the habit of sponging yourself in summer, keep it up. It's even more valuable now.

Next, don't be afraid to let the air get at your body. When you're undressing, don't rush to get into pyjamas. Let the air play on your skin for a minute or two.

Don't let early darkness tempt you to cut out your regular evening walk and plunk into an armchair by the fire. If possible, always walk to work. It's a splendid tonic for the skin and lungs, and it avoids the "fug" and infection of buses and trams.

Don't rush into heavy woollies and overcoats. Keep them for really bitter weather. You want to harden the skin and keep it well ventilated.

It's important, when winter comes, to give yourself half an hour to an hour more sleep. Many of us, in fact, get less sleep. Instead of getting home at 9.30pm from golf, tennis, or walks, we go to the pictures, whist drives, &c., that keep us out to nearer 11!

Once in a while, that's all right. But a succession of late nights is bad.

Don't be downhearted if you take a cold just now. It's not necessarily a bad start to winter. More than likely it'll give you immunity for months to come. But if you're liable to colds, now's the time to have a vaccine. If you put it off you won't get the full benefit over the winter.

How's your weight? You're best to start winter at normal. So if you're up or down try, in the next few weeks, to get to your "fighting" weight.

Your job has a lot to do with your health in winter. People who are "in and out" stand up better – like bus drivers, policemen, postmen, labourers, joiners, plumbers, and so on.

Office workers and shop assistants are not so well off. Their quarters have to be warmed and they lose the bracing effect of cold air. Factory hands aren't so lucky, either.

But if you're in the second group you can help a lot by taking plenty of baths, or rubbing yourself briskly with a wet towel.

And spend your spare time in active exercise outdoors. If you've a family, don't get worried if they have to swot, provided they also play games. And don't keep them indoors unless it's damp.

How about food? Fruit and vegetables are good winter campaigners. The little extra cost is cheap in the long run. You don't need to eat much, but have them regularly and fresh if you can.

Drink plenty of water and other fluids. They needn't be dead cold. Eat a fair amount of sweet things to produce heat.

Finally – don't hug the fire. Get out and face the winter. You'll come through it a lot better.

THE MODERN VIEW, BY DR LYNDA

DOES dreading something give you health trouble? Probably.

Positive mental attitude is a philosophy which claims that an optimistic outlook attracts positive change. It has been proven that people with a positive attitude have a measurably higher chance of survival and recovery and it has a significant effect on overall health.

Or perhaps the 1950s Doc was missing the fact that the mood of his patients would have plummeted in winter (known as seasonal affective disorder).

He was also right about not cutting down on exercise and "plunking into your armchair". We do little enough exercise as it is, and exercise benefits lots of things, from mental health to your heart, even if it is just a walk round the block.

Colds and flus are airborne viruses so people working in enclosed areas will be more susceptible to catching them than people who work as an individual or in the open air, hence the warning about travelling on trams and buses and working in offices and shops and factories. Skin has little to do with it, neither does taking lots of baths and . . . rubbing yourself with a wet towel?

Vitamin C, although commonly thought to be good for colds and flu, has more of a role in protecting skin and healing. It's Vitamin A that's good for fighting infection and helping your immune system work properly, found in yellow, red and green veg and cheese and oily fish.

So the modern view would be to feed your body the right raw ingredients, be active and be positive and give your body a better chance of remaining healthy throughout the winter months.

This Spring Tonic Works Wonders

March 9, 1958

YOU want to shake off the bad effects of winter. You want to get rid of the poisons inside you. You want to get back your old energy and fighting fitness. Well, one thing that helps more than anything is the sun.

For folk like you and me, it's worth a thousand pep pills, or a hundred bottles of tonic.

Right now our defences against illness are down to 75 per cent of what they should be. Yet only two days out in the sun will bring these defences up to 85 per cent.

That shows the tremendous value of a two-day holiday to anybody recovering from flu.

If you get out into the sun now you actually become a new person inside. You shed old tissues and grow healthy new ones.

That's because sunshine helps the body to make vitamin D.

The next thing you know is that all the germs that cause sore throats, laryngitis, tonsillitis, sinusitis, head colds and bronchitis are fighting a losing battle.

But that's nothing like the whole story.

All winter, poisons have been gathering inside you — mainly in your muscles. That's why you feel tired and aching in the morning.

Sunshine penetrates a lot deeper than you think. It gets through to the blood and acts like an iron tonic. The blood corpuscles, in turn, really become red and healthy. And the poisons are washed away in the new surge.

In fact, a week or so in the sun will practically clear away all the rubbish of a winter. That's why even old folk lose their aches and pains after a spring holiday.

"But it's too cold to sit out in the sun", you'll say.

I don't want you to sit out – not even in a sun trap. You get more good when you're on the move.

The reason is that the blood is moving along better, and all of it is getting a share of the good.

What about boils, pimples, and blotchy skin? I doubt if there's a better treatment than being outdoors in the sun.

Sunlight kills the germs and makes for healthy skin. But the sun isn't much use through windows. Five minutes of it outdoors is worth more than two hours indoors. And the most expensive lamp is a poor substitute for the real thing.

Here's a surprising thing. Outdoor sunshine is good for the blood pressure. Generally it will bring down the pressure. Yet, oddly enough, it helps folk who are tired and depressed because of low pressure.

The rays act like a gentle massage on some folk, and like a cold shower on others. Whatever is needed, the sun has a wonderful knack of achieving it.

If your nerves need toning down, it does the trick. If your morale needs bucking up, the sun's rays are better than most tonics.

Even your appetite is bound to improve.

Plenty of sun means you get far more value from anything you eat, particularly milk, eggs, butter and cheese.

And youngsters thrive in the sun. They even grow taller and stronger, for sunshine means good bones.

But all of us, even folk in the grandma class, "grow" in the sense that our repair department is jolted into action.

A day out in the sun – and you're almost sure of a splendid sleep, too. That in turn is another tremendous help to your repair services.

If any of you are hard worked, or worried, or in the middle of a big problem, I'd advise a couple of hours in the sun. You'll last the pace better – be fitter for the task, and even be more efficient.

Lastly, the sun is tremendously important for morale. It dates back to the days when our ancestors were lucky to survive a bad winter. When the spring sun came, there was new hope. That feeling still persists in every one of us.

The more you're run down, the quicker you'll benefit from the sun. But the fitter you are, the less you'll notice the difference. No matter how you feel now, get all the sun you can, and by early summer you'll be 100 per cent.

Then, after the end of June, you have the chance of building up reserves for next winter.

It's easy, it's wonderful – and it doesn't cost a penny.

Things We Don't Use Nearly Enough In A Rainy Winter

November 11, 1951

TOO many people think our health from now until April depends mostly on the weather. They're quite wrong.

Seventy-five per cent depends on what I call winter wisdom. Cultivate that and you've a better chance of escaping chills, rheumatics, and all the aches and illnesses so common in the next six months.

What is this winter wisdom? Let me tell you about one of my patients, Mrs C.

She dreaded the winter more than any of us. About October she always started to have colds, swollen ankles, and rheumatics. I noticed her living-room had a strong floor draught. And do you know what I prescribed? A footstool.

"When you're resting, always get your feet off the floor", I told her. She did, and benefitted tremendously. So could we all. A footstool is a winter priority – not only for old folk and those with a weakness in the ankles and calves, but for the healthiest of us, too.

For every room has a floor draught of some kind.

And here's another point. Every house has a "cauld chair". It's seldom father's. Some other member of the family is invariably sitting in the cold.

That's why one of the best buys now is a draught screen. You'd be amazed at the extra comfort it gives and the freedom from colds and chills that results. It's as good as a crackling fire on a cold night.

And if you're a "cauld chair" victim, it'll enable you to sleep better.

Some people have "winter eyes" – sticky and gritty in the morning, headaches and even styes. The reason is – lack of a reading-lamp.

A centre light is not the best thing. We live in artificial light through the winter, and if it's not to harm us the angle has to be right. The best angle is behind your shoulder.

Now here's an old-fashioned one. I sometimes advise men in offices to wear spats. They're a first-class guard against cold feet. They prevent rheumatism of the back, as well as of the legs.

And nobody should scorn an umbrella. If I had the choice of an umbrella or a raincoat, the umbrella would win every time. It keeps the rain off the neck. A raincoat doesn't.

And a wet neck causes tiredness and muscular rheumatism.

Now here's a point that may surprise some people. We perspire more in winter – due to heavier clothes, over-heated offices, &c.

Perspiration goes cold on us far more quickly. Winter wisdom here is – wash more and bath often. You'll double your chances of beating winter chills.

Even folk afflicted by chapped hands should wash often.

Don't cut down on the water you drink in winter.

Actually, most folk drink less because somehow it doesn't seem to taste so good. But less water means extra work for the kidneys, more chance of self-poisoning. So we fall easier victims to germs.

Our food is apt to be less crisp and hard from now on. So let's clean our teeth oftener – and for at least two minutes at a time.

A tip when you're going out into the cold. Take a teaspoonful of olive oil. It heats you up and helps the digestion.

A cold often starts in the head and goes down into the chest. So, if you get a head cold, rub the chest at night with olive oil and the cold may never get down to your chest.

Take hot gruels for a sore throat or cold. They act like an internal poultice.

I often think we should all use more of this old-timer food, gruel.

Finally, have more company in winter.

We're all apt to be too much alone. That's bad for the mind – and for the body.

Come On And Enjoy The Bad Weather

December 13, 1959

"I WONDER if I'll get through the winter scot free?" We're all asking that question this month.

And I could tell in a minute what your chances are.

The lucky folk are those who have good circulation. It's probably the most important factor in keeping fit in winter.

Just look at the advantages.

1. The blood romps through the arteries and veins. In cold weather the blood never stays long enough in one place to get chilled. Remember, it's chilling of the blood that brings winter troubles in a hundred ways – from pleurisy to rheumatics.

2. You'll never feel sluggish with a good circulation. For the blood has a job not many folk know about. It helps to get rid of all the waste products in the system.

3. A good circulation means you're more likely to be cheerful and optimistic in winter. That's because the brain depends on good circulation for the best available blood – and it gets just that.

4. Quick distribution of blood adds up to a good defence against germs, whether it's a cut on the finger or a sore throat. The blood gets to the trouble spot in quick time and snuffs out the infection before it gets the upper hand.

5. Good circulation also means good muscles. It's a strange thing, but good muscles are more important in winter than in summer. It's muscle contraction that generates heat to keep us warm on the coldest day.

6. A good blood flow is half the secret of being hardy. That's why Mr Brown can go about in just a jacket when you're wearing a topcoat. His pores close quickly to the cold air. They're never caught wide open to a chill.

"Now, how can I improve my circulation?" you may ask. It's easy – but don't expect anything spectacular.

Modern techniques and new medicines may help. But the two sure ways are as old as the hills – they are exercise and fresh air. Exercise tones up the muscles and that means the heart muscle, which pumps the blood along.

Next, don't be afraid of winter.

Fear upsets the nervous control of the circulation. That's why, when you're happy, you don't feel the cold nearly so much. The moment you're miserable on a bitter day you're far more likely to catch a chill.

The circulation slows down. Blood stays too long near the skin and gets chilled. Then the cold blood passes inwards and chills stomach, &c.

Another way to help your circulation is to cultivate a straight back. Don't cramp the lungs. Shoulders held well back help the blood flow.

Drink plenty of fluids – fruit juice, particularly. Have your fair share of cheese, butter, eggs, beans, peas. All these give energy to get you out and about – even on dull days.

Fluids help digestion. Maybe you didn't know it, but indigestion can make you feel cold.

Don't dodge baths in winter. A good clean skin makes you less liable to chills.

Don't wear too tight shoes. And I think woollen gloves are best.

The reason is, you can help the blood flow at any time. Simply curl and uncurl your toes. Open and shut your hands.

The secret is to generate your own heat. Walk, dance, and keep your hands and feet moving.

Even if you're in the seventies, don't sit about the house too much. Do wee odd jobs. Even knitting helps.

Keep these points in mind, and your blood should flow easily. And it'll all add up to enjoying winter, not fearing it.

What A Silly Thing To Do In A Cold Snap

November 30, 1952

ALL this week I've been on the go from morning till night. Right, left, and centre, folk have been knocked out with colds, chills, neuralgia, lumbago, and rheumatism. Without exception, the victims blame the cold snap.

But in many cases I think they should really blame themselves.

The average person should get through the winter pretty easily. If we don't, it's often because of the silly things we do in winter!

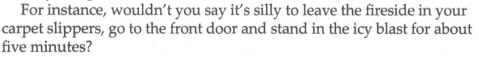

For instance, wouldn't you say it's silly to leave the fireside in your carpet slippers, go to the front door and stand in the icy blast for about five minutes?

Of course you would. Yet many of us do just that about once a week, and don't realise it! We have friends in for the evening. About eleven o'clock, we see them to the door. We don't like making the goodbyes too abrupt, so we stand there for a while.

Our skin is hot and the pores wide open for attack.

Women especially are silly about this. Because a cold or chill takes 36 to 48 hours to develop, we don't realise we've got it because of the delayed goodbye.

Always keep in mind that a chill often comes via the feet. So if you're tempted to stop and have a chat in the street on a cold, wet day, don't stand for more than a minute or two.

That's one of the silly things many of us do in winter.

The ground is always cold. And the cold can get through the best of shoes, especially if it's a wet cold.

Indoors you're most vulnerable to a chilling of the feet during the five minutes after you get up in the morning. This is because the circulation hasn't got going for the day.

For this reason, it's a mistake to let your bare feet touch the lino. A pair of slippers at the bedside is a MUST for winter health.

Lots of folk make a big error in winter when they don't change their undervest before they go to bed.

An active skin is a fine defence in winter. If you keep on a vest all week the cushion of air between the wool and the skin gets stale or squashed out.

Change every night in winter.

When you put on the underwear again in the morning, there's a fresh cushion of air against the skin. That's grand for circulation.

It's silly to be excessively energetic in bitterly cold weather.

The risk of slight heart strain is at its greatest.

Supposing you go sledging with the youngsters. If you're 30 to 40, one hour is more than ample. Over 40, no more than half an hour.

Warning signs that you're overdoing it are breathlessness, a catch in the throat, a thumping of the heart.

"Heart" folk should always warm their outdoor clothes before they go out. The cold air makes a sudden demand on the heart. They should also start the outdoor journey leisurely. It's folly to hurry from the house.

What about "chesty" people?

One of the commonest mistakes they make is to talk when out of doors in rimy weather. Silence for them is certainly golden.

To open the mouth in frosty weather is an easy way to bring on bronchitis or whatever they're subject to.

Now, here's an experience you'll often have on a cold day. One minute you're aglow with health – then suddenly you feel chilled.

That's a warning – and it's silly to ignore it.

Somewhere you're being attacked by damp – get home, and don't spare the horses. Change clothes and get a rub down. If possible, have a bath.

One or two points about eating in winter.

Take at least an hour and a half over your Christmas dinner. It's wrong to eat an unusually big meal at the normal rate.

It's wrong also to eat your normal amount after a party the previous night. Eat only half of your usual in food next day. Make up the balance in fluid.

The Worst Mistake We Can Make When On Holiday

June 20, 1954

SOMETHING odd happens to many of us on holiday. For the first three or four days we're on top of the world. Then we feel heaviness for the rest of the holiday.

Probably a vague dissatisfaction, even depression, plus a desire to get the holiday finished.

Well, it's as simple as this – we're just overeating.

That's common on holiday and the woman of the family is most likely to suffer.

There's a natural increase in appetite. There are extra meals, bigger meals. The housewife is having meals made for her instead of making them. The liver is overloaded. Hence the depression as well as the heaviness.

A good idea to save the liver is to miss the last meal of the day. But don't scrimp breakfast.

In addition, I advise half a teaspoonful of salts in a glass of warm water first thing in the morning on an empty stomach.

You see, on holiday the meals are apt to be irregular and different in size to your normal. This can lead to constipation.

If we're pretty active, a little constipation is not all that serious – but it so easily gets worse, and it can "dull" the whole system. So try that pinch of salts.

I don't think we should spend too much of our holiday in a car, especially a small one. Everybody, whether they realise it or not, has a faint but deep feeling of claustrophobia.

You realise this when you step out of a car after a long run – what feeling of relief you have! Two hours inside a car, then 15 minutes' break, is reasonable.

But long runs in a car – well, it's not my idea of a good holiday. There's less fresh air, more draughts. Some muscles are overstrained, other muscles go flabby.

Dangers are – (1) constipation, (2) breathing troubles and (3) muscle and joint troubles. Even the nerves can be upset.

One reason we don't have so much energy during and after a holiday is that we develop catarrh, even in a minor degree.

The air passages of nose and throat have to deal with new irritations. For instance, you may go from town to country where the air is filled with pollen and tiny seeds. That's something new to the system.

Now that shouldn't bother the average holidaymaker. But the unfortunate thing is that nearly every one of us smokes far more than usual on holiday.

It's these extra cigarettes that really start the catarrh, and prepare the way for the effect of the seeds, &c.

So make it a rule on holiday – light up no more than your usual quota of cigarettes.

Another holiday pastime that pulls you down is walking the streets aimlessly. It's all very easy to go round the shops, but, remember, it's much harder work than you realise.

And there's another thing – the nerves don't like crowds.

There's irritation at every other step. The folk in front aren't fast enough. You're always on the qui vive for bumps.

No, it's not my idea of a holiday!

If you feel tired on holiday it may mean you're not getting enough sleep. For though few folk realise it, on holiday we feel better if we take an extra hour in bed.

We're usually burning up more energy, so we need that hour for extra stoking up.

In giving you all this advice, don't think I'm a spoilsport. But a little holiday wisdom of the kind I've mentioned won't only make you healthy afterwards, you'll also enjoy your holiday twice as much at the time!

The best way to fend off fleas in a picture house

April 18, 1954 — **Is there anything I can do to fend off fleas? I work in a picture house and as soon as the weather turns warm, I get constantly bitten.**

Various preparations kill these pests, but they may all irritate the skin if used regularly. Ask your chemist to try you out cautiously with one or two preparations.

January 13, 1952 — **Is it advisable for two people recovering from tuberculosis (having been ill for 9-12 months) to marry, especially in a hot climate?**

Another year should be allowed to elapse. During this time specialist treatment and supervision are essential.

October 28, 1951 — **I've started wearing a scarf again, but it isn't keeping me as warm as I expected. What's the best type of scarf?**

A loosely-knitted woollen one. The loose texture traps air and insulates you against the cold.

October 19, 1952 — **My pre-fab bedroom has a ventilator. Is it necessary to leave the window open when I go to bed?**

In good weather, yes. In bad weather, no (especially if it is windy, frosty or foggy).

February 26, 1956 — **I live alone in a big bed-sitting room. During the recent cold weather the temperature there (day-time) was between 48 and 50 degrees. I'm over 80 and have angina. Is this temperature sufficient?**

No, unless you're in a cosy bed all the time.

September 1, 1957 — **One of my toes always becomes badly affected with chilblains in frosty weather. Can I do anything now to prevent this?**

See that your footwear is comfortable and roomy at all times. Avoid putting your feet (when cold) against a hot bottle, near a stove or fire, or into hot water. Walk regularly every day.

June 18, 1950 — **Can you give any advice to those of us who are afraid of thunder?**

Thundery weather has a depressing effect on the system. You can get headaches and a feeling of oppression. But don't let this give way to a feeling of fear. Lightning kills or hurts remarkably few people, your chances in a thunderstorm are far better than when crossing a busy road.

July 16, 1950 — **If the weather is cloudy, I get severe headaches. They usually come before rain, and go away after. What can I do to stop it?**

This is due to the amount of electricity in the atmosphere. It affects us all, depressing or "elevating" us. Some are affected more than others. It's nothing to be alarmed about, and there's nothing you can do about it.

June 16, 1957 — **My wife suffers from hay fever, asthma and bronchitis. Would it be unwise to take her with me on a camping holiday this summer?**

It all depends where the holiday camp is to be. By the seaside or on the moors might suit excellently.

November 29, 1953 — **Every summer I've irritation in my arms and shoulders. It goes away in winter. What's the cause?**

Direct sunlight does this to some folk. Calamine cream, applied each night, is likely to help.

August 22, 1954 — **In an article you said blackcurrant jam makes the perfect drink for winter. What's the recipe?**

Put one heaped tablespoonful of the jam in a tumbler. Pour in boiling water and add two teaspoonfuls of sugar.

February 3, 1952 — **I've had recurring hacks on each side of my mouth for the past months. I'm 57. What's the cause and cure?**

Probably the changeable and hard weather is responsible. In which case, treat with boracic ointment or glycerine and borax. If it persists, consult your doctor in case you're below par.

February 5, 1950 — **My husband goes out to play snow-balling with the children. He comes back with raw, red hands, but otherwise full of beans. Is this bad for him?**

Normally, no. So long as he gets off wet shoes, socks, &c., and dries himself thoroughly whenever he comes in, he's OK.

September 7, 1958 — **Which country would be most suitable for a person suffering from fibrositis from head to toes, and who is also developing a chronic wheeze?**

I'd plump for California, where the climate is equable and sunny.

January 21, 1951 — **Can you tell me how to get rid of a red nose? My nose runs in cold weather.**

Don't polish it with a moist hankie. Don't blow too strongly. Get an inhaler to dry up secretions which are too strong in your case.

May 1, 1955 — **Is walking a good exercise for rheumatoid arthritis?**
Yes, except in wet or windy weather.

— Chapter 5 —

The Heart Of The Matter

EXCITING football matches and films are dangerous for the hearts of middle-aged, male doctors, lawyers, business men and foremen. Industrial workers and navvies will be fine, and housewives (because their worries are trivial!) should also be OK.

Heart disease, and coronary thrombosis were much misunderstood conditions in the 1950s, so there was quite a bit of conflicting information given — take hearty exercise, don't exercise too much.

But there was also good advice, if couched in terms unfamiliar nowadays. You should avoid having a "flabby heart", for instance, or a dull mind. A good sign of heart health was the ability to walk 20 yards without letting your heels touch the ground. Give it a try!

Reading between the lines, however, there was a growing awareness, understanding and concern over heart problems.

Two of the articles, one from 1951, a second from 1957, are largely "tests" so readers could work out if they might be at risk.

This was a sombre message – that lives were being claimed, lives that could have gone on for several more years, if not decades, if warning signs had been heeded or a few simple steps had been taken. The 1950s Doc was trying to save his readers.

These articles were paid great attention. People had seen the effects of heart maladies all around them. Their own friends and relatives who died too young.

When The Doc asked his "12 questions" there were men and women who were very worried about their answers. These are the sorts of articles that had anxious patients queuing in droves, desperate to see their GP as soon as possible.

Many Of Us Damage The Heart Without Knowing We're Doing It

January 15, 1956

IT'S a curious thing, but though most of us are frightened of heart disease the thought of heart strain rarely strikes us.

Yet the danger of straining your heart is ten times greater than the danger of getting heart disease!

You can be cruel to your heart in ways you probably never realised.

I examined a patient last Wednesday. He was a bank clerk, who had never done any hard physical work. He was gentle, and his movements were slow and deliberate. He never ran for buses or lifted heavy furniture.

When I told him he was suffering from heart strain, he refused at first to believe me!

"How could that possibly be?" he asked.

"Well," I told him, "I don't know your domestic background, but your brain is slogging your heart to death".

When I examined him in my surgery, he lay flat on a couch. In that position the average heart pushes round a gallon of blood in a minute. His heart was having to push round two and a half gallons of blood in a minute!

If that happened when he was lying still, think of the strain when he was on the move.

He was the inoffensive type – wouldn't say boo to a goose. He would swallow an insult and restrain his anger – indeed, a man who prided himself on his self-control.

But – and here's the point – all the things that irritated him rankled in his mind. And nothing strains the heart more than suppressed emotion.

Heart strain is more common now than ever.

One reason will surprise you. Today you can be cured of an illness too quickly! You often feel better in two or three days, when it used to take a fortnight.

Any illness involving feverishness poisons the heart. So, although you apparently recover in two days, the heart is weakened, and really needs a fortnight to recover!

It's silly – and after you're 45 it's dangerous – to go back to your usual activities too soon.

The four common illnesses where you're apt to strain the heart are – flu, pneumonia, tonsillitis and throat troubles, and scarlet fever.

What's more, with these illnesses the danger of heart strain is even greater than the disease itself.

If you do rush back to work before your heart is fit, the first thing the body calls for is more blood.

But the heart is flabby and can't increase the force of its beat.

So it can only speed up the beat – and the big heart muscles may be strained.

The sad fact is that if you strain the heart in this way after you're 45, it'll never be the same.

What about sheer physical strain and its effect on the heart?

First a word to the housewives. Never carry a shopping bag up a hill if it weighs more than 14 lb. It's a terrific strain on the heart.

The effort of holding the heavy bag tightens the chest muscles. This in turn restricts your breathing. And the moment you've to hold your breath the strain is increased.

Menfolk should remember this, too. Never try to lift a wardrobe if you can't breathe when you're lifting.

And if you feel the veins on your neck standing out – call a halt!

When you're tired and have to tackle a heavy job, for any sake begin slowly.

The cruellest thing you can do to your heart is to galvanise it into action with a sudden spurt of running or a quick, heavy lift.

Unless you're very fit, it's most unwise to dash for a bus after a heavy day's work.

Many a man strains his heart when he least suspects it. He has a few pints of beer at the local, then notices the clock. "Goodness, I'll have to run", he says. What he doesn't know is that too much fluid in the tummy hinders the action of the heart.

So take it easy, mister!

Once we get past the 45 mark, it's most important we should avoid heart strain.

Think of it this way. If we stretch a new elastic band 100 times, it goes back to its shape easily. But try this with an old elastic band and soon it remains stretched.

That's exactly what happens to a middle-aged heart.

Now for smoking and alcohol. You can smoke ten cigarettes a day and your heart won't suffer.

But twenty a day are bound to make it beat fast. So it's perhaps doing double work in a day.

A splendid safeguard is to give smoking a rest for two or three hours at least – say in the forenoon.

Excess of alcohol, particularly spirits, harms the heart in a different way.

You can be as thin as a rake, yet if you're a heavy drinker you're almost sure to have a fatty heart. This kind of strain can be really dangerous – even a killer in time.

So there you are.

The way to have a good-going heart is through moderation, a good nature – and, remember, if you're elderly, pause every twelve steps when going up a hill or climbing stairs.

THE MODERN VIEW, BY DR LYNDA

THE 1950s Doc is really talking about two different heart problems here.

1. Chronic heart "strain", or failure, when the heart is not able to pump effectively, causing a build-up of fluid in the lungs and legs, resulting in breathlessness, tiredness and puffy swollen ankles.

2. Sudden acute episodes of stress on the heart, resulting in a lack of oxygen to the heart muscle itself, causing heart attacks, angina and electrical faults which result in sudden problems and sometimes death.

His understanding of how heart disease happens and the physiology of it all is almost completely wrong, but in fairness to him there have been incredible advances in investigative procedures in the last 50 years.

Due to better understanding and knowledge of how the heart works, preventative measures have been revolutionary in reducing deaths and morbidity by heart disease.

In 1955 more than a quarter of all UK deaths were due to heart attacks, a further quarter of deaths were due to other cardiovascular problems (heart, stoke and other circulation issues). Nowadays less than a third of all deaths are caused by these three issues.

And not all of it is down to "moderation and having a good nature"!

It's Just About The Worst Thing You Could Possibly Do For Your Heart

February 8, 1959

A FEW weeks ago a middle-aged man I know dashed out of the back door to his car. He was late and, to crown all, the car battery was flat. The self-starter wouldn't work.

So he got hold of the starting handle and furiously began to crank the engine. He gave it all he had and more.

Suddenly he felt far from well. So he went back to the house and sat down.

In two hours he was dead.

His heart had given up. It couldn't cope with his sudden spurt of effort. Nothing is worse for the heart than to be jolted quickly into maximum effort.

And nobody over 35 can do it and get away without some ill effects. If you're one of these folk quick off the mark, change your ideas now.

Otherwise, you're almost certain to be a poor soul after 55 – if you live that long.

Quick starters become old quickly. The last third of their life is plagued with troubles.

First, they suffer from a dilated heart.

That means he'll have distressing breathlessness when he makes any sort of effort.

Second, they're easy victims to respiratory troubles.

If there's one thing even worse than too quick a start, it's too quick a start when you're in a temper.

That's because you hash the heart and don't realise it – you're too angry.

Suppose you say to your wife one morning, "Here, I'll give you a hand with the spring-cleaning and beat the living-room carpet". Well if you start hashing into it, you're silly. You're not used to that sort of exercise.

But if your wife nags you into beating the carpet, and you go to it with vigour and an angry thought – the strain on the heart when you do it is practically doubled.

A sudden dash for the bus is bad. A spurt for the bus after a heavy meal is far worse.

In fact, a burst of temper on a heavy meal is a strain on the heart after 45. Lose your rag before lunch if you must – but never immediately after.

Anybody with a record of bronchitis or asthma is also wise to avoid sudden bursts of energy.

The lungs are under a double strain. The heart tries to make good the deficiency of oxygen and suffers for it.

What about heavy lifts?

Never lift anything heavy enough to make you hold your breath. Otherwise your heart is too hard-worked.

And do the lifting with the legs – not the arms or back. That's the secret. It's the straightening of the big muscles in the legs that does the lifting.

Any other way is likely to make trouble in the heart region, blood vessels near the brain, or, more particularly, in the back.

Never lift any weight more than eighteen inches in front of you. When you have to lean forward to reach for a lift, you're liable to displace a disc in the back.

Now, how do you get up in the morning? Do you jump out of bed or do you groan and stretch and crawl out?

This'll surprise you. You can pat yourself on the back if you're in the No. 2 lot.

The springers-out-of-bed are doing the wrong thing. It's the worst start to the day they can have.

Any change of position after a period of immobility is best done slowly. The blood flow shifts – and the slower the better.

Watch a cat getting itself started after a sleep. That's what we should try.

Even getting up out of a chair should be done slowly. Bounding out of a chair can make the healthiest folk feel dizzy. That's because

Indigestion Sufferers !

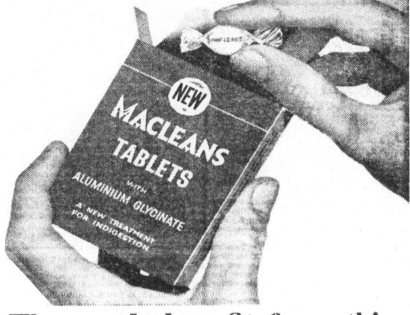

Thousands benefit from this remarkable new treatment

All over the country, indigestion sufferers in their thousands are switching to New Macleans Tablets.

No wonder! New Macleans Tablets give them "follow-through protection" against acid indigestion. Not only rapid relief from their indigestion pain, but also *prolonged* relief for hours, literally hours.

A great advance in the treatment of indigestion, it has been made possible by the development of Aluminium Glycinate, a new and remarkable antacid compound.

"Follow-through protection" describes the prolonged relieving action of the Aluminium Glycinate in New Macleans Tablets. This exclusive compound *controls* stomach acid and *holds* it at natural levels. Thus New Macleans Tablets stop any return of indigestion pain for hours.

Small and pleasantly flavoured, they should be sucked or chewed. To combat a sharp attack of indigestion, chew one tablet, and immediately afterwards suck another. At all chemists, cartons 3s. 6d. handy roll pack 1s. 3d.

New Macleans Tablets
stop pain quickly . . . then give you follow-through protection

MACLEANS LTD., GREAT WEST ROAD, BRENTFORD, MIDDLESEX   NMT 2/14/8

the blood surges away from the brain. In old folk, this can cause a nasty fall. And anyone with hardened arteries shouldn't do these things.

Any sudden shift in the blood flow might be serious for them.

P.S. – The slow start way of life affects more than physical effort. If you're a brain worker, start in bottom gear and work up. If you start in top gear, you tire mentally before the end of the day.

THE MODERN VIEW, BY DR LYNDA

A FEW problems here. Suppressed emotion, temper, losing the rag in the afternoon and short bursts of strenuous exercise, in the main, do not cause heart failure directly, as the 1950s Doc suggests. But these things can sometimes cause other problems, resulting in acute coronary problems.

Nowadays we know the main causes of heart failure are smoking (and yes — even 10 a day are implicated), alcohol, raised blood pressure, modern diets with excess cholesterol, sugars, obesity and reducing exercise and physical activity.

There are "almost truths". The advice to "Do the lifting with the legs" is good, although the trouble will be with the back not the heart.

"Old folk getting out of a chair or bed too quickly can make you dizzy" is called postural or orthostatic hypotension. It happens when your blood pressure falls due to a change in position. When you are young, your body and blood vessels can react quickly to a change in position, but as you get older the response is slower and the blood vessels are not able to maintain the flow of blood to the brain, making you lightheaded and dizzy and in extreme cases you might faint or fall.

It's made worse by the number of medicines that you may be on, some of which exacerbate the drop in blood pressure, especially water tablets, medicines for high blood pressure, prostate problems and Parkinson's disease, to name a few common ones.

Lifestyle is the key to heart disease prevention.

As I've said, heart disease has reduced over the last 50 years but I suspect the next generation may not be so lucky as they seem to think that taking a cholesterol pill "allows" them to have that cream bun.

The increase in obesity, and its outcomes like diabetes and hypertension, will, I think, mean we'll see more heart disease in the future as we rely on medicine and technologies to keep us well rather than taking responsibility for our lives and our lifestyles.

Am I Likely To Get It?

March 25, 1951

AMONG my patients last week were a business man, a woman teacher, and a labourer. Their jobs and lives couldn't have been more different. Yet each asked the same question:-
"There seems to be a lot of this coronary thrombosis nowadays, doctor. Am I the kind of person likely to get it?"

It's a question more and more folk are asking.

Because there's certainly far more coronary thrombosis than ever before.

In the last 30 years the number of cases has increased 20 times. In the past 10 years it's doubled. From 20,000 to 40,000 people now die from it every year.

That sounds alarming, so let me say at once – the odds against getting the disease at all are well over 1,000 – 1. And the disease isn't necessarily fatal.

Now, which of my three patients is most likely to get it?

I say without hesitation the business man. Because not only is C.T. mainly a male disease (eight cases in every ten), it's often a penalty of "getting on", especially in professional men.

The very qualities which lead to success encourage C.T. – long responsibility, hard brainwork, worry, edginess, drive, the urge to be always on the job, and the neglect of relaxation.

When too much of this is added to other stresses, it makes the heart tired. The main heart (or coronary) artery narrows, and a moment comes when the blood flow slows down and clots.

That's why so many cases occur in doctors, lawyers, business men, and even foremen.

It's also essentially a disease of middle life (the fifties and sixties) when such men are at the top. Under 40, there's little need to worry about C.T., although you can start the conditions which may lead to the disease later. Over 70, the chances are remote.

Why isn't a navvy or heavy industrial worker just as liable to C.T. as a professional man?

Because, no matter how hard he works, he doesn't lay himself open to wear and tear of nervous energy.

Few women take C.T. for the same reason. Home life is natural to them, and although they worry, it's usually superficial.

Is there anything C.T. types can do to avoid it?

Yes. My favourite prescription is – "Make your pleasures simple".

It's often the addition of other excitement to the strains of work that puts too big a call on the heart.

Heavy eating, smoking and drinking too much, exciting football matches or films – all these things stimulate and put an extra strain on a heart that's already carrying a heavy burden.

Hard work itself, playing games, gardening, hiking, fishing – these shouldn't increase the chances of C.T. There's nothing emotional about them, you see.

Another thing. Too many men of the C.T. type refuse to take adequate convalescence after illness. They go back to work when the heart is still out of tone – and so C.T. is encouraged.

Because of all the stresses and new excitements of life we need more than ever today a healthy regular life, fresh air, freedom from useless worry – and let me repeat, simple pleasures.

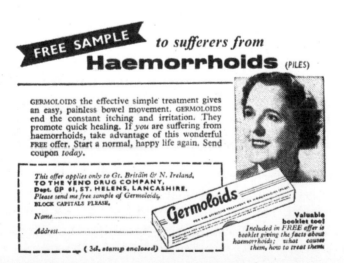

Twelve Questions To Ask Yourself
May 5, 1957

HARDLY a day passes but you hear of somebody collapsing from coronary thrombosis.

Maybe the thought has struck you. "Is it likely to happen to me?"

Your answer – "yes" or "no" – to the following questions will give you a fair idea.

But, first of all, let me stress it's a combination of several of these things, not just the answer "yes" to one.

Do you find you can't stride up a hill?

This can be an early sign of a liability to bad arteries. The blood is finding it harder to get through to the heart muscle. Breathlessness isn't so important. The warning sign is more a vague physical weakness.

Have you ever had a short, fierce pain in the centre of the chest?

Perhaps it passed off, and you feel as fit as ever. Take the warning, though. It can be an early sign of C.T.

You may have had an attack and didn't realise it. Maybe only a tiny artery was blocked or took cramp. No serious damage done. Still, it's better to slow down your pace.

Are you 14 lb. overweight?

Overweight means flabbiness – this tends to bring on a change in the artery walls and weakens the strength of your blood flow. The flabbier you are, the more chance of a blood blockage as you get older. So no second helping for you after 50. Eating more than necessary turns our "chemist's shop" into disorder. This, in time, is almost certain to thicken the arteries.

Are you a fast eater?

If so, you miss the first stage of natural digestion – the help from juices in the mouth. Doctors often suffer from C.T. One of the main reasons is we often have to eat hurried meals. Even mushy foods should be chewed.

Do you like fatty foods, even in summer?

This is one taste I'd advise you to change. Too much fat, particularly animal fat, is bad for arteries. Only youngsters can expect to get away with this habit.

Did any of your blood relatives die of a heart collapse?

If so, take a little care after 40. No need to worry unduly, but you've got to face it – you may be a little more vulnerable to C.T. We inherit not only the same nose, &c., but the same kind of arteries, circulation – even the same chemical action in our system.

Have you no great taste for vegetables and fruit?

It's a pity if the answer's yes. These are the main foods to keep the arteries supple well into later life. They're a natural laxative, and we need their chemicals to provide good circulation.

Are you daft about pastries, suet pudding and rich foods?

Don't overdo it. Too much starch means overweight – and a strain on you. Also, you may be taking into the system too much cholesterol – a chemical that is blamed by some authorities for thickening the arteries.

Do you seldom drink water?

Plenty water daily gets top marks, along with vegetables and fruit, for keeping arteries in good trim.

Do you have your first cigarette before breakfast?

Not a good sign. Over-smoking makes you an easier target for C.T. It speeds up the heart, harms digestion, starts chemical upsets. The actual nicotine may also affect the big heart muscle. Cut down to 20 a day.

Are you always "tight for time"?

It's folk who never have a minute to spare who are likeliest victims. Late to get up, late for the bus, for work – it all adds up to anxiety. This sets up tension, even in our arteries. Also, the organs and glands that turn our food into energy, &c., are overworked.

Do you sleep less than 50 hours a week?

It's your weekly amount that matters. Less than 50 hours means that the brain and arteries suffer. Arteries need time for repairs just as much as muscles.

Now, let's add up the "yeas" and "nays". If you've more nays than yeas – congratulations.

And, remember, C.T. is rare in men under 40 and in women under 50. But if you're in your 20s and do silly things for years, you may land in trouble later on.

It Always Seems To Strike So Suddenly

April 11, 1954

WE seem to hear more and more about people suffering from clots in the blood.

Let me say right away that a clot in the blood is not necessarily a death sentence.

Far from it! About 75 per cent of such cases clear up themselves.

Clots tend to form in three areas – (1) the arteries near the heart, (2) round the valves of the heart, (3) the brain.

The gravest danger area for a clot is the 12 inches of coronary arteries round the heart. These arteries feed the heart muscle.

A clot blocking the flow causes complete collapse. Even so, we can now sometimes foresee the danger.

You see, the great problem is that a clot, if untreated, gathers size like a snowball as it passes along.

Don't believe anybody who tells you of a new drug that can dissolve a clot. What we do is to give an injection that prevents the snowballing effect. And if conditions are favourable the clot may disappear before it reaches the danger area.

Nature does this on its own. The most important thing is to keep the clot from moving. If we can do that there's always hope.

And with apparatus devised within the past ten years we can pin-point a clot – and take steps to "fix" it, and prevent it increasing in size. Rest, quietness and the anti-coagulant drug can well be the life-saver.

Older people, about 70, are particularly susceptible to a clot on the brain. But even that need not be fatal.

The collapse may not be as severe as coronary trouble – perhaps a series of little strokes lasting a fortnight.

The surprising thing is that the patient can recover, and quite quickly, too.

What has happened is that the clot has blocked a blood vessel and is preventing part of the brain getting its "food".

But the blood can eventually find side-routes to the affected part – hence the apparent miraculous recovery.

All older folk can do a lot to avoid this trouble. A main cause is slowing down of interests and exercise. In other words – coddling themselves to the point of stagnation.

Warning signs are headaches and giddiness. After recovery the patient may lose his old-time mental keenness. Still, that's not to say he's finished. It's up to relatives to do all they can to get him "interested".

Now No. 3 (the brain).

It really starts in the heart. The patient has been warned of heart trouble – the kind due to a clot hovering round one of the valves.

This can cause little discomfort. And therein lies the danger. The patient gets impatient with the doctor's "go easy" advice.

Over-exertion, sudden anger – and the patient may be dead within 20 minutes.

What happens is that a tiny clot is driven out of the heart, smack into the brain – gets stuck like a cork. And that's the end.

There's another kind of collapse which is distressing but which often gives hope of recovery.

It's called a stroke, but is really a cerebral haemorrhage. Here the shock to the brain is not a clot, but a bursting of a thin or diseased blood vessel.

The likeliest victims are folk in the sixties, or folk who for a long time have had high blood pressure, and who tend to be highly emotional, or highly competitive.

After the collapse, there is paralysis of an arm, a leg, or all one side, even the whole body.

No relative should despair. It is possible that in one month there will be some movement, in three months quite appreciable relaxing of the paralysis.

In six months I've often seen the body able to move reasonably well. And in one year, sometimes almost complete recovery.

In these cases of recovery, it's essential that the patient disciplines himself into an easy, calm outlook. If that is achieved, the chances of a recurrence are considerably reduced.

What are the causes of clotting?

If the inside walls of our arteries, &c. become rough, we increase the chances of clotting. Factors making for this roughness are infections due to bad hygiene, poisoning, due to possibly excessive smoking, drinking. And also poor kidneys.

Moderation. Plenty of water to drink. Control of temper. These are some of the helps.

The Simple Secret Of Having A Strong Heart

June 29, 1958

WHAT'S your age? 37? Or 57? Whatever you are, make sure you get your fair share of exercise. If you don't you can be in for real trouble.

And the older you are, the more important it is to get reasonable exercise.

It's important in the 50s. Vital in the 60s and can mean life or death in the 70s.

You see, our muscles degenerate very quickly. You know that after a week in bed. A month or two without exercise can thin down a muscle from its minnow shape to a mere thread.

In two years you can land yourself with a flabby heart – just by lack of exercise. The big heart muscle actually withers. This doesn't only show itself in breathlessness and unfitness, but in the brain, too.

So if you begin to lack your old buoyancy, just ask yourself: "Am I getting enough exercise?"

It's really a vicious circle. The mind gets dull through lack of exercise and the inclination to take exercise can fade right out of your life.

You find yourself waiting 15 minutes for a bus rather than undertake a ten-minute walk.

When you reach that stage you're going "down the hill", no matter what your birth certificate says.

Four of our main troubles today are linked with our circulation – thrombosis, high blood pressure, hardened arteries and strokes.

If you don't take exercise you're twice as liable to any of that four.

Take the arteries, for instance. Forty per cent. of overweight is due to lack of exercise.

But surplus fat doesn't only gather on your tummy. It gets among the linings of all your arteries. Result: degeneration of the arteries. They lose elasticity. The heart has to work harder to pump the blood through. So up goes the blood pressure.

The walls of the arteries may also lose their smoothness.

Next thing, blood can collect into a clot, and start a dangerous journey along your bloodstream. That's where the risk of a stroke comes about.

The danger time for all of us is between 45 and 55. So be as active as you can in middle-age and your chances of dodging artery trouble are good.

We've recently discovered slow movers are far more liable to varicose veins.

So, ladies, take the hint. You're more liable to them than men – and it could be because you don't walk so briskly.

It's the same with constipation. If you're always on the go, you shouldn't be troubled. It's muscles that work the bowels – and walking keeps muscles in good trim.

Another thing. Did you catch everything that was going last winter? If you did, you can do better this winter.

Start now to get out and use your legs. It's the tonic that costs nothing. Yet it gives better resistance to infection than anything else. Keep up the walking all through winter.

It's worth remembering, too, that nothing wears you out more than doing nothing.

Suppose you come home after a harassing day. You're mentally tired. Well, fight that feeling to flop into a chair for the rest of the evening. By all means have half an hour with your feet up. Then out you go and do some physical work.

You'll sleep better. Your nervous tiredness will give way to pleasant muscle tiredness. And you'll be fitter for the problems of the next day.

What's the test of your fitness?

You don't need to do 100 yards in 12 seconds to find out. Just try to walk 20 yards without letting your heels touch the ground. If you're able to do that without being unbearably sore below the calves, you're not too bad.

If you're lying back on the grass in summer do you find it a problem to get up?

If you do, you're slipping into unfitness. Unless, of course, you're an old age pensioner.

And if you have a hard job getting out of an armchair, it's really high time your muscles were exercised.

Lastly, a gleam of hope for old folk.

We've found that exercises can do wonders for the over 70s. At most city hospitals there's a special department to give new fitness to folk who thought they were finished.

The danger for anybody over 70 is stiffening joints. The great thing is to exercise the muscles round the joints – particularly knees and ankles.

The Most Important Warning Of All

September 6, 1959

FEW of us go on and on without some trouble threatening. The lucky ones are those who heed the first warning – the most important warning of all.

Many of my patients over 40 are scared of coronary thrombosis.

"How can I tell if I'm heading for it?" they ask. Well, the first warning could be a tiny attack of C.T. It's a feeling of alarm that comes across you. You sweat, feel unwell and have a pain across the breast bone.

But only for two or three minutes.

Then you feel as good as ever – and forget all about it.

But don't forget it. Ask advice from the doctor. A change of diet or in your way of living can prevent a bigger attack.

There's another kind of heart trouble that gives its first warning in a different way.

You've spurted for the bus, or had a violent quarrel. Now you feel a pain across the chest and down an arm.

The pain means your heart is trying to tell you the blood is finding it hard to keep moving around.

A serious breakdown of the heart can be avoided – provided you heed the red light and do what the doctor says.

We haven't the same chance with a stroke.

Collapse can sometimes come completely and unexpectedly. But there is one sign that may show itself. It's small, but vital. All that happens is that a hand or foot goes dead or weak for no apparent reason.

This "dead" feeling can last for hours or maybe only five minutes.

It might not be the "stroke" alarm. But it could be. So if you're over 50, have a word with your doctor.

For younger folk, this "dead" feeling is generally of no importance.

High blood pressure doesn't give any definite warning. But here's something you should know. If you have long spells of being tired and headachy, there's good cause for a check-up on your blood pressure. It's possible it's too high or even too low.

Now, if you waken up off and on in the middle of the night with a pin-pointed indigestion, it may not be just a case of ordinary indigestion.

It could be that an ulcer is making its first protest.

Some folk have the idea that if they're always hungry the trouble could be diabetes. That's not the case. To be perpetually thirsty is the warning – and needs treatment.

Here's a good guide for the coming winter.

Most troubles then are infectious, and if they're nipped in the bud you save days of illness.

This is how you can do it. The first sign of flu is easy to identify. It's a feeling of ice-cold water tumbling down your spine.

The moment you have this sensation, take a hot drink, a couple of aspirins, and get into bed.

Stay there for 24 hours.

An ordinary cold usually starts off with a dry throat or nose. That's not too obvious. But when the first sneeze comes, too, take the same cure as the one for flu.

This time, 12 hours in bed should do the trick.

Lastly, two warnings from the eyes.

No. 1 is when they feel gritty. That could be a first sign you're needing glasses, or stronger ones.

No. 2 is much more serious. You're walking in the dark and notice halos round the street lamps. Also halos round the lights when you get into the house.

It may be glaucoma, and it calls for the doctor, within two days at most. If, in addition, you have a severe headache and vomiting, it's an emergency.

P.S. – Remember, these warnings could be false. Even so, it's silly to take any chances.

The Five Main Dangers To The Heart
December 13, 1953

DO you know a lot of folk could live five or ten years longer than they do? Yes – if they'd just take a few elementary precautions about the heart.

There are five main dangers to the heart – and they can all be avoided.

Take the case of Mr B. In his 20s and well into his 30s he was keen on all kinds of sport. In his 50s he was tall, fit and strong. Yet before he was 60 he collapsed.

"I wouldn't have believed it", a friend told me. "Mr B. looked the fittest man in the district".

This happens too often. And the reason is overdoing it constantly in your 30s. Driving yourself too much because you want to be champion at tennis, badminton, &c., &c. Carrying on long after you're tired out.

You see, the heart is really a muscle. It develops with exercise when we're young.

Now, that's ideal for a long life – provided we don't overdo the exercise grossly. If we do, the heart muscle gets too big. And after 50 this kind of heart tends to toughen, and the fibres are replaced by fat.

The second danger is to keep going too long.

You'd be surprised at the number of folk who, after 40, try to keep up with men ten years their junior. You may get away with it for years. But it tells in the end.

When we do violent exercise the heart has to dilate to cope with the increased turn-round of the blood. Under 40 the heart recovers its normal size quite easily. After that, the heart may remain enlarged if the exercise is too violent.

Then the valves are more inclined to give way. They lose the ability to open and shut as they should.

Now I'd like to tell you about Mrs C., a housewife in her early 50s.

Like many other women, she's never taken part in sport or active pastimes, even in her youth. She married young, and has spent all her life in housewifely duties.

Nothing wrong with that – but to Mrs C. and all women like her I give this warning. In your 50s never make a sudden burst for bus, tram or train.

Never try a sudden lift of anything really heavy.

You see, your heart hasn't really been developed as a muscle should. So by the time you're in your 50s it isn't fit for a sudden strain.

The fourth danger is over-eating.

After fifty you should cut down every dish you take by 10 per cent. After sixty, by another 10 per cent. That way, you'll help your blood pressure and cut down the risk of hardened arteries.

Just as important – after 55 there's a risk if you take a huge meal, then do strenuous exercise immediately afterwards.

You see, the distended tummy presses on the heart (which is a bit older than it was)! And so the heart may not be able to cope with a sudden extra call.

This could happen at Christmas dinner, with a strenuous game afterwards. So take it easy if you're getting on in years.

Mr L. is typical of the fifth danger. He's (1) successful, (2) excitable, (3) smokes too much, (4) worries too much about his work.

He got coronary thrombosis.

One of the reasons was that, over a long period, he quickened the rate of the heart by concentrated thinking, with not enough relaxation. You can get away with it up to 45.

After that age – go on with your concentrated brainwork by all means, but make sure that at least three evenings a week your mind relaxes at some entirely different pursuit.

Your Temper Has A Lot To Do With Your Heart

October 19, 1958

BE good to your heart. That goes without saying. But do you really know how?

For it's not what you think that can damage the heart.

For instance, hard physical work doesn't usually harm it at all.

The one thing the heart can't abide is the wrong kind of emotion. That either speeds it up – or the brake goes on and it stops.

You can run up a flight of stairs and feel breathless, but the heart can stand it. Yet run up stairs in a blaze of temper, or in a state of grief, and you do untold harm.

That's why you hear of folk sometimes collapsing on hearing of a relative's death.

That's why, when a husband loses his wife, he can literally die of a broken heart.

Folk have died because someone took them by the throat. They weren't strangled. It was the heart that stopped, partly through fear.

Bad news should always be broken gently – and by a friend, not by a stranger. This is particularly important when an elderly, lonely, or sensitive person is to get the news.

Harass the brain with mental problems, and the heart suffers.

It speeds up. It goes like a motor scooter instead of with the action of a smooth-running car. That explains the mystery of so many business men having heart trouble.

"Goodness, that's strange. He never strains himself", folk say.

But they don't realise that mental strain is worse than hard, muscle work.

Now, what about the effect that illnesses can have on the heart? Three illnesses can damage it.

No. 1 is flu. Fortunately, the heart recovers. But here's a warning. After flu, or any feverish cold, never do anything to tax your strength. Our heart muscle is temporarily poisoned. Excess effort can damage it permanently.

Illness No. 2 is bronchitis. The chronic kind leaves the lungs over-expanded. The heart has a harder job pumping blood round. It's the same as pumping up a bicycle tyre. It's easy when the tyre is soft, but tough work when the tyre gets hard.

Illness No. 3 is acute rheumatism. The kind that has a fever along with it. This needs careful watching and long convalescence. Not for the rheumatism, but the possible damage to the heart.

What about physical effort?

Well, here's a guide that may well save a life. Go by your birth certificate and not by your "fitness". You may feel able to tackle a tough lift. But if you're 50 or 60, you can't do it without some risk.

A frightening aspect of some heart troubles is that weakness can be there and you don't know it.

Here's one test you can make. Never tackle a job where you have to hold your breath to do it.

If you do, you seriously risk heart strain.

Now for elderly folk.

You know not to go up hills at a gallop. But did you know not to go out into bitterly cold air? And did you know a strong wind is extremely exhausting for your heart?

Anybody with high blood pressure should know that a tonic is bad for the heart!

Unless it's prescribed by your own doctor, the H.B.P. brigade should never experiment with tonics. They can whip up the heart and bring about a crisis.

For years we've been considering what's bad for the blood vessels, and, because of this, bad for the heart.

Animal fats, eggs, curries, and alcohol have all been blamed. But we're still not sure.

What we do know is that over-eating over a long period damages the arteries – and then the heart. So does taking huge meals over a short period.

Is a woman of 40 too old to get married?

March 4, 1956 — **Is a woman of 40 too old to get married and have a family?**

No, but she hasn't very much time to spare before it'll be too late.

March 23, 1958 — **Would touching the toes be beneficial to a man of 72? His tummy is getting out at the front.**

Strenuous exercise of this sort would be unwise for so old a person. Far better to eat a little less.

September 18, 1957 — **I'm troubled with dizziness when going to bed and on rising. Is there a cure? I'm 78.**

No. At your age changes of position should be made gently to allow the circulation to catch up.

June 28, 1959 — **Can you tell me what causes "the fidgets" in my legs or what I should do to cure them? I'm female (45).**

A certain degree of instability of the nervous system is common about your time of life. Suitable tablets, taken intermittently, are available.

December 30, 1956 — **My legs tremble when I go out for a walk and I shake a lot. I'm also dull of hearing. I'm 53.**

All these symptoms would suggest you're prematurely old, if I didn't feel sure that they're nervous in origin. Get the once-over from a doctor and believe (and do) what he tells you.

April 1, 1956 — **During the difficult time for middle-aged women, at what age should the nerves settle down?**

There's no fixed age, not even an average one. Fortunately, sensible women, with outside interests, need suffer little or no upset.

November 13, 1955 — **I'm troubled with dizzy turns. If I hold down my head for a short time everything goes round and round and I've to grab something to keep from falling. I'm 71.**

At your age, stooping is unwise, and you must avoid it. Take a daily dose of Gregory's powder in a little warm milk.

October 13, 1957 — **I'm 19 and quite pretty but I've terrible shadows below my eyes. I've tried going to bed early but it makes no difference.**

Are you sure these are really there, and sufficiently marked to be unbecoming? Mirrors play queer tricks, we don't always see ourselves as other see us. Cut out tobacco and alcohol and eat lots of fresh fruit.

November 7, 1954 — **For a time I've had a numb feeling in all my toes. When I bend them there's a tight feeling, but it doesn't restrict my walking. Is this a normal condition at my age? I'm 72.**

At your age the circulation to the extremities is often affected, but in your case this seems to be trifling. Keep your feet clean, powder them well each morning and avoid tight footwear.

February 10, 1957 — **I've noticed my father (57) gives an occasional slight jerk of his head. He is not aware of it. He suffers from gastritis.**

Old people sometimes develop this as a habit, or it may be a sign of nerve changes. In the latter case, a suitable drug, taken regularly, alleviates the condition or occasionally checks it. Ask your doc.

June 4, 1950 — **I am 19, and subject to excessive perspiration. What can I do?**

Teenagers sweat more than other people because they're more sensitive and emotional than other ages. Nervousness and lack of poise are primary causes of perspiration. In later years lack of fitness is a commoner cause.

February 24, 1957 — **Can you suggest a mild place in Scotland to retire to? I'm in my sixties, and when I get a cold it always goes to my chest.**

The Black Isle or Moray Firth coast are both good. Or Fort William, Oban or Inveraray, if you prefer the west. Again, Ayrshire has suitable places to offer, or parts of the Tweed valley.

August 9, 1959 — **I've a crepey neck, owing to age (50). I can't afford a good cream, but would like to improve it.**

Olive oil is reasonably cheap and can be gently rubbed in each night.

September 25, 1955 — **I've pain at the lower end of my back and in the sole of right foot. Strenuous work makes it worse. I'm over 60.**

Changes in the backbone, due to wear and tear probably, are responsible. You should be taking things a little easier now.

April 6, 1958 — **Where can I get in touch with a reliable plastic surgeon who will perform the operation commonly called face-lifting? I believe it entails 14 days in a nursing home. Approximately, how much will it cost?**

Such an appointment should be made through your doctor. No reliable specialist will treat a case otherwise.

March 23, 1958 — **Ever since I was hit by a motor car, my bowels have been very loose. I still feel a pain in the leg injured in the accident. I'm a mother of nine, aged 55.**

You are over-anxious about the accident and possible complications, giving yourself this nervous diarrhoea. A simple sedative from your own doctor might help.

— Chapter 6 —

You Are What You Eat

DO you know the best meal to eat in winter? It's stovies, with onions through it, and a glass of milk.

Do you know why we feel the cold more than we used to? Or the sure sign that you've made a worthwhile soup? Or the test for good porridge? And why the best sweeties are black-striped balls?

All that information is here, and all are the opinions of the 1950s Doc.

The advice on what, and what not, to eat might raise the eyebrow of a modern-day nutritionist, though.

And the opinions on the effects of eating might be described as "straightforward". There's no mollycoddling, no euphemistic language, no political correctness here. You are what you eat, and if you eat too much then you get fat.

The Doc of the 1950s didn't pull his punches about the consequences either. If a man is fat, then he will have a shorter life. A woman who is too thin, on the other hand, should be pleased to put on a few pounds in order to improve her figure.

Lots Of Folk Keep Their Stomach In The Wrong Place

June 15, 1952

Mr C. came to me in great alarm last week. "I can hear the blood hammering in my ears like a great drum", he said. He was afraid of blood pressure.

After I'd examined him, I told him – "It's happening because you're misusing your stomach".

You see, the heart and the stomach are only an inch apart. They hang like pendulums, and they're served by two branches of the same big nerve.

Distend the upper part of the stomach, and it presses against the heart – it may even force it out of position.

When this happens, the heartbeat is amplified – hence the drumming in the ears.

The stomach and heart also get too close when you eat a meal while wearing tight clothing.

The natural position of any empty stomach is high. As it's filled with food, it should drop down. But if you're wearing a tight belt, the stomach can't drop. It stays "upstairs", and as it fills it presses against the heart.

The result is you feel puffy after dinner. You may even feel that there's something wrong with your heart. But it's the position of your stomach that's at fault.

And if you carry on with this, and keep your stomach in a

permanently wrong position, you may, in time, do damage to the heart.

We're used to thinking of our heart and stomach as fixed, so it may seem strange to think of them moving about.

But the phrase: "His heart's in the right place" has more meaning than you'd think!

That's the case of Mr T., who was coming home fagged out after doing overtime. Because he was "all in", his wife was putting huge, appetising meals in front of him – to build up his strength again.

That's bad. A tired man can't cope with a big meal.

Far better to have a drink of milk and a biscuit when you come in – and the meal an hour later.

And when you do get the meal, take your time. It takes one second for liquid to reach the stomach from the mouth – but about six seconds for solid food to cover the same distance.

So if you swallow a mouthful of food oftener than once every six seconds, you're creating a queue at the entrance of the stomach. Time yourself. How many swallows do you take in six seconds?

Other things the stomach doesn't like are foods it can't break down.

If you swallow pips, hard skins, tough bones, &c., they're thrown back when they get to the stomach's exit – because they're not soft enough to be passed on.

A piece of hard material may come to the stomach exit six times before the tummy says, "Oh, well, carry on then".

That's a lot of extra work.

And every time the hard stuff tries to get through there's a jolt on the muscles, and sometimes spasm pain.

The kind of food you eat can, without your knowing it, have a nasty effect.

Certain foods taken together distend the stomach. One of the commonest faulty mixtures is fruit juice and milk.

The fruit juice curdles the milk before it reaches the tummy.

If you have meat in a meal, don't drink tea with it. Too much tea weakens the gastric juices.

And with meat on the menu, the gastric juices need all the strength they've got! What's more, tea is apt to toughen the meat.

If you must drink tea at a meat meal – drink it afterwards, and only one cup, please!

THE MODERN VIEW, BY DR LYNDA

THE 1950s Doc was way off in his anatomy here. Or was he?

Certainly "blood hammering in his ears" is not caused by "misusing your stomach". It's called pulsatile tinnitus and is usually nothing sinister or serious, and there IS feasible treatment for it.

Yes the stomach and heart are served by branches of the same nerve but they are separated by a very large strong muscle called the diaphragm, so distending the stomach cannot cause the heart to be displaced.

The only way that the heart can be displaced by the stomach is if there is a fault in the diaphragm and part of the stomach is pushed into the chest cavity — commonly called a hiatus hernia.

It's common in people over 50 and most don't know they have it. Occasionally it can be caused by a birth defect, but is more likely to be caused by obesity and as The 1950s Doc said, tight-fitting clothing may aggravate the symptoms of reflux and indigestion, especially after a large meal.

Treatment is the usual nags — stop smoking, lose weight, eat smaller portions, drink less coffee and alcohol and less stress.

A thing of concern to me as a GP in the 21st Century is the use of medication instead of lifestyle change. People think it's OK to regularly over-eat and use medication to reduce the acid in their stomach instead of keeping their weight down or not overindulging in the first place.

There have been studies which have shown an increase in bone fractures, gastric cancers, dementia and effects on the absorption of vitamin B12 and iron (not all proven) with long term use.

Surely it's best to lose a little weight and look after yourself.

As for the mixing of tea and meat, and milk and juices, I don't think there is any proof of this causing any issue. It's the sin of gluttony and overindulgence which cause problems.

It May Look Pretty, But It Doesn't Do You As Much Good

October 5, 1952

I'D like to see all my patients sitting down every day to the old-fashioned kind of meal.

For, as I go my rounds, I find we're getting far too elegant in our tastes nowadays.

Some of us would be a wee bit ashamed to sit down to a plate of "stovies".

Yet stovies are a dish fit for a king. Eat stovies through the winter, and you're less likely to suffer from chest colds or bronchitis.

It's the onions that do the trick.

They stimulate the cells of the lungs and bronchial tubes, and keep them fighting fit.

Add a glass of milk and you have the perfect winter meal.

Remember, too, the old-fashioned boiling beef! It used to be popped in the broth pot for stock – then served up as meat for the second course.

Now it's out of fashion.

What a pity! We got every ounce of good from the broth. And maybe the beef afterwards isn't so tasty, but it certainly is the easiest kind of meat for the digestion.

There's grand value, too, in the fat on boiling beef. It's the easiest fat of all to take.

I think folk today feel the cold more than we used to. Part of the reason is the modern fussiness about fat. The old-time mother used to insist on all the family eating the last scrap of fat. "Clean your plates" was a must.

Now the distaste for fat is pandered to.

There's mutton fat, lamb fat, beef fat, bacon fat. Surely we can take at least one of them without screwing up our faces? Get the children into the fat habit. They need it as much as we do.

And as good a "piece" for the children as any is the cheapest. A plain piece of bread dipped in dripping.

Our grannie knew it. We shouldn't forget it. The colder the day, the more it's needed.

If you've no bone for the broth, a little fat will go a long way to help.

Sure signs of good broth are these little circles of "oil" floating on the top. Grannie had no time for clear soup. And she was right.

Broth should be thick. A bone gives the flavour and the root vegetables give the nourishment – turnips, carrot, potatoes. And never forget peas.

For porridge, coarse meal is best. Here's the test for porridge. Your spoon should practically stand up in it!

If you're bothered with rheumatism you can get vitamin B in powder form. Sprinkle a little over your porridge. That's a habit that will help you.

Bread isn't far from being a perfect food – if we eat the crust. The crust definitely helps digestion. You should never let the bairn away with refusing to eat it!

Lots of us have a scunner at the skin that forms on pudding. Well, eat it! There's an awful lot of good in that skin. It's changed into valuable protein.

Apples are fine for beating constipation. But, again, only if you eat the skin. That's the part that keeps your innards working well.

Oh, yes, I could go on for a long time about the good old-fashioned food – mealy puddings, herring fried in its own fat, home-made dumpling, &c.

Even the old-fashioned sweeties are unbeatable – like grannie sookers and black-striped balls.

They're sweetness and energy in its best form.

THE MODERN VIEW, BY DR LYNDA

EVEN today our diet is slowly killing us as a species, mainly due to malnutrition and obesity. However, despite it all, life expectancy in the UK is up from 64 years in the 1950s for men to 80 years now, and 84 years for women.

The greater availability of fresh fruit and veg, more the focus on stopping smoking and increasing exercise, and the better treatment of infections are probably the main causes rather than diet. But the rise of fast foods and ready-made meals, may well influence life expectancies in the future.

That fussiness for fat the 1950s Doc mentions has been a good thing in retrospect. But there are as many myths about diet and food as there are truths. Did you know that cholesterol is mainly made in your liver, rather than ingested in food?

Cholesterol is a fatty substance known as a lipid, which is vital for a host of normal functions in the body.

It's used in making hormones, cell membranes, absorbing important vitamins and in the making of Vitamin D, for example.

It's carried around the body by two special proteins called low density lipoprotein (LDL) which takes it from the liver to the cells that need it and high density protein which takes the used cholesterol back to the liver to be broken down and disposed of.

If there is too much LDL and high cholesterol levels, then the excess fat is deposited in artery walls causing narrowing and hardening of those arteries, resulting in strokes, heart attacks and kidney damage, among other things.

But not all dietary fats are bad. The real baddies are saturated and trans fats, mainly found in meat, cheese and dairy — which, unfortunately, are what the 1950s Doc advocated as good for you.

This sort of research was in its infancy back then. Meat fat increases LDL levels and causes the problems.

Many factors combine to increase heart disease risk, not just cholesterol, so stopping smoking, losing weight and getting more exercise is much more important. They also lower cholesterol.

And then, of course, there are statins, tablets which lower your blood cholesterol.

It does slightly grate, as a physician, to see that people believe taking a tablet negates the responsibility we all have to look after ourselves and change our lifestyle.

NO!

However, perhaps my mother's saying of "a little of what you fancy doesn't do you any harm" holds true, as we do need to eat some fat.

And faddy diets and cutting out things completely surely can't be good for you.

As for sweeties, I agree the old fashioned ones are unbeatable — but that's a personal taste rather than a health directive.

Moderation is the rule, I think.

Here's Something For You To Chew Over

December 16, 1956

SUPPOSE you saw a lion in a field eating grass. That would be unnatural, wouldn't it?

It's just as unnatural for you and me to stop eating meat – for nature meant us, as well as lions, to eat meat.

If you tire early in the afternoon or feel listless and depressed, as likely as not it's good red meat you're needing. Especially steak or roast beef. They're the meats for energy and staying power.

Only two things can really give you rich blood – green vegetables and beef.

But things like steak and roast beef have an extra advantage. In their juices are substances that pep you up and give you a joy of living, as well as pure physical energy.

Now, don't get me wrong. Don't stuff yourself with meat. A small portion a day does a world of good. Too much has the opposite effect. That's because red meat isn't too easy to digest.

And before you rush away to the butcher's, let me ask you this question. Are you fiery tempered?

If you are, steak and roast beef shouldn't be a regular dish for you. You've already got more than enough of what beef can give you.

For you, too much red meat is likely to raise your blood pressure. It may be bad for your arteries, too, because medical opinion is swinging round to the theory that excess protein with fats is a possible cause of high blood pressure and hardened arteries.

Between now and April, a first-class meat to take is ox liver, particularly if you're bothered with colds. We all need vitamin A badly in winter. It's our main defender against internal infection.

No meat is packed so full of vitamin A as ox liver. Indeed, of all our foods, only carrots can compare with it.

If you eat a little liver, say twice a week, you're unlikely to be plagued with bloodlessness or stricken with neuritis.

The secret is that liver also has vitamin B2, which is so valuable for blood and nerves.

Liver should be grilled, stewed or steamed, but never fried. Oh, I know fried liver is very tasty, but it loses some of its value, and abuses your digestion that way. And, please, no fried onions with your liver if you have a tendency to indigestion!

What about the semi-invalid and old folk whose digestion can't cope with meat?

The great thing for them is tripe. Thoroughly cooked, tripe is possibly the best meat for all-round value.

But it must be cooked slowly and for a long time. If not, you'll get little benefit.

Is there anybody in the house who's had weeks of over-work or flu or is under par? Ox liver and tripe are the best meat courses for them.

Next, the good old boiling beef – the kind mum puts in broth.

For healthy folk, it's a grand nourisher and warmer in cold weather. But many of us feel it doesn't agree with us.

Can you guess why?

Because we get an overdose of the goodness! We take the broth, then the meat immediately after.

That's far too much for most digestions. Beef broth shouldn't be followed by a "red meat" course.

Fish is far better as the next course.

Whenever you have indigestion, you should realise you're not getting the benefit of your meal. That goes particularly for red meat.

That's why I wouldn't advise anyone to have red meat at tea-time. Tea makes red meat extremely indigestible. Your tummy, in fact, has to deal with "leather". Your digestive fire gets clogged up.

So your system, instead of getting vitamins, gets body poisons.

Chicken isn't so marvellous as you might think. It's not nearly so energising as steak, for instance. But it has one great advantage – it's easily digested.

That's why chicken's the thing for anybody who's feeling poorly, and they get more value from it.

Most meats are best grilled and slightly under-done.

Did you know, however, that the right way to eat meat is to cut it into little pieces on your plate? The cutting severs the fibres, and the small pieces are more easily chewed.

And chew you must – even mince!

Of course, pieces of mince are small, but there's more to it than that. Meat must mix with saliva from your mouth. That's the secret of enjoying your meat, and also getting the staying power and energy from meat.

It's a wise housewife who buys the steak and then asks for it to be minced before her eyes. Sometimes there's gristle and fat in ready-prepared mince.

Maybe it's cheaper and good value for the money. But there's nothing to beat steak that you see getting minced.

THE MODERN VIEW, BY DR LYNDA

THE meat versus no meat argument wasn't new, even in the 1950s.

Humans evolved eating plant and animal sources of food, so by eliminating one or the other we run the risk of becoming deficient in key nutrients.

It is perfectly possible to have a well-balanced diet without meat by supplementation of some minerals and vitamins.

So let's look at the pros and cons of meat eating and how much the 1950s Doc got right.

Meat is a great source of protein, minerals and vitamins for a healthy body. It's classified into three types — red meat which contains high levels of iron-rich proteins and saturated fats; white meat which is lighter in colour and comes from chicken, turkey and tripe etc.; and processed meats which have been modified through salting, curing smoking etc. for preservation and to enhance flavour.

Too much red meat (high in saturated fats) has indeed been linked to increased bowel cancer, heart disease and diabetes, so he wasn't too far wrong when he said it was likely to raise your blood pressure and be bad for your arteries.

Studies are making links between eating too much red meat and cancer, and there is a stronger link for processed meats like sausages and bacon, which have a higher level of salt and fat and should definitely be limited to once a week.

On the up side, red meat is a great source of iron and vitamin B12, which is impossible to get without eating meat or taking supplements. Liver is a great source of vitamin A, iron and a whole host of B vitamins, as the 1950s Doc says, and good for your immune response.

But I'm not sure about whether the cooking method is terribly important.

However, high temperature cooking produces more hydrocarbons, which are highly carcinogenic and may damage some of the more fragile vitamins and minerals.

So he's right, too, about the fact that red meats are best served under-done. But remember to cook white meats thoroughly.

There are some statements in the above article which I have to say don't ring true. I'm not sure that you can get an overdose of the goodness by eating red meat after a beef-based broth, and you do not lose any of the benefit of a meal if you have indigestion.

There's Only One Right Way To Get Slim And Stay That Way

April 6, 1958

YOU slip the penny into the slot and watch the dial go round, 10 stone, 11 stone, 12 stone. "Oh, dear", you sigh, "I wish I could slim".

Somebody tells you of a marvellous way to shed the extra pounds – and the great battle begins.

Ladies, you're wasting your time! At least, the odds against you are 50 to 1.

You all make the same mistake – you're in too big a hurry! Shed two stones in a month of drastic dieting – and I'll bet by the end of the year you're as heavy as you ever were, if not heavier.

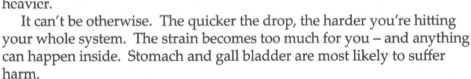

It can't be otherwise. The quicker the drop, the harder you're hitting your whole system. The strain becomes too much for you – and anything can happen inside. Stomach and gall bladder are most likely to suffer harm.

There's only one way to slim, and stay that way.

It's what I call the slow and steady way. It's so slow it may take a whole year.

But here's the point: the "beef" won't go on again. For the first two weeks shed no more than two lb. For the second fortnight shed no more than one lb.

Then, for the rest of the year, reduce by not more than ½ lb. every week.

Don't deprive yourself of any particular food. Eat your usual kinds. Just eat a little less. It's as simple as that.

Then you're still getting a healthy, balanced diet. Some folk cut out one meal a day, the one that suits their routine.

My advice is – stick to your three meals. Don't cut out a course at lunch, either. Instead, make each portion a little smaller.

But stick to that, nothing more. You daren't have even a sweet drink "on the sly".

Always weigh yourself at exactly the same time of day on the same scales. This is important, because even a pint of water can push the scales round by 1 ¼ lb!

Keep cutting down the portions until you reach your target. By the end of the year, reducing won't be a torture – it'll be the normal thing. And you're set for life.

Massage doesn't help. Fat is a fluid and rubbing simply shifts it somewhere else.

"Will I have to do exercises?" That's a question I'm often asked. Nearly always my answer is, "No".

In fact, for a woman who's two stone or more over her mark, exercises can easily strain the heart.

But there's one kind of fat where exercise is the answer. That's the fat of the average middle-aged man.

He's pretty neat in his figure – except for that spare tyre round his middle. His cure costs nothing. It's simply a lot more walking – and a slightly larger stride.

Provided it can be done comfortably.

Remember, though, still curb your appetite after your exercise. One plain biscuit is equal to a mile's brisk walk. So don't eat two biscuits after a mile, otherwise you're worse off than ever.

Fancy diets are all very well, but they have three main flaws.

1. You get tired of their monotony.
2. There may be a danger of vitamin deficiency.
3. You tend to have a hunger-and-burst way of living.

After two weeks of a fancy diet you're so glad to get back to normal you become a bigger eater than ever.

Don't believe these fairy stories about excessive weight being caused by upset glands.

This is very, very seldom the case.

Every one of us after 50 tends to eat too much. If you're in this age group, start now to eat less.

Sometimes it's a matter of life or death!

If you don't keep your weight down, you're far more liable to this horrid lot – high blood pressure, weak heart, diseased arteries, rheumatism (especially in the back and legs), bronchitis, diabetes, and of course, premature old age.

In fact, excess fat is the biggest single killer in Britain today.

And yet it needn't be if only a lot of us didn't eat more than is good for us.

Don't Think You're Safe Just Because You're Thin

November 13, 1955

FIFTY PER CENT. of us have one very bad fault. And it doesn't give us a fair chance of first-class health or a long life.

Have you guessed what the fault is? It's downright overeating.

And here's something that may surprise you. Don't imagine because you're thin as a rake that you can say "Oh, that doesn't apply to me!"

It can, you know.

For you can grossly overeat, and it need not show when you spend a penny on the weighing machine.

Not only that, it's as serious for the thin overeater as for the chap who puts on weight.

If you're thin, overeating is more likely to cause hardened arteries than in the case of the fat man.

The fat person's danger is heart trouble.

How do you feel after your midday meal? Sleepy? If the answer's "Yes", it's quite likely you're overeating.

Never forget – sluggishness after lunch is a warning sign. Headaches are another.

Have you noticed that some thin people who eat big meals never put on any weight?

One of my patients got the shock of her life when she came to me. She was worried about being underweight. She wanted pills or a tonic or a special diet.

My cure was very different. I told her to stop eating too much – particularly rich food.

For it was an excess of this food that was keeping her thin. In two months she was pleased as Punch with her extra poundage – and better figure!

There's nothing miraculous about the cure. Her excess food was over-working her liver and kidneys so much; most of it was being wasted. But once her intake was reduced, these organs improved – and were able to cope with the food and pass the benefit round the body.

So if you're on the bony side, why not try eating less – not more?

Time and again patients tell me they don't eat a lot. Well, over-eating is NOT just the amount – but the KIND of food.

Remember, the rich, fattening foods are: cakes, potatoes, bread, margarine, butter, milk puddings, meat puddings, fruit puddings, pork, fried fish and chips, fat bacon and ham, butter beans, nuts, chocolates, creams, sweets, scones, and crumpets.

Certainly take your fair share of them – but don't overdo them.

Now, here are foods which are not fattening:- lean meat, veal, chicken and poultry, fresh peas, cabbage, cauliflower, salads, tongues, meat pastes, liver, tripe, tomatoes, beetroot, most root vegetables, cheese, clear soups, and boiled fish.

A good tip – particularly for anybody worried about tiredness and headaches – is eat "light" at breakfast and lunchtime and have the main meal in the evening.

There's no doubt that after 5 p.m. is the best time for a tuck-in. You see, while you're asleep, the food is distributing its benefits and energy to the body.

You'll waken in the morning full of beans. And the energy will pretty well last for 24 hours.

But if you can't have your main meal in the evening, try to cut out one course at lunchtime. Two courses are ample for most of us.

And when you're in the 40s, cut down your intake. It can mean surprisingly good health later on.

As for the old folk, it's dangerous for them to eat too much.

How can we tell when we've eaten enough?

Everybody gets a signal in the stomach. But the warning only lasts about a minute and a half. Ignore this feeling of "enough!" and you won't get another.

Folk who take a lot of liquid with their meals don't get the signal so strongly. So they're much more prone to overdo things.

There are three kinds of folk who should never have a big meal.

First, those with heart trouble. An overloaded stomach can easily bring on a heart attack.

Second, those with a tendency to asthma and bronchitis.

Third, the folk with ulcers. A big meal can mean a burst ulcer – and that can mean curtains!

Finally, eat a little less than you normally eat in winter and a lot less in summer.

That goes for every second adult who reads this!

Age Matters Far More Than You Think

January 13, 1952

WE all want to get the most out of every year of our lives. But many of us don't – because we don't recognise the limitations of our age. And that causes an awful lot of ill-health.

Take food, for instance. From 5 to 20 we're safe to eat to our hearts' content.

From 24 to 40 we should cut down by a fifth – and by a third from 40 to 60. After 60 we're asking for trouble unless we eat only half of what a youngster eats.

Here's why.

Up to 20 there's growth and maximum activity. You can hardly eat too much. In the 20s there's plenty activity – but no growth. After that even activity slows down.

So, if you over-eat after 40, you're risking two things – high blood pressure and hardened arteries.

Too many people are lulled into false security because they don't put on middle-age spread. They think they can eat as much as they used to. But the danger is still there – middle-age spread or not.

Even the nature of the food we eat should change as we grow older.

Best foods up to the age of two are milk, orange juice, and cod liver oil.

Up to 14, lots of milk. From 14 to 45, as much beef as possible, considering present-day shortages.

After 45 we all need to be more careful of our digestion and circulation.

We can help ourselves very simply by carrying ourselves straight. As we grow older we lose half an inch in height – and the longer we can postpone that, the better for our fitness, and we can do it by carrying ourselves straight.

A word now for the old folk – take a little cheese and a fair amount of milk, and as much butter as you can get.

Cheese gives energy without bulk. Milk is the ideal all-round food. And for fat, butter is the most easily digested.

And, Grannie, PLEASE cut out fried foods!

Some people reconcile themselves to going "down the hill" after 45. There's no need to. Most of us can enjoy our best health between 50 and 60. We don't take colds so easily then.

Our system seems finally to get rid of threatened ulcers, heat spots, hay fever, and asthma. We've little or no chance of developing T.B.

There's little likelihood of being troubled with the severer forms of rheumatism – if they haven't started before 50.

There may, of course, be mild twinges – but not the crippling type.

Nervous ailments which affect the circulation and digestion are apt to die off in the 50s.

This surprising improvement is due to a change in mental outlook. We've more confidence in our job. We're more contented, more mellow – even more sensible!

But there's one thing we can't avoid.

If we do go down with illness, we've got to realise that, the older we are, the slower the rate of recovery.

At 25 we might recover from a good-going flu in four days. After 45 we shouldn't think of even being "on the way" until after eight days. If you're over 60 you must give yourself at least a fortnight's convalescence from flu.

Next, see how your need for sleep changes with the years:-

Infant, 20 hours a day.

Up to 18 years it's 9 hours.

18 to 50 years, under 8 hours.

50 to 60 years, 8 hours.

60 to 70 years, 9 hours.

After 70 years (rest or sleep), 10 to 12 hours.

And our mental make-up changes, too. Our ability to memorise is best up to 14 years. Our ability to study, 14 to 25 years.

But when in middle-age our powers of judgment and selection are at their very best.

Don't Worry About The Tattie Shortage

May 6, 1956

IN the past few weeks the potato shortage has been the talk of my surgery.

Mothers are wondering if the family's health will suffer if they don't get enough potatoes. Let me say right away – don't worry. We could do without potatoes.

That doesn't mean they aren't good for us. Far from it.

Although potatoes are mostly starch and water, they contain a little protein – the body-building stuff. They also have the important vitamin C, which keeps your blood in good condition and your skin clear.

So eat them by all means. But if you can't get them, remember the substitutes are just as good.

These are milk puddings, bread, scones, rice, tapioca and fruit.

Now, how many potatoes should we eat – and when?

Too many increase the risk of becoming overweight. And that can be the cause of a host of troubles.

If you're over 40 it can lead to increased blood pressure and strain on heart and liver. Diabetes, too, can be a result of eating too many tatties.

For the average person, I would say a quarter to a third of a pound of potatoes a day is sufficient.

During the war, a family I know were big potato eaters.

Each one of them accounted for 7 lb. of potatoes a week. A pound a day! Today they are all overweight and all on a diet.

Indeed, if you're overweight and dieting too, it is more important to do without potatoes than bread.

What are the best ways to eat potatoes?

If you want to get most out of them, boil them in their jackets. They're not only more nourishing, but more easily digested.

Another good method is to roast them in their jackets, the way hikers do, in the hot embers of a fire.

How about chips?

Yes, they're tasty, aren't they? But unless they're carefully made, they can be hard and indigestible.

That's because frying gives them a hard skin, which taxes the digestion. Not only that, but the starch inside the chips is toughened. That loads even more work on to the stomach.

However as long as you have a good digestion, and chew them well, chips shouldn't do you any harm.

Take a tip, though. Don't bite a chip in half and swallow it, hoping your stomach will do the rest. It won't! A hard chip can lie on your stomach for as long as four hours while the digestion wrestles with it. So they're hardly advisable at bedtime!

Children under nine months should not be given potatoes, unless a little in their soup.

And kiddies under school age are best not to have chips. Chips are all right for school agers and folk in their 20s and 30s, but after 40 go easy.

And if you've a stomach ulcer – or you're over 65 – give them a miss.

Potatoes, particularly if boiled in their skins, are grand for growing, active children. The starch is easily turned into sugar by the system and gives abundant energy.

But as there's no fat in potatoes, it's a good idea to add a lump of butter, or marge, or even dripping, after they've been served. Granny knew what she was doing when she did this in years gone by.

Above all, Mum, don't chip and fry yesterday's left-over boiled tatties, if you can possibly avoid it.

The fat clings to them, and because they have been cooked before, it gets right to the inside.

This toughens the starch even more than with ordinary chips. It's much better to slice the leftovers and have them cold in a salad.

There's a popular theory that the best of a potato is just under the skin. Don't believe it! It's the same through and through, except for the skin, which is very indigestible.

Yes, Some Foods Are A Lot Better Than Medicine

November 18, 1956

DO you take laxatives regularly? If the answer's yes, then try to stop the habit right now – unless you're over 70.

Few folk realise that a laxative acts like an irritant.

Here's an illustration. If you drop hot tobacco ash on your hand, you draw your hand away instinctively to escape a burn, don't you?

The bowels do something the same with laxatives. They hurriedly pass along the irritant.

And if the bowels have to do this every day, they're inclined to lose their tone and their reaction is impaired.

You can beat constipation in a more natural and healthy way.

First thing in the morning take a cup of tea, and drop a pinch of Epsom salts in it. It won't taste the tea. This isn't a laxative. It's what I call a starter.

But the tea must be fresh – and not too strong.

I think, too, the best breakfast dish is porridge. Try making it with coarser oatmeal. It stimulates the bowels into action.

There's no need to take a big plateful. But you can't beat it as a regular start-off to the day.

Your porridge will have a good deal of Vitamin B. This tones up the nervous system.

Maybe you have not realised it, but a poor nervous system increases the risk of constipation.

It's often worthwhile, too, to change your bread for a time.

Try the wholemeal variety. It also has roughage and Vitamin B. All in all, I think it's the best of all breads for keeping you regular. Don't overdo it, though. Once slice is all you need at a time.

Take a little extra butter or margarine with it – but not salt butter.

What about meat? The best for constipation is fatty bacon. The fat gives the bowels plenty of good exercise – the very thing they need.

And never let your system get dried up. Three pints of water a day aren't too much, including your cups of tea.

Workmen who do hard, physical jobs should drink even more.

Have your pint of beer, too – but go easy on spirits.

Probably the best finish to the day is a glass of hot water just before you turn in. If you keep your "inside" moist, there will be little need for laxatives.

Exercise, too, is often better than medicine.

"That's all very well", you may say. "But I'm getting past the age for that".

But touching our toes isn't too hard for most of us, is it? It's first-class exercise for tummy muscles. If these are kept in reasonably good trim, your bowels won't balloon up – a common cause of constipation.

Or try this. Lie flat on your back and pedal an imaginary bike. It's easy. It's comfortable. It's good for the whole system.

But it's particularly helpful for the lower "stomach".

Older folk can get a laxative effect without taking exercise at all. Simply rub the tummy. Start in the centre, and rub round and round, increasing the size of your circle. But it must be a clockwise rub. Two minutes of this massage is all you need.

No matter what your age is, though, a walk last thing at night is first-class.

Try to stride along. Walking from the knees isn't much good. Anybody who has a good step that swings the thighs rarely needs to take a laxative.

Too many cigarettes are bad for the bowels. But I'm all for a cigarette after a meal. If that's your habit, keep on with it. On the whole, it can be as good as a medicine.

Doctors are now discovering that constipation is not as harmful as was once believed.

Some folk can go 48 hours without their bowels acting – with no ill-effects. Some can even go three or four days.

And for goodness sake, don't worry. There's a decided link-up with brain, nerves and bowels. So worry can affect the bowels adversely.

But see your doctor about prolonged constipation. It may be caused by your way of living or something in your general health.

And laxatives are not the best answer to that. By all means take laxatives when they're really needed – but only once in a while.

The moment you think it's becoming a habit – cut it out.

How To Tell If You're Getting Flabby
June 15, 1958

DO you know what's most likely to ruin the second half of our lives? No, not a disease. Flabbiness!

And the sooner we find out if we're going flabby, the better. Because it likes to creep up on us unnoticed. So, let's try these tests –

No. 1 – Relax your legs and touch the big muscle of your calf. It should be firm but no firmer than a child's rubber ball. Now tense the leg. The muscle should be as hard as a properly blown-up football.

No. 2 - Stand erect and feel the small of the back. If there's a hollow there, you're OK. No back should be absolutely straight.

No. 3 – Lie flat on your back, legs out. Are you soft around the tummy? If so, you're flabby in the worst place. But if you pass this test, bring up the knees. Now feel the tummy. If there's a roll of fat there, you're not as fit as you could be. If there's no "spare tyre", you're in tip-top condition.

No. 4 – Point your chin upwards. Now feel under the chin. Any fat there? If there is, try to do something to improve your fitness.

For fat round the neck tends to make you mentally flabby, too.

But it's not so bad as a fat, pudgy face. It can be a sign of all-over flabbiness.

You see, the skin has small muscles of its own. If these aren't kept in trim the skin sags. In rushes fat to fill up the spaces. Before you know where you are, flabbiness has set in.

Flabby muscles are a menace to health.

They bring on bad digestion, poor circulation, heart trouble, even mental depression.

After 40 it's flabbiness that's often responsible for you catching colds. Unlucky folk develop chronic bronchitis.

In the 60s it's the joints that start to complain. The knees stiffen, the arches of the feet may collapse.

Yet none of this need happen. There's no magic way to beat flabbiness, but here are three golden rules:-

1. Walk as often as you can. Keep the legs in good order, and every muscle benefits.

2. Once you're past the 45 mark, eat less. It's a strange thing, but when a man reaches 45 he tends to give up exercise, yet he wouldn't dream of giving up some of his food. And over-eating is five times riskier than playing tennis (or running for a bus) at 55.

3. When you sit in a chair or in a bus, try to feel that hollow in your back. Long spells of sitting bent forward ruin the tummy muscles.

Here's another way to avoid going soft and flabby. As you get older, don't fall into the habit of not washing as often.

A clean skin is as important as exercise and gives you the urge to keep active. That's because the skin muscles are toned up.

It's more important to be really clean at 60 than at 30.

Of course, when you reach 70 you can't tackle what you used to in exercise or sport. But the great thing is – never give up.

Above all, make the effort to beat flabbiness now. You'll be glad you did – five, ten, or twenty years from now.

Were you tired out at the end of the week?

Well, try taking a glass of Milk *every* *day* and see what a difference that will make to you.

You'll feel a lot better if you drink more Milk

Three Things That Will Help To Keep The Heart Young

September 20, 1959

"I DON'T know how she does it at her age".

"You'd never guess she's over 60".

"That man never seems to get any older".

We'd like folk to say that kind of thing about us, wouldn't we? They will – if we keep our heart young! And really, it's not so hard to do.

Of all the theories about keeping the heart young, doctors are now agreed on one point. Exercise is by far the most important. The heart muscle needs a little extra effort daily to keep it in good condition.

That's the secret.

Old folk must get out – even if only for a quarter of an hour. The woman in her 60s must have her evening walk. The man in his 50s shouldn't give up his golf. The man in his 40s shouldn't give up his tennis or cycling.

Even after operations, the idea is now – "The sooner the heart gets a stimulus the better".

So Mrs Jones doesn't get days in bed after an operation, as she would have at one time.

She gets up at the first chance – to exercise the heart. All in all, if you exercise the heart you'll have good circulation, fewer ailments, better lungs and better resistance to infection.

The second big help to the heart is – Don't eat too much, particularly after you pass the middle forties.

If you put on weight the fat first goes to the abdomen, the heart's next door neighbour. A fatty tummy presses on the heart and prevents it expanding as it should.

Next, the fat spreads round the heart itself. Result – more cramping.

And if you continue to gorge, the fat may creep into the actual heart muscle. Then there's little or no chance of getting rid of the fat.

On top of that, your heart is having to cope with maybe two or three stone of extra weight. No wonder it ages!

"Och, but that doesn't affect me", I've heard women say. "I can eat and eat, and never put on an ounce of excess weight".

Don't delude yourself, ma'am. Your trouble's not a fatty heart. It may be a poisoned one. The liver and kidneys can't deal with all the poison left by the excess food. So some of the poison filters into the heart – and ages it.

The third way to help the heart is – give it good blood. This is easy. Fresh air, red meat, and green vegetables are good for the blood. But remember it takes a long time to build up good blood once you've allowed its quality to fall.

Now we come to what to avoid.

Never allow any throat infection to become chronic. Even if it's "not too bad", have it seen to. Otherwise, your heart is bound to be poisoned – even if it takes 20 years.

Worst of all is a rheumaticky throat. Fortunately, this complaint isn't so common nowadays.

To a lesser degree, bad teeth age the heart in time. So does a running ear or a discharge of any sort.

All these must be cleared up.

Plenty of water to drink, 15 minutes of peace and quiet every day, lack of worry, moderation in alcohol and smoking – all these also save the heart a lot of wear and tear.

But exercise is best of all.

I can't stand the cold, what should I eat?

September 11, 1955 — **I'm 70 and can't stand the cold. Is there anything I can take?**

Eat plenty of butter or margarine, and drink milk. Fatty meat in moderation will also help.

January 27, 1952 — **Does one put on weight again after dieting? I've lost three stones, and I'm sticking to my diet as far as food is concerned. But I'm inclined to go back to sweets and cakes.**

Many people believe that after getting their weight down, they can return to eating sweets and the like. Not so. While a diet to lose weight must be strict, a diet to maintain the "reduction" must still be moderate. Extras, like sweets, tend to increase your weight again.

January 15, 1950 — **The shops are stacked with fruit — all very dear. From the medical point of view, are grapes and nuts the best buy?**

No. There's nothing to beat the apple. Its juices have splendid protective qualities against illness in the danger months ahead. In addition, it's best for stimulating digestive juices and cleaning the mouth. Orange comes next. Grapes have a bigger percentage of sugar, but fewer protective properties. Nuts are a body-building food rather than vitamin-providing.

July 28, 1957 — **Can you tell me if eating raw oatmeal can do any harm?**

Not if you've a good balanced diet in other respects and have a healthy digestion.

May 31, 1959 — **I'm 21 and drink a half-pint of milk with every meal, including supper. Also, I have milk if I go to a café. Now I'm getting fatter round the face and people say it's through drinking too much milk.**

If your weight is going up, too, the milk is responsible. But it's unlikely to cause fat cheeks only.

September 7, 1958 — **There are times when I've a terrible itch. It seems to be worse when I eat a lot of sweet foods. Can it be a germ?**

No. It may be due to too much sugar in the blood, or to a form of "hives".

May 26, 1957 — **Is there any advantage in tea without sugar and milk?**

Without sugar, it tastes more refreshing and you won't put on weight. Without milk, it can be a little irritating to the stomach.

September 4, 1955 — **Would an adult's health be seriously affected if he lived entirely on good-class tinned foods?**

No, provided a balanced diet is taken.

October 23, 1955 — **I use so much salt with my food that friends say it's bad for me. Is it? I'm 29.**
Probably, and certainly it will affect your health as you grow older.

May 2, 1954 — **Are peanuts nourishing?**
Yes, very. But also indigestible.

July 31, 1955 — **What is "yoghurt" and in what way is it beneficial to health?**
This is one of several forms of curdled milk, soured by the action of bacteria. It has been used as a food and also for treating diarrhoea.

August 21, 1955 — **I hereby beseech you in accents humble, Is there a cure for my tummy rumble?**
If otherwise your health is good,
Take time and care about your food.

January 22, 1956 — **Would a vegetarian diet be harmful to health?**
It depends on how strict the diet is. Most authorities consider that a really suitable diet should include milk, cheese and eggs, and many insist on some meat and fish, too.

February 5, 1956 — **My husband drinks tea with every meal, including soup. Can this be a reason why he can't get his weight up?**
It might well be, especially as he may use it to wash down solids before thorough chewing. Try to wean him off the habit.

August 13, 1950 — **What foods shouldn't be eaten on an empty stomach?**
Grilled cheese, fries, pastries, suet pudding, sauces, pickles, new bread.

May 24, 1959 — **For health reasons I'm on a vegetarian diet, but am losing weight. What can I take to rectify that?**
Extra milk, butter, cheese, eggs and cream daily. Balance them with fresh fruit, so as not to upset digestion.

January 21, 1951 — **Does boiling take the vitamins out of milk?**
It takes some vitamins out of the milk, but this deficiency is more than replaced with a very small quantity of cod liver oil and fruit juice.

May 15, 1955 — **I eat two large oranges every day, skin as well. Can this do me any harm?**
If you leave out the skins and thick white pith (which are very indigestible and have no real food value) you'll benefit from the oranges daily.

November 2, 1958 — **Living in digs, I cut out meat from my diet. I have eggs, cheese, milk and occasional fish. A friend tells me everyone needs meat. Is this necessary? I'm a sedentary worker.**
No, your diet is sufficient, if you supplement it with daily fresh fruit.

— Chapter 7 —

Coughs, Colds, And The Fear Of Flu

THE avoidance of colds, and what to do to dodge the dreaded influenza, were by far the most popular subject matters for Doc articles throughout the 1950s.

Flu was a nationwide fear. The great epidemic of 1918-19, known as the Spanish Flu, still loomed large in the national psyche. Survivors of it were parents and grandparents in the 1950s and remained greatly worried about what might happen if it struck again.

But not recovering from a cold quickly was often your own fault, according to the Doc — you might have used too much hair oil, not had haircuts often enough, or sat face-on to an electric fire.

You didn't have to stop smoking, but a lot depended on how far down you smoked the cigarette. Whatever happened, though, you shouldn't try to cure your cold with gargles, sprays and inhalants — that could just have made you worse!

The worst sin of all, though, was not taking a deep breath before blowing your nose.

A Word To Everybody Who Is Down With The Flu

September 29, 1957

EVER heard of explosive flu? It's the only type that kills – and it can do so in 24 hours. It can strike so quickly that you literally drop down in the street.

Terrifying, isn't it?

But I'd like to say right away that this kind of flu is extremely rare. In 999 cases out of 1,000, flu doesn't kill. It's a self-limiting infection. It runs its course in three days.

By that time you haven't a flu germ left.

Apart from explosive flu, it's the complications that can cause death during an epidemic. It's these complications that can ruin your health and change a three-day illness into one that may last weeks, months or even a year.

The most common complication is one you'd never guess – mental depression.

During the three days flu germs are on the go, they send out a nasty poison. This poison seeps into the bloodstream.

So, right from the tip of your toes to the top of your head, you're poisoned.

The brain suffers greatly. And the depression can last 14 days.

But the important thing is to realise this is a natural complication. Otherwise, in extreme cases, there's a risk of a nervous breakdown among folk who are by nature worriers.

If you've a worrying job, on no account go back too soon. Your morale is at zero for about 14 days. In a way, you're mentally weak.

The heart muscle is the next big danger.

It, too, is saturated with flu poison. Your heart is then not able to stand up to strenuous exercise. So it's asking for trouble to chase about soon after flu.

You can land yourself with a permanently tired heart. Even young and athletic folk should stay off football, &c., for at least three weeks after flu. Teenagers and the over fifties are the easiest victims of this complication.

And beware of the false sense of well-being that will come on the fifth day after you go down with flu.

Pneumonia is the most dangerous complication.

The flu germ has battered down our resistance.

Then in comes one of the pneumonia germs – and it finds it easy to get on top.

It usually comes on the second or third day. The patient is very ill, and looks it. He's breathless. Sometimes his hankie shows a blood-stained spit.

And here's a warning for anybody nursing a flu victim. Blue is the danger colour. If the ears or lips are slightly blue, get the doctor at once.

Twenty years ago, the chance of getting over pneumonia after flu was only 50-50.

Today it's ten to one in your favour. All the same, it means three to six months of pretty poor health.

What's more, even with modern drugs, there's still a risk of the heart breaking down under the treble strain – of beating flu germs, neutralising poisons in the bloodstream, and having to fight pneumonia.

The best defence against this complication is to follow one simple rule:- In the first three days of flu, on no account get out of bed.

Almost as bad, but more common, is the risk of bronchitis.

If your attack is at all severe, you can never feel safe until the whole fortnight's convalescence is over.

Even then, it's wise to ask the doctor for a check-up on your chest. I know one patient who skimped the fourteen days' lay-off – and the check-up.

He lasted at work for two days and landed himself with chronic bronchitis, which he has to this day.

Generally, children and old folk are most susceptible, and with old folk it can easily be fatal.

Another thing, along with pneumonia, bronchitis after flu can cause T.B., particularly among teenagers.

Sinusitis, tonsillitis, and laryngitis are other risks. And you yourself will have the best idea which is likely. For, immediately after flu, the other germs that follow on are almost certain to attack your particular weak spot.

Lastly, about half of all the folk who get flu face a risk of starting up chronic rheumatism. Here again it's the poisons to blame. That's why you ache so much.

So never risk a soaking or a chill after flu. If you have a tendency to rheumatics anyway, take the full period of convalescence.

All these risks can arise if the flu attack is severe.

But in the main there's little danger of even minor complications if you're sensible.

THE MODERN VIEW, BY DR LYNDA

THE winter of 2017-2018 was the worst year for flu since the 2009-2010 swine flu epidemic, with roughly 200 per 100,000 people contracting flu, despite the vaccination programme.

If you were unlucky enough to be admitted to Intensive Care with flu then you had a one-in-four chance of dying.

Lots of what the 1950s Doc says here is nearly true.

Flu does strike quickly, is usually self-limiting and it's usually the

When you feel the first signs of a feverish chill or cold take Beecham's Powders. The unique formula of Beecham's Powders soon brings the worst symptoms under control. Because of their powder form they are quickly assimilated and speedy in action. Get a supply of Beecham's Powders now!

2 Powders for 5½d.   Cartons of 8 Powders 1/7

complications that cause deaths during an epidemic. He was also right about the three major complications of pneumonia, cardiac problems and depression — but he definitely got the physiology all wrong.

"Explosive flu" is a term he made up, but probably he was talking about the sudden deaths in otherwise healthy young people caused by what is thought to be an "over-the-top" immune response reaction to the virus where the body becomes overwhelmed by the chemicals it produces to fight the virus and which attack the host's healthy tissues.

It is not a poison secreted by the virus!

The complications are usually in people with pre-existing disease of their heart and lungs, or who have a suppressed immune system due to disease or drugs, and are usually due to co-infection with some other bacteria.

I'm not sure about the sense of wellbeing on the fifth day, but I guess that's when recovery from the initial viral infection starts and before a secondary infection kicks in.

Today, the rates of recovery from pneumonia and chest infection are even better, thanks to treatment of the complications with antibiotics and supportive care in hospital for the seriously ill.

But now we are in danger from so-called "superbugs" emerging due to the overuse of antibiotics.

Again, I'm not sure if the advice about not getting out of bed would prevent the complications, but rest is certainly important for recovery.

However, bronchitis does not cause TB (tuberculosis).

You might be more vulnerable to contract TB after a bout of flu, but it's a disease entity on its own, caused by another bug altogether.

Interestingly, the 1950s Doc was correct about flu causing depression.

Post-viral fatigue and depression are usually short-lived and well documented — and not just found in those with a predisposition.

Sometimes, for patients with an underlying mood instability or a particular psychological profile, it can cause a chronic mood disorder and is often associated with what has many names, i.e. ME (myalgia encephalitis), post-viral fatigue and fibromyalgia, which I assume is what he means by chronic rheumatism.

Fortunately, these things are not common and still present treatment problems for the modern doctor.

The mainstay of flu treatment today is still prevention by vaccination, and rest, fluids to combat dehydration and now Paracetamol which eases aches and pains and reduces fever to make you feel better.

Keep That Holiday Feeling
August 4, 1957

YOU'RE back from holiday. You're feeling at
the top of your form. Wouldn't it be grand
if you could stay at the top? Well, you can!
August is the month to start to maintain
your holiday fitness.

Take my word, you don't fight off January colds
in January. You fight off colds now – in August, when you're 100% fit.

So let's not waste time.

First, make sure you have at least two baths a week. Every morning,
give yourself a sponge down. If you're under 30, make it a cold sponge.
From 30 to 65, a tepid one will do.

Every night at bedtime, change completely to the skin. Wear nothing in
bed that you've had on during the day.

Why all this attention to the skin, you may ask?

Because you can't fight winter infections without a good skin. After
your holiday, your skin is in tip-top condition.

It's had a fresh air "bath" every day. The pores are lively, they open and
close quickly to every change in temperature.

So the secret is to keep them that way by morning sponging and baths at
night. It's too late to start in October, because of the risk of a chill.

And don't be in too great a hurry to get into winter woollies. On a
colder day, put on an extra pullover.

All this is really one of the best tonics you can have – a tonic to the skin.

And the benefit goes deeper than that. Your circulation is pepped up.
No matter where the first winter germs attack you, your "defence armies"
get to the battle area in record quick time.

But what if you're one of the unlucky people – your holiday was a
washout? Then all the more reason for giving your skin an air tonic. You'll
be well advised to take something extra, too.

Two tonics are specially good at this time of the year. For pepping up
general fitness try the three syrups.

If you're feeling "slow and heavy", then Easton's syrup is just the thing
for you. Take the tonic for, say, a fortnight at the end of this month.

There's also a splendid tonic for wee Johnny of school age – chemical
food or iron and phosphate.

For general fitness, however, vitamin C is hard to beat. It's essential for
keeping up that holiday fitness. You can take two such tablets a week all
winter. Better still, take it regularly in its natural form.

Twice a week, make a point of having at least one thing from this list – lettuce, orange, two tomatoes, half a grapefruit, juice of a lemon, cabbage. Later on, eat Brussels sprouts. And in mid-winter, blackcurrant juice heads the list.

No need to take all of these things, of course – one item will do.

Vitamin C is important in this respect. Comparatively few foods (like bread, butter, meat, fish, &c.) have it. So, have another look at that list.

Lastly, try hard to avoid a bad autumn cold. It can use up all the good your holiday has done you. Vitamins A and D can help here.

A week's course of them immediately after your first little cold can set you up for the winter.

But the unlucky folk who are prone to colds are better advised to start taking A and D tablets now. Foods for them are liver, kidney, butter, carrots, dried apricots, prunes.

But don't depend too much on tablets to give you fitness. It's far better to get fresh air into your lungs and about your skin, and now's the time to get the habit.

THE MODERN VIEW, BY DR LYNDA

SORRY, 1950s Doc, there is little evidence that a cold sponge-down in the morning would help protect against colds and flu.

Remember the days when there was usually no heating in the bathrooms and bedrooms and single glazed metal framed windows often with ice on the inside in winter? (Sadly, I do). It was a form of torture, not a remedy!

And there's a lot written about cold showers or a cold "dook" (Scandinavians love them) but no evidence they have a protective role against colds and flu.

The "cures" and remedies are suspect, too. Easton's syrup contained quinine (supposedly to help appetite and a general stimulant), iron (listed as a brain food) and strychnine (a general stimulant). There were cases of fatal strychnine poisoning in children from it!

Generally, our diet should be much better than in the 1950s, so the use of tonics and vitamin supplements are not really necessary.

Vitamin C is mainly used by the body to promote wound healing.

It's Vitamin A which boosts the immune system. It is found mainly in dairy products eggs and oily fish. Vitamin D is used to regulate calcium and phosphate to keep teeth bones and muscle healthy. I'm not sure it has any role at all in the immune response.

Iron helps make red blood cells to carry oxygen around the body and has little to do with the production of white blood cells, the ones which fight infection.

Prevention is best achieved by looking after your diet, taking regular exercise and getting the flu vaccine. If you do get the cold or flu then you could help contain it by staying away from your workmates and vulnerable family members.

Things You Should Never Do When You Have A Cold

January 17, 1954

JANUARY is the month for colds. But some folk will still be sniffing and sneezing well into February. If they are, then, really, it's their own fault!

A cold may last a week, but should never last more than 10 days.

Are you one of the unlucky ones? Well, don't imagine your constitution is poor. It's far more likely you've been making mistakes.

I had a man to see me on Thursday. He couldn't shake off the cold.

I noticed his hair was well plastered down. He'd far too much cold lotion on his head. Be careful of that during icy weather, it chills the head and keeps a cold going.

But don't miss a haircut because the weather is cold.

Too many men make this mistake. They put off having their hair cut. The head gets coddled, and when the cut comes, the scalp feels the draught all the more.

Get your hair cut oftener – once a week instead of once a fortnight, but a little less off each time.

The head is very important when we have a cold. Whether you normally wear a hat or not, you shouldn't go out in rain or white frost without some protection on your head.

But suppose the cold does get a grip of you. No. 1 "Don't" is – for goodness sake, don't sweat it out!

A very hot bath, a couple of aspirins, and bed with extra blankets are all very well when you feel a cold coming on. But that's the only time it's safe.

A "sweat" in the middle of a cold can easily weaken you and bring on pleurisy or pneumonia.

No. 2 "Don't" concerns the eyes. Cut down TV, pictures and reading. The eyes are not in the best of trim, and strain reacts on your cold. When your eyes water with looking at TV, &c., you're prolonging your cold.

Another thing. It's unwise to sit face-on to an electric fire or a gas fire, because of rays which irritate the lining of the nose, &c. Much better to sit with your back to it.

Now for the use of hankies. A cold has three stages – the sniffly, the stuffy and the discharging. At stages 1 and 2, don't blow – only wipe!

When you're stuffy, your nose is not full of phlegm. It's the air passages which are swollen. Blowing makes them worse.

Heavy smokers often find a cold lasts too long. "I just can't cut down", they tell me. Well, here's a tip. When you've a cold, smoke as many as usual – but only half of each cigarette. You won't be a martyr, because it's the first few puffs that give the satisfaction. But no "ends", please. Throw the second half away.

Pipe-smokers can help themselves in the same way – only the first half of the pipe, please!

The reason is this – your body is putting up a fight. Half a fag or half a pipe cuts down the intake of all poisons, particularly as most of the "harm" is in that last half.

Another good tip is to ignore the nonsense about feeding a cold. Overeating is just what the cold germs like!

As for exercise – a little less than usual. That's better than none at all.

THE MODERN VIEW, BY DR LYNDA

SOME interesting concepts here, but what did the 1950s Doc get right?

I love his definition of the three stages of a cold — the sniffy, the stuffy, and the discharging. Quite right.

A cold does last 7- 10 days, but the cough can stay much longer due to increased mucous production stimulated by the virus (part of the immune response).

A hot bath and aspirin are good for a cold by inhaling steam to loosen the mucous and soothe the bronchial tubes.

Aspirin has some antiviral properties and reduces fever. Today we'd probably advocate Paracetamol rather than Aspirin as it can cause problems for people with asthma or tummy problems. For children, in particular, it has been linked with Reye's syndrome, a condition similar to meningitis or encephalitis.

Women have as many colds as men so I'm not sure plastering cold lotion on the hair or having it cut less often would make you more or less prone to a cold.

Sweats are a sign that there may be more than a cold or pneumonia developing, but certainly won't bring it on, per se.

And I loved the use of hankies. Who can remember their mother pulling out a used hanky out of their pocket and smothering your face to wipe of the snottery discharge then popping it back in her pocket to fester until it was needed again? Thank goodness for paper tissues.

As for smokers, the problem is picking up cigarettes in the first place. And "most of the harm is in the last half"? I suppose only smoking half a cigarette does cut the amount of poisons you inhale.

He's right that it's the first few puffs that give the satisfaction, but smoking will increase the length of the illness and make your lungs more prone to catching colds and infections in the first place.

It Can Save Five Years Of Your Life

December 14, 1958

YOU wouldn't like to lose five years of your life, would you?

Then make sure this winter you don't land yourself with two attacks of bronchitis.

One attack is distressing, but needn't be serious. Two attacks can leave their mark permanently.

It's a medical fact that chronic bronchitis reduces expectation of life by five years.

And, honestly, there's no excuse. It's the easiest thing in the world for the average patient not only to avoid the first attack, but more important, that dangerous second attack.

You hear folk say, "My cold's gone down to my chest".

That's not so. The cold germ never goes that far. It's other germs that come in with and are stirred up by the cold germ and attack the bronchial tubes – right down to the lungs.

So, next time you get a cold, heed the warning sign. The moment you feel a slight tightness in the chest, get to bed.

Other signs are a vague pain in the breast bone or you can't breathe OUT. Once you get to bed half the battle's won. The body has rest and surplus energy to deal with bronchial germs.

If you don't go to bed, you're an easy target for more and more of them.

Aspirins are grand for a head cold. But for threatened bronchitis, Dover's powders* are the thing. They soothe the cough, and they're inclined to make you sweat (that's a good thing). Just as important, they're mild sleep producers. Take one powder every four hours. But only for the first day.

You can help tremendously, too, with a poultice on the chest. Kaolin is grand. The earlier it goes on the better.

Drink at least five pints of hot fluid a day. Blackcurrant or lemon juice drinks are best.

Lastly, don't forget a daily laxative.

Now the battle's half won. Get in the doctor in, and he'll win the other half for you.

Bronchitis, properly treated, isn't half the terror it was three years ago. Since 1955 new antibiotic drugs have been developed. Today we can cure some cases that were once considered hopeless.

Even chronic bronchitis can now be eased, where it was once impossible. By 1969 the experts believe we'll cure three out of every four bad cases of chronic bronchitis.

If you crack down on bronchitis at the start, it needn't be much worse than a cold.

It you don't you can easily have a cough all winter.

The worst feature of neglect is that the damage to the lungs can't be mended. After a bout of flu, you'll be liable to pneumonia.

You can sometimes take some risk when you're getting over a cold. It's madness to take the same risk with bronchitis.

The danger is you're always apt to think you're better than you are. You say to your wife, "I'm all right. I'll get up tonight".

Before you do that, take this test. Put your hands behind your back, below the shoulder blades. Now take a big, deep breath. If your palms can feel a "rustle" in the lungs, stay in bed.

Once you get on your feet after a bout of bronchitis, here are the six golden rules: -

1. You need as much rest as after an operation – at least two weeks.

2. For the menfolk – change over from cigarettes to a pipe for three months. The ladies should cut out all tobacco.

3. For a good while sit downstairs in the bus. Use non-smoking railway compartments.

4. For two months, never do anything that leaves you winded. Your heart muscle needs a long time to recover.

5. Don't go out at night when there's white frost or fog.

6. Change into dry socks and different shoes whenever you come home from work.

If you're ever unlucky enough to land with bronchitis, it's a good idea to take a tonic all winter.

Two kinds help. Either cod liver oil emulsion or a preparation of vitamins A and B.

Also remember this. Bronchitis is easy to cure.

But you've got to make a job of it – or there can be years of trouble ahead for you.

Dover's powders, which contained opium, are now banned in the UK. Their inventor was Dr Thomas Dover (1660-1742).

A Guarantee Of Not Getting A Cold

November 5, 1950

DON'T think I've found a new cure for our commonest ailment. I haven't. But if you follow my advice to the letter, I can guarantee you'll have nothing worse than a sniffle this winter.

The source of the cold is a germ.

Don't let it in and you won't catch cold.

How can you keep it out? The cold germ has two entrances into the body. One is the nose. The other is the mouth.

You're remarkably well protected in the nose. Minute hairs in the nostrils, mucus, bones, and adenoids form four lines of defence. So, you see, germs have a pretty rough time getting in by the nose.

And if we all breathed constantly through our noses and not our mouths, those four defences would be sufficient.

Unfortunately we can't. We've to open our mouths sometimes – to talk, eat and so on.

But too many of us use this opening to breathe with, too. That's where the danger lies. The mouth has only one defence against germs – the tonsils. They work wonderfully well, but if we're to keep free of colds, they must have help.

How, then, are we to reinforce this single line of defence? There are five ways.

1.   Breathe through the nose as much as possible.

2.   At work, at home, in bedrooms, living-rooms, buses – wherever you are – have good ventilation.

3.   Blow your nose on rising and at least two or three times during the day. Blow one nostril at a time. When you've finished blowing, take two or three deep breaths of fresh air.

4.   Throughout winter clean your teeth often every day.

5.   Most important of all, gargle and wash your mouth at least three times a day, after each meal – and oftener if possible.

Most folk think mouthwashes and gargles kill the germs in mouth and throat. They don't. They merely wash the germs out. In order to kill them, the solution would have to be so strong it would damage the skin.

Use a weak solution often, rather than a strong one once.

And when you're using mouthwash and gargle together, always use the mouthwash first.

If you do it the other way round, it's like dusting the room then sweeping the floor.

The best to use?

For a mouthwash your own toothpaste is as good as any. Swill it well round, then take a mouthful of water. Rinse again.

Or use any of the good mouthwashes at half the advised strength.

When they're in tablet form, don't do as one man did and suck them. He couldn't eat for days!

A half-pint glass of tepid water containing a level teaspoonful of salt is a cleansing and soothing gargle.

Swap the salt for the same amount of baking soda, and you have an excellent gargle for loosening phlegm and mucus. A mixture of both is probably best of all.

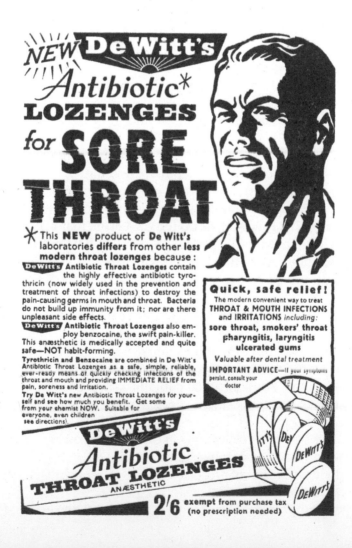

October Is Too Late
September 13, 1959

THERE is one way we can avoid a bad cold in the coming winter. By a course of anti-catarrhal injections.

Some firms are having them arranged for their staff. It's a good idea.

But it must be done now. Even October is too late.

Here's why. If, just after the first injection, you get the "smit" from someone, you'll land yourself with the worst cold you've ever had. So, after getting the injection, it's wise to walk home from the surgery.

And for 24 hours afterwards, stay away from buses, cinemas, &c., in case you pick up a cold.

When the course is completed you should be all set for a winter without bad colds.

"But how is it you beat the cold when everybody knows the cold germ hasn't even been pinpointed yet?" a patient asked me.

It is, of course, true that nobody can kill the cold virus. But a simple cold is mild and of no consequence.

It's the germs that follow close on the cold virus that cause the real trouble. The injections build up defences against these germs.

Usually you need six visits to the doctor. The first injection is one-sixth of full strength, and each succeeding injection gets stronger. The needle goes in the arm.

There's no swelling, but your arm might be a little bit stiff for up to 24 hours.

Should everybody have these injections?

Half of us wouldn't benefit, for the good weather has helped our all-round resistance. And one in 20 patients would even be made worse by the injections.

But your doctor knows if you'll benefit from them.

For those who need the injections, the course will mean fewer colds. And the few you do have will be trifling.

But the greatest benefit of all is less chance of bronchitis, tonsillitis, and other germ illnesses.

When you beat colds, you're a long way to breaking catarrh, too.

Nearly every one of us has catarrh to some degree. It's annoying, dirty, and bad for general health.

One snag when blowing your nose is that you may drive the phlegm backwards, even into the air passages of the face.

Result – a bigger hold-up than ever.

Six gentle blows, with both nostrils open, is the best way. Don't go in for nasal douches. Most doctors are wary of them, simply because a patient is likely to be too vigorous.

What about morning phlegm? Well, you're lucky to have that.

It shows there's been a cleaning-up operation overnight. Always make a point of getting rid of it.

Now, many of us have a choked nose, yet hardly any phlegm comes down.

This isn't a cold. The inside of the nose is swollen. There's little you can do about it. But your health won't suffer unduly.

If you're a cigarette smoker, cut them down. You'll feel the benefit in two or three weeks.

For some bad cases of catarrh, there are special exercises. Roughly, you do breathing exercises, lying on a couch with head and shoulders lower than the rest of the body.

Don't try these on your own. But if your doctor says "yes", then these drainage exercises can bring wonderful improvement.

Anybody as old as 80 can help catarrh by adopting a regime of ordinary breathing exercises.

Fresh air, breathing in by the nose and out by the mouth – deeply, but not forcibly – is worthwhile starting now. Try it at any time and anywhere when you remember.

As a variation, when you inhale, fill out the lower part of the chest – the opposite of the usual way. This lower breathing often brings up phlegm from the depths of the lungs.

Starting next month, go in for good soled shoes.

If you let your feet go cold and wet at 9 p.m., by 9.30 p.m. your nose will likely be blocked.

Catarrh is a thousand times more common than it was in our grandfathers' day.

Because there's more irritation all round. We can never go back to the fresh-air life of the old days.

But at least let's take every chance of it.

And, if necessary, there are always these six injections, too.

Always Take A Deep Breath Before You Blow Your Nose

September 16, 1951

"DOCTOR how can I avoid colds this winter?" Many patients are asking this question.

And my answer is always the same – look after yourself in September! If you dodge colds this month you've a good chance of being free of them all winter.

We all get cold germs at this time of year. In small doses they help us! They build up body resistance for bigger attacks later on.

About one person in ten never has a bad cold all winter because he wins the first round in September.

Those who do catch a bad cold in September lay themselves open for the rest of the winter.

So it's up to ourselves to avoid colds. We can do it in two ways:-

1. Watch the membrane at the back of the throat and nose.

2. Never allow the army of cold germs to become too big.

We get most colds because we neglect No. 1. The membrane holds back the germs and later "washes" them out. That's why we blow our noses.

But too many of us blow the wrong way. We blow both nostrils at once, and blow twice as hard as we should.

This injures the cells of the membrane.

The injured cells can't resist the cold germ. In fact, we blow our defences away and bring on a cold.

The right way to blow your nose is – first take one or two slow, deep breaths. Then blow one nostril at a time, and gently does it!

A blow in the fresh air is worth three in a stuffy room.

Another thing. Cut down smoking indoors. Smoke irritates the membrane, so does a stuffy room heated only by gas or electricity.

That's why you should also keep away from the cinema when you're tired.

You think you'll get pepped up. But when the rest of your body is tired, the throat membrane is also too tired to stand up to the smoky atmosphere. You treble the risk of a cold.

Now for the second plan – how to keep germ reinforcements from landing.

Keep at least two feet away from a sneezing person. Seventy-five per cent of sneeze germs die quickly unless they land on a human.

If you can, sit in the back of a tram or bus.

Wash your hands oftener from now on, particularly when there's a lot of cold about. Germs land on your hands – often from shaking hands with other people.

Use twice as many hankies. If you're snivelling, take two in the forenoon, two in the afternoon.

Drink as much water in winter as in summer.

If you must have an artificial fire in the room, remember a shallow dish of water prevents the dryness which irritates nose and throat.

If you feel a cold is getting a grip, go to bed for 24 hours.

A day in bed on Sunday if you're below par is excellent. During the week, even two hours earlier is a saver.

Finally, you must find out for yourself what's the best thing for you to take to strengthen your defences.

It may be vaccine, vitamins or gargles, or malt, olive oil, cod liver oil, sun rays, or fresh fruit.

Don't dread the winter. Get out and enjoy it.

Having something to look forward to is half the battle.

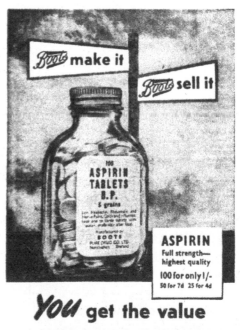

Sitting In Front Of The Fire Is No Cure

January 11, 1953

NO doubt about it, we got off to a bad start this winter.

Winter weather came in two months earlier than usual. And it has stayed almost without a break.

Usually our body has to resist only three months' hard continuous winter from January to March. But already many people's resistance is down to a "March level".

We're feeling the effects in four ways.

1) Some of us are tired.

2) Others are catching a succession of colds one after the other.

3) Adults, who never had rheumatism before, are complaining of aches and pains.

4) Some housewives and children are bothered with headaches.

Everywhere I hear moans about the long winter – and fears for the next two months.

But cheer up! The human frame is built to stand up to colder and longer winters than we get in this country.

Cold weather itself can't ruin our health if we're sensible. With a little effort we can increase our winter stamina from the usual three months to five. And that's long enough to take us into spring.

Remember this. Nearly all winter illnesses are due not so much to cold, as to less fresh air and exercise.

These two things are the real key to winter health.

Yet many of us are so apt to be fed up with the cold that we huddle over the fire. We live and eat in the same room, often for the sake of warmth.

But simply warming the skin isn't the way to beat the cold. On the contrary, it can let the cold in.

Do you know some people can't sleep because they've sat too long in front of the fire beforehand? They've opened the pores, and this lets the heat out!

A brisk walk outdoors and a plate of porridge when you come in. That's the secret for winter stamina!

Heat yourself from the inside, not the outside.

Folk who complain of feeling tired and "low" mentally sometimes think their blood is to blame. That's not so.

It's their muscles. Flabby muscles pull down the system, including the brain.

And it's lack of exercise in winter that leads to flabby muscles.

The easiest victim to any illness, whether it's a cold or pneumonia, is the person who's tired and depressed – winter fatigue brought on because the muscles are not up to standard.

One of the healthiest men I know is a 70-year-old. He's glorying in the winter because he's daft on curling.

He's in better condition than he is in summer! He doesn't feel the cold. He's getting plenty of fresh air and exercise. His system is well above his usual par.

A good walk in winter is in some ways more valuable than in summer.

A nip in the air tones us up. We've less perspiration. The air is more germ free.

Keeping on the move is also important if you're bothered with mild rheumatism. Fifty per cent. of winter rheumatism could be checked by exercise.

Keep the circulation going – that's the secret.

A word to mothers. Don't deny the babies fresh air in winter. Nine babies out of ten don't get enough.

I know the pram can't always be put outside – but why not let baby sleep in another room?

Babies who sleep in the "one-room-for-the-family" tend to be chesty in winter. Their digestion is poorer and their sleep is less sound.

A lot of us find it difficult to get up on winter mornings. The reason isn't the cold – but lack of fresh air. We've been sleeping with the windows closed.

So let's all make up our minds – more fresh air and exercise these next three months.

Most Of Us Fight Catarrh The Wrong Way

October 18, 1953

THE complaint that plagues us most is not, as you'd think, the common cold. Away ahead of that is chronic catarrh.

Nine out of ten city folk have it in some form.

It may pull us down 20 per cent in fitness and brightness. It's the cause of a great deal of depression. Some poor souls are made utterly miserable.

Without being pessimistic, I must admit there's really no cure. And no hope of a cure in the near future.

It's the price we have to pay for being civilised!

But there are comforting facts. It is not medically classed as a disease. In a way, it saves us from more serious illnesses. And we can get relief. We can minimise the depression, the headaches, the choked-up feeling.

Catarrh is really an irritated "inside skin".

Think of your skin as the harling of a house, and the wallpaper in the room as the inside skin, which is normally thin.

It should also be moist to prevent friction and trap invading germs, and smooth to allow these germs to be washed away.

Nowadays, dirt and fumes, artificial heating and indoor work all tend to irritate the nose and other linings.

The inner skin gets thickened; the lubricant becomes thick and sticky. And so you have catarrh.

The air passages in some cases are no bigger than a darning needle. Catarrh makes them even narrower.

So either we have to breathe harder to get the same air, or we only half-breathe. And this is one reason for the feeling of depression.

Connected to the nostrils are air spaces in the bones of the forehead and cheek, also in the base of the skull – all lined with this inner skin.

When these get sticky, the germs collect instead of being drained away. The brain is deprived of the necessary amount of oxygen. No wonder we feel depressed, stupid, headachy!

We should try to make the catarrh as mild as possible.

Best remedy by far is – improve your general health a wee bit more.

Avoid foods that irritate your tummy. No fancy stuff. No fries. Cut out pepper, spices, vinegar, &c. Cut down smoking.

If your catarrh is really bad cut OUT smoking. I've been told by patients that a cigarette brings relief to catarrh. Yes, but it's only temporary. You'll be worse in 20 minutes.

What happens is that the smoke has induced a flow of thinner phlegm by irritation. That's all.

Quickest and best "first aid" is to go to an open window and take in slow, long, deep breaths through the nose. Let the air out through the mouth.

It's the easiest thing in the world to make your catarrh worse. One way is douching the nose without a doctor's advice.

Another is blowing the nose violently. Never do that. The nose should be wiped, not blown.

Inhalants are all right at the time when the catarrh is really bad and you want temporary relief. But I don't advise their continual use for ordinary chronic catarrh.

And you should not try nose drops on your own.

Safest and best is the old-fashioned steaming; boiling water with any of the old favourites:- eucalyptus, oil of pine, menthol, camphor.

But don't have the mixture too strong – it's really the steam that helps. And never "steam" when you have to go out afterwards.

Every time you wash your face, clean the inside of the nostrils to a depth of half an inch – and no more!

Folk who get catarrh badly should remember this winter – never sit facing a gas fire or an electric fire.

Sit with your back to it or side on.

It's A Good Idea To Stand On Your Head

February 26, 1956

A YOUNG man came to my surgery last Wednesday with bronchial catarrh. Phlegm had settled on his chest. He had spent a miserable night coughing and hawking – but the phlegm wouldn't budge.

"What can I do, doctor?" he asked.

"The one way to shift your catarrh", I told him, "is to stand on your head!"

My patient thought I was joking but I persuaded him to try my cure. Back he came the very next evening. "Doctor, it's amazing. I got rid of the phlegm all right".

We're nearly all cursed with catarrh at some point, particularly in the nose, throat and chest.

You needn't worry much about it in the nose, or even the throat. But beware of chest catarrh.

That phlegm simply must be got up.

It's one thing that can easily bring on pneumonia.

Try poultices on the chest – cough mixtures, too. But if all else fails, try the head-down trick.

You can do this in any way that suits you.

Here are two methods:- kneel on the floor and get far enough down to rest your elbows on the carpet. Stay there, head downwards, for as long as you can count 100.

That's long enough.

The other method can be tried in bed. Lean over the bedside, and literally hang the head and shoulders upside down.

"Oh, that's all very well", you may say, "but what about the blood rushing to the head?"

It'll do you no harm, but about two minutes is long enough.

And don't do it oftener than three times a day.

Of course, this relief is not suitable for anybody with a weak heart or blood pressure. But for all others, it's remarkable how it can ease the chest.

When you get a bad dose of catarrh, you feel wabbit. Maybe you wonder if you should stay off work?

That all depends on the colour of the phlegm you bring up.

When it's dark coloured, very tough and at all rusty, go to bed at once.

That's because the germs have got at your chest and there's a battle going on. The phlegm is really the casualties – germs and white corpuscles. Unless these casualties are got rid of, they fall farther down in the chest – even into the lungs.

That's when pneumonia can develop.

The colour of the phlegm is a good guide. If it's clear, the trouble isn't deep-seated.

The yellower it is, the more likely some of the sinuses are involved.

For any favour, don't be polite and swallow phlegm rather than spit it out. Yes – spit! But, of course, into your hankie or a piece of tissue paper.

It isn't that the phlegm will harm your stomach, but some will fall back into the bronchial tubes.

What about the man who has chest catarrh two or three times every winter?

That's nothing serious in itself. But he's getting it too often. He needs feeding up. Or he's unfit. Or he's doing something that's lowering resistance. Or he's eating the wrong kind of food.

To any mother who has a boy with a weak chest, here is some advice:-

Give the laddie good food and plenty fresh air. That's better than medicine.

Now, nasal catarrh – probably the most common of all. It isn't always a cold. It's usually caused by germs or irritation.

Next time you're feeling "thick" upstairs, try this test. Blow your nose. If nothing comes down, it's pretty certain there's no germ trouble – just irritation.

The irritation that afflicts us most is cigarette smoke. If you cut out smoking, your catarrh is almost sure to disappear in three months.

But if that sacrifice is too great, it'll help if you don't blow smoke down your nose.

Try to stop inhaling, too, for that irritates the lungs and can set up chronic catarrh.

Anybody plagued with catarrh, and who isn't prepared to give up tobacco, can at least change over to a pipe. Pipe smokers don't irritate their breathing apparatus nearly so much.

Sometimes catarrh can become quite an epidemic. There's one on the go right now. It's like gastric flu, only there's no high temperature. It comes on suddenly, and there's vomiting.

Catarrh of the stomach is to blame, due to a new germ that's got into the tummy. If this hits any of the family, don't be alarmed. It doesn't last.

Above all, however, remember this is about catarrh. It's not serious – but it CAN be.

This Is Why It Takes You So Long To Get Rid Of A Cold

March 2, 1958

"DOCTOR, why do I take so long to get rid of a cold?

You won't guess the answer to this one. Because nobody takes long to get rid of a cold!

The virus is dead and gone in 48 hours. Why, then, do the sniffing, sneezing, and wheezing drag on and on?

Simply because the cold virus, when it gets a grip, can stir up about 36 different kinds of germs – all rarin' to cause trouble.

It's these other germs that keep the "cold" going. You might get as many as a dozen colds on top of each other.

More likely these other germs carry on of their own accord – and attack the throat, chest or lungs.

So, to all who find it hard to throw off a cold, here's why.

You were too slow on the uptake.

The cold is not a serious illness. It's easily squashed. But you didn't take the warning – that first volley of sneezes. Had you gone to bed right away you wouldn't be sniffling now.

A day and a half between blankets at the start is worth a week in bed later on.

You didn't give up smoking.

It takes a strong will to say "No more fags until my cold is better". But, my goodness, what a difference it makes to the duration of a cold. The linings of the nose and throat have a hard enough time fighting the germs.

You should have helped them by the "no fag" rule. Smoking irritates the linings – your first line of defence.

You ate too much. You drank too little.

Time and again I see my patients make these two mistakes. "Feed a cold and starve a fever" is bunkum. If you overload the tummy, your resistance falls to zero. Your cold's bound to get worse.

When I visit a patient down with the cold, I always look at his tongue. Nearly always it's dry. He isn't taking enough drinks.

When there's a battle going on in the body there are thousands of casualties. These have to be washed away. So keep going with plenty fluids like water and fruit juices.

You didn't keep your feet warm.

Cold feet at any time of the day are bound to keep a cold going. The blood gets chilled at the feet, and chills all the organs on its way back to the heart. Cold feet lower your resistance by at least 50 per cent.

We can't explain why, but there's a close nerve link-up between feet and nose. Cold feet chill the inside of the nose and your whole head can go all stuffy in seconds.

You overdid the cures.

Many a patient tells me she "tried everything" for her cold. And I've a good idea that's just the reason the cold kept on.

Gargles, sprays, and inhalants are, of course, all right in their way. But if they're too strong, or used too often, they tend to irritate nose and throat – and kill the defenders instead of the attacking germs.

You went to bed cold.

Perhaps the fire was low, yet you had to see the end of the TV. The No. 1 danger of getting a worse cold is not, as you'd imagine, a sudden chill. Far more likely it's the slow creeping cold that does the harm. A drop of two degrees in the temperature increases colds by 5 per cent.

You didn't like to be by yourself.

It's ten times easier to beat a cold on your own. That's half the value of going to bed or staying indoors. But you carried on. You picked up other folk's germs, and you were an easy mark!

Frankly, the man who lets a cold run on doesn't deserve much of our sympathy. For, by and large, it's his own fault – and he knows it. He looks for fancy cures that won't upset his way of life. The real cure means some upset, but it's well worthwhile.

Nearly Everybody In My Waiting Room Is Complaining About Being Tired

March 8, 1959

"I'M feeling kind of washed out these days". That's the great complaint this spring. Practically every second person is feeling tired out. I've never seen anything quite like it before.

The reason? Poisoned heart. That's what's causing the tiredness – and slowing down recovery after flu.

Not only that. Thousands of us are almost immune to flu. But our fight against it has left our heart muscle poisoned.

So don't get any idea of an overnight recovery from this tiredness. A quick pep-up is the worst thing you can try. What's needed is a slow building-up. A tonic to pep up the system is like flogging a tired horse. You could do yourself harm.

Here's the way to get back to normal.

First:- take an hour's extra sleep every night for two weeks. I don't think there's anything more important. During the following fortnight take an extra hour occasionally.

If you don't do this, you'll just have to take the consequences. You could be left tired for at least another two months.

Second – drink more than you normally do.

Water is best. It helps the kidneys to get rid of the poisons more quickly.

As an extra help, prefer vitamins to tonics. Every day for a fortnight or so take two vitamin B tablets and one vitamin C tablet.

B is good for poisoned nerves. It also helps to lift depression and the fed-upness that go with this tiredness.

The vitamin C tablet has a different purpose. We're very vulnerable to extra infection just now. That C tablet daily may make all the difference.

For the same reason, I don't think you can do better than change over to orange or grapefruit juice in the morning. The water flushes the system. The fruit helps your defence against more germs.

What about food?

Keep your meals simple. Milk and eggs are favourites to build you up and replace lost stamina. Have a glass of milk between meals. Have two eggs a day. Take a little more sugar. Have your drinks sweeter, but make your tea and coffee weaker.

Instead of a cigarette, change over occasionally to sweets. Boilings, barley sugar, and butterscotch are all first-class for the tired man or woman.

Quite a few folk are walking about with mild pneumonia – and don't know it!

That's where their tiredness comes from.

So, if you have the slightest suspicion that your lungs aren't in good shape, try this test. Take three slow, deep breaths. If, by then, you start coughing – or feel a pain in the chest – it might be the dregs of pneumonia, or even worse – bronchitis setting in.

Go to your doctor for a check-up. If he suggests an X-ray, don't get alarmed. Do as he says.

No cough should be tolerated more than a fortnight. You must tell the doctor about it. Otherwise the tiredness can stay with you until mid-summer. Don't cut out smoking unless your doctor tells you. But ease up on it a bit. The nicotine in tobacco speeds up the heart.

Now, here are other ways you can help to get rid of that tired feeling.

Try low-breathing occasionally. Breathe in and fill the "stomach". Exhale and feel the stomach going in.

This is grand for turn-over air in the lungs, also for getting rid of phlegm in the bronchial tubes where they branch through the lungs.

Get as much fresh air as you can. Even ten minutes at a time will help to give you a healthy heart again.

Take it easy. And for any favour don't try to make up for lost time – in the house or at the office. Stop when the clock says so.

Lastly, fight depression by thinking cheery thoughts. Remember, lots of us are in the same boat – and spring's just around the corner!

How to tell if a dying person has a chest cold

September 27, 1959 — **Does rather quick and laboured breathing, some hours before death, indicate the patient (aged) has a chest cold or flu? Or is this the natural way of a peaceful passing?**

It is the usual terminal condition, brought on by congestion in the chest due to the failing heart.

February 9, 1958 — **While ill with pneumonia, I found I'd lost the power to sneeze. The "aaaah" came perfectly normally, but never the "choo!" Was this related to my illness?**

I've never heard of such a complication, but queer things can happen to all of us. Fortunately, this needn't worry you since it isn't serious.

March 18, 1956 — **Is flannel the best underwear material for chesty folk?**

No. Loosely-woven wool (or other material) is better, and unlikely to hamper free movement of the chest walls.

December 14, 1958 — **What's the healthiest way to breathe? Is it in and out through the nose, or in through the nose and out through the mouth?**

Normally, through the nose all the time, except when eating and talking. As a health exercise, deep breathing is useful. Draw in air through the nose, and exhale through the mouth, with lips parted but not gaping wide.

April 1, 1956 — **I often cough up small pieces of what looks like cheese. They don't resemble phlegm or catarrh.**

These are probably phlegm, despite the appearance. But get your chest X-rayed to make certain it's normal.

May 17, 1959 — **My mother had lumbago and flu. She's 60. Since then she's had severe pain at the base of her spine and bladder trouble. She's tired and sleepy. She's overweight.**

She must not drift along like this. The bladder trouble can be dealt with, and she can be helped and encouraged to reduce her weight. All who have had severe influenza this winter have tended to be tired and depressed, but that wears off.

May 9, 1954 — **What's the best thing to do for a stomach chill?**

Get cosy in bed. If acute, take ½ oz. castor oil. In all cases have fluid diet (chiefly milk and water) for 24 hours (in sips only, if vomiting).

March 31, 1957 — **Does a person with cancer have a cough? I've had this dry, irritating cough for nearly two months.**

It depends where the cancer is. Many other (and more common) things can cause a cough, but you need a throat and chest examination.

January 5, 1958 — **My wife suffers bronchitis. Would having a budgie in our RAF living quarters have anything to do with her being allergic to something?**

If she's asthmatic, the bird might be to blame. But pure bronchitis is usually due to germ infection. One of the new antibiotics might help her.

August 21, 1955 — **Which is better – sea air or country air – for folk with lung T.B.?**

In most cases, country air — preferably at an altitude.

September 7, 1958 — **Sometimes I feel something's sticking in my throat. When I swallow, it seems to move a little, but afterwards the feeling returns. What could cause this? Could it be connected in any way with a bout of flu?**

Yes the flu has probably left some infection in the throat. Gargle twice daily with a glass of warm water, to which ½ teaspoonful each of salt and baking soda have been added.

November 5, 1950 — **I found one morning that I had gone deaf. My deafness was going away when I felt a slight head cold coming on. Is the deafness a warning?**

It's usually the other way round — you get a cold first and then deafness. You may simply have wax in the ears, the head cold being coincidental. See your doctor about getting your ears cleaned.

November 2, 1958 — **Would you consider a person (20) during an attack of bronchial asthma, with pulse 120, respiration 28, and temperature 101 to be on the danger list?**

No, but ill enough to require medical attention.

October 20, 1957 — **How can I tell the difference between a bad cold and flu?**

It's often difficult. Influenza usually (but not invariably) strikes suddenly. A rise in temperature above 98.4 degrees Fahrenheit would indicate flu and the need for bed.

January 19, 1958 — **I'm very troubled with catarrh and sinusitis. Does an electric blanket or electric heater have a bad effect on this?**

Dry heat of any sort seems to make this worse. So do certain rays from electric fires. The latter travel in straight lines (more or less) and their bad effects can be avoided by keeping behind the fire, or at least, to the side.

— Chapter 8 —

Secrets Of A Good Night's Sleep

IT isn't necessarily true that sleeping with your head to the north is best for you . . . which will be good news for people who had never suspected this might be the case.

This chapter has its fair share of . . . questionable . . . advice, but it also has a lot of clever and insightful stuff.

Counting sheep is condemned as useless, sleeping tablets get similar short shrift (and another sound thrshing from our modern doc Lynda) but the benefits of warm feet, a cool head, pleasant thoughts of holiday beaches, and following your body's natural rhythms all find favour.

And everyone in the 1950s, it seems, slept on their right side. But only if they were healthy — unhealthy people slept on their back. And on a soft mattress. And snored. But often indulged in the terrible mistake of a non-stop search for pleasure!

A Simple Answer To Sleeplessness

December 11, 1955

YOU'D hardly credit this, but one patient in every eight tells me – "Oh, doctor, I can't sleep a wink!"

Then they all ask me for sleeping pills.

And the truth is that only one in fifty who demands sleeping pills needs them.

There are only three types of people who really need pills for getting off at night.

No. 1 is like Mr B. He's highly strung. He has a difficult job to hold down, with lots of worries. But he can't help taking these worries to bed with him.

He needs the oblivion that sleeping pills give.

Type No. 2 is the elderly woman like Miss S. She lives alone. Her sleeplessness is due to nerves. Pheno-barb does her a world of good by giving her a feeling of security.

Type No. 3 may surprise you.

Although we don't realise it, many of us have a primitive fear of the dark. You can be six feet tall, weigh a healthy 14 stone and be as tough as nails. Yet your sleeplessness can be due to this deep-seated fear.

Children should never be given sleeping tablets.

And I don't think that anybody in the twenties or thirties really needs them either. After 60 it's a different story.

For one case in twenty who "can't sleep", drugs do help. As we get older it's more difficult to sleep. That's because there's less muscular fatigue for the body – and the mind is as active as ever.

We lack the two things that make good sleep easy – muscular fatigue and a quiet mind.

Yet, even for these difficult cases, there's a simple answer.

What if you have a spell when you can't get to sleep because your mind is racing? One aspirin, with a cup of hot milk, is better for you than swallowing pheno-barb.

Then there's the odd occasion when you're physically jumpy at night. Your nerves are on edge and you toss and turn.

Get up and take a hot bath. Your nerves are being irritated by body poisons. A good soak gets rid of these. Afterwards have a cup of tea and two aspirins. That'll send you to sleep.

Anybody who's a slow sleeper can usually benefit by taking a hot drink and hot foot bath half an hour before bedtime.

We all have our natural bedtime. That's when the heartbeat slows down and the pulse rate and body temperature fall. Your time may be 10.30, mine might be midnight. Whatever their time, slow sleepers should stick to it.

Everybody who doesn't sleep well should use a really soft pillow.

It doubles your chances of dropping off quickly. Irritating pressure against the ears is reduced to almost nil.

Most of us sleep on our right side. But here's a tip. Start off on the wrong side! Two minutes is enough. Then over you go. Even a little thing like that can help a lot.

And always sleep in the same direction. Don't let your wife cajole you into changing the bed round. It's not necessarily true you sleep better with your head to the north. But whatever direction you're accustomed to, keep to it!

What about counting sheep? I've never yet met anybody who benefited from doing that!

In fact, the concentration demanded of the brain to visualise the sheep is bound to keep you awake!

If you must count, count your breaths or the tick of the clock. Your own breathing is the perfect pace for inducing sleep.

Now, what about late meals?

It's always a mistake to go to bed on an empty stomach. This keeps you awake. And it's often the reason for waking you about five in the morning.

A light meal (say, hot milk and biscuits) is a good thing half an hour before turning in.

Fresh air, too, is essential to sound sleep. But don't open the bedroom window until you're ready for bed. And you'll not sleep well if you have the bedclothes high – that is, over your head.

Warm feet, cool nose and head – that's the thing.

THE MODERN VIEW, BY DR LYNDA

MOST people experience problems with sleep at some point in their life though it's usually short-lived, but up to a third of people have prolonged sleep disturbance.

The most common causes are anxiety and depression but we often turn ourselves into insomniacs by drinking coffee or alcohol or eating chocolate full of caffeine.

There are no official guidelines on how much sleep you need, as long as you are rested and able to function well the next day. But most adults seem to require 6-9 hours, with children requiring more and the elderly requiring less.

The 1950s Doc was right about a few things, though. Sleeping tablets should never be used by children and young adults except in very exceptional circumstances. Phenobarbitone, which was highly addictive, has been replaced by newer, equally as addictive, and questionably safer, drugs.

But they do not treat the cause and, over time, become less and less effective.

In many cases they cause daytime sedation and drowsiness, linked to accidents and falls in the elderly and confusion and depression in the long term.

They should be used in the short term only, and the types of people the Doc says "really need them" probably don't need then either.

So what makes for a good night's sleep?

Regular exercise during the day and keeping the mind active helps. Try to go to bed and get up at the same time each day, which helps you get into a routine. And no naps or snoozes during the day. Try to relax in the evening, with no strenuous activity 2-3 hours before bed. Have a bath, read a book, have a light supper avoiding caffeine (mainly found in coffee, tea and chocolate) and some light stretches or yoga might help.

Make sure the bedroom is comfortable dark and quiet, and your bed is comfy to lie in. There are many relaxation and meditation CDs/aids that might help too.

I'm pretty certain that having your head pointing north doesn't matter! As for counting sheep, I find reading some medical journals does it for me.

There are specific conditions which cause insomnia and require specific treatment. Anxiety can mean difficulty getting to sleep, and depression which causes frequent and early waking needs treated with talking therapies and antidepressants. Ladies of a certain age might benefit from hormone replacement therapy if their flushes are causing problems at night.

Sleep apnoea is now a recognised problem causing insomnia, daytime sleepiness and fatigue, and is treated with a CPAP (continuous positive airways pressure) machine.

And there are a host of unusual disorders like myoclonic jerks and restless legs which can be treated...but not with sleeping tablets.

And, yes, I agree. Warm feet, cool nose and head. That sounds just about right.

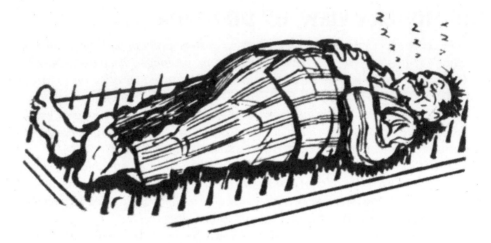

There's Nothing Like A Hard Bed
March 1, 1959

HOW many folk will sink deep into their soft bed tonight and think it's the last word in comfort?

Many will, I know, yet they couldn't be more wrong.

Let me say right away – there's nothing to beat a firm, or even a hard bed. Not only for comfort, but for good health.

Any doctor or surgeon who's treating a patient for sciatica will always tell him to lie on a firm bed.

It not only helps to cure the sciatica and any shoulder and neck pains. It helps to prevent them.

In many cases sciatica and lumbago follow a twist, an injury, or even cold and damp. Well, the outcome is less likely to be serious if the complaint is dealt with right away in a sensible bed.

Freedom of movement is essential to us all in bed.

Certain parts of the body – elbows, heels, hip-bones – don't like pressure. They can become painful after a while. So, to neutralise the pressure, we turn in our sleep. And we can only do this if we have a sufficiently firm support.

If a hollow has formed lengthwise in bed, it's difficult to move freely. Next thing we know we've got cramp.

Even if you're apt to sweat excessively in bed, it can be due to a sagging mattress. That's because you're lying in one position night after night. You can't turn when you should.

People who sleep on a hard bed rarely have nightmares.

Maybe you've slept in a hard bed yet tossed and turned the whole night. Don't blame the bed. Although you seemed to be restless, you've probably had a better night's sleep than any billowy bed could have given you.

Now, how do you make this kind of healthy bed?

Where a firm bed is ordered, the doctor generally advises you to put boards under the mattress. It's better if the boards are placed across the bed rather than lengthwise. Then there's less chance of them bending in the middle.

It's a good idea, too, to bore a few holes in the boards. This lets air pass through.

But don't whip the boards out and chop them up for firewood if you're uncomfortable for the first night or two.

A firm bed takes a bit of getting used to. But, believe me, you'll know the benefit in a week or so.

A man came into my surgery with an aching back. It was a slipped disc. He admitted he slept on a cushy bed. I got him to put boards under his mattress that very night. Before the week was out, he was back at the surgery almost jumping for joy!

What had happened? A few nights' comfortable, relaxed sleep allowed the disc to slip back into place. And it was the firm bed that did the trick.

But you don't even need to make a special bed. For persistent aches and pains in the shoulders or back, try a week of sleeping on the floor. If you don't have a hair mattress to put down, use two rugs folded to give four-ply.

Make sure you're not lying in a draught.

When you're buying a new bed, buy a good mattress. It can be springy, but see that it's laid on something that doesn't sag.

You'd be surprised how many people, used to a hard bed, don't take a holiday. All because they can't sleep in a strange, soft one!

Well, I know a man who has to travel a lot. He takes his bed-boards with him. He had them specially made with hinges so that they would pack in his suitcase.

So, when you go on holiday, why not ask the hotel to give you bed-boards?

P.S. If anybody doubts the comfort of a hard bed, ask an old soldier. And you don't find many of them with sore backs, do you?

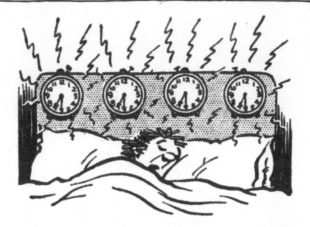

Yes, There Will Be One In Every Family

September 28, 1952

IT'S surprising the number of folk who suffer from "morningitis". At least one in nearly every family has it.

You know the symptoms when you wake up – wabbit, "thick" head, sour mouth. And that irresistible urge to take an extra five minutes in bed.

The hangover effect only lasts about half an hour. Because of that we're inclined to accept it. But we shouldn't. Morningitis can take the edge off our whole day.

If it's persistent, we're letting ourselves get under par. All sorts of troubles can result. It's ten times commoner today than a generation ago.

And men are the chief sufferers (or culprits). For every wife who's reluctant to get up, I'd say there are a dozen husbands!

What's the cause or morningitis?

At the end of every day, the body has suffered wear and tear. It's time for the "repair squads" in our system to start working – the moment we hit the pillow.

If we wake up as bright as a cricket, that's a sure sign we've given these repair squads every help to do their job well.

How can we help those repair squads to make us bright and breezy in the morning?

Well, for one thing, many of us like a smoke last thing before we go to bed. That's as bad a start to a night's sleep as we can get.

The fumes may lie in the deep sections of our lungs all night.

Yet, if we cut out that last cigarette, the craving will keep us awake. What on earth are we to do?

Simply this. After you smoke your last cigarette, go to the door and take three good deep breaths in the open air. You'll be amazed at the difference in the morning!

Next, a very important thing is to make your last hour before bedtime pleasant in thought.

Shut out the worries of the day. Forget your grievances or any other disturbing emotion. "Let not the sun go down upon your wrath", is a grand saying for a good sleep and a bright wakening.

You see, that last hour is the one that affects your subconscious. The quality of your sleep depends on keeping that subconscious quiet.

Some of us like reading in bed. Then let your reading be pleasant. No thrillers, please. And nothing heavy.

The moment you think to yourself, "I'd better stop", obey that hint. Don't force yourself to read even another page.

"What about me? It takes me so long to get off to sleep". I can hear dozens of you say that.

Don't be alarmed. You can lie awake until one o'clock in the morning and still get a good sleep. It's not the time but the quality that counts.

But start thinking, "Oh, it's one o'clock. I'll never get up in the morning", and you're sunk. The quality of sleep is bound to suffer, for the subconscious will be nagging away the rest of the night.

We all know physical effort leaves poisons in the body. They cause aching muscles and change the heartbeat.

Mental effort leaves poisons in the brain, too.

When we sleep the physical side is quiet. Yet the brain can go on working. Result – instead of these poisons being all cleared away, they are piling up!

For this reason try not to be apprehensive of the coming day! That will ruin your sleep, and is behind that desire to snuggle under the clothes when it's time to get up.

A light supper is ideal. Enough to give the tummy juices something to work on and no more.

Remember, too, the more tired you are, the more need for open windows. A stuffy room can give you aches and pains in the morning on top of a "thick" head.

Never use sleeping tablets left over from an illness. The "dope" was given to work on the pain, and induce, say, three hours' sleep. When you're healthy, the dope has no pain to work on.

The effort to break the dope-sleep strains the system!

As for bedclothes, cut out these old-fashioned, heavy quilts. Don't overdo the blankets.

If you're too warm, the body has the needless job of keeping you to the proper temperature.

That Tired-Out Feeling

November 20, 1955

NEXT time you have a heavy day, take a good look at yourself in the mirror.

Is one eye smaller than the other? If the answer is, "My goodness, so it is!" – then you're overtiring yourself.

Always remember this, though. You can tire yourself out for one day, or you can be slogging your system for years, but you're not always the best judge.

Your wife, mother or next-door neighbour will notice the warning signs long before you do. When anybody tells you, "You're looking tired", don't brush it off with a laugh.

Fatigue can hit you in two ways.

First, you're more vulnerable to infection. It's almost certain, for instance, that your last bout of flu only came on because you were tired. And you got that crop of boils, and that bad cold, for probably the same reason.

The real menace is, however, a chill.

When the muscles tire and the system is crying out for relief – for goodness sake keep yourself well wrapped up. From now on, put on a scarf when you're going home from work. Gloves, too.

A tired man waiting for a bus on a cold night is asking for trouble.

What about you, mum? D'you know where you get most of your chills? Going to the door without a cardigan on. Or going out for a bucket of coal without a scarf.

That, plus the fact you've probably had a hard forenoon.

Even to cut your finger when you're tired is dangerous. You double the risk of blood poisoning.

All the same, there's little need for you to worry about a shortish spell of fatigue – provided you keep warm. And, of course, rest.

The first warning of over-tire you'll likely get is when your eyes feel itchy.

The next is when the voice starts to protest. It doesn't get fainter, as you'd imagine. It gets louder.

But if the voice does start to go faint, then the fatigue is really serious.

Here's another test. Hold your hand out at full stretch. If it trembles, you can bet your boots trouble's not far ahead. Get a warm drink right away.

You see, a lot of the tiredness is due to lack of fluid. Once you make up that deficiency, your tiredness will decrease.

How can you beat tiredness when it isn't possible to go to bed?

Go outside and try to yawn about 20 times! Yawn until the tears come. Anybody who can work this trick will be amazed at the freshness that follows.

Another way is to change your footwear. There's no better relief than getting off your shoes and putting on slippers.

Yes, and put your feet on a stool for a while.

No matter how tiring your day, you'll come to no harm if you get a decent sleep. There's one snag, however. One person in every three is inclined to be "too tired to sleep".

If you're like that, have a hot bath (even a foot bath). Take a warm drink and two aspirins.

Believe me, those two aspirins will do more good than sleeping tablets.

If at all possible, sleep on your own. And don't have too much weight on the legs. You can't get a good sleep with bedclothes that are too heavy.

What if you have a whole week of tiring, exhausting work?

Well, it doesn't usually do anybody much harm either, provided they get a restful weekend. The only danger to these seven-day sloggers is that the strain may hit their hidden weak spot.

Women's weakness is migraine – these blinding headaches so difficult to relieve.

Men (of all ages) tend to develop neuralgia up one side of the face. The easiest victims are business men with worry as well as hard work. So, to anybody in that category, the cure is not aspirins – it's rest.

Now for the most vulnerable person of all – the fellow with an uncertain temper.

If you're inclined to be temperamental, NEVER go off the deep end if you've had a week of strain.

The risk is that fatigue, plus bad temper, can burst a tiny blood vessel in the brain. That means a stroke, possibly even the end.

Lastly, nervous breakdowns.

Overwork won't break the nervous system, provided you've a single aim, you're reasonably happy and successful – and you have a regular weekend break.

Believe it or not, a more likely reason for "nerves" is a non-stop search for pleasure, or any kind of escapism.

If You Have A Nightmare . . .

January 1, 1956

MR F. went to bed pretty late one night. And he had a dreadful dream. He dreamed he was lying in a deep hole and someone was burying him alive. Shovelfuls of earth came down on him, filling his mouth and nose. He couldn't move. He was suffocating.

In what he thought was his last moment he caught a glimpse of the person who was burying him. It was his wife!

Mr F. had the same dream the next night, and the next, and the next. He came to me. He was a very worried man, scared to go to sleep.

But his main concern was about his health. "Am I heading for a nervous breakdown, doctor? Do you think there's something abnormal about me – some deep-seated complex?"

I know he was beginning to wonder if his wife were to blame – that there might be a hidden dislike somewhere.

Well, should any of you have a nightmare – and you might at this time of year – remember what I told Mr F. No matter how abnormal your dream is, don't for any favour start imagining things.

Most theories about nightmares are bunkum! In 999 cases out of 1,000 a nightmare is caused either by irritation from outside – or inside – the body.

There are many people who, like Mr F., have suffocating nightmares.

The most likely cause is that you sleep with the bedclothes too high on the face. Or your pillow is too soft. When you turn your face into it, breathing is restricted.

Now, except for babies and very sick folk, there's no real danger in this.

Instinctively you make a violent move to get air.

But just before you do get more air, the brain gives a warning of suffocation – and the nightmare begins.

Other reasons for this kind of nightmare are beds that sag in the centre, too heavy bedclothes, a bed that creaks badly, or a rattling window. Even sleeping on your back can do it. The jaw drops open, the tongue hangs slack and tends to block the air passages.

And don't tie your pyjama cord too tight, either. The restriction round the middle can start a bad dream.

So, before you begin thinking it's time to see a psychiatrist, see to your bed and bedclothes.

But of all the things that cause nightmares, it's almost certain your stomach is to blame three nights out of four.

A healthy tummy is quickest to protest when it's ill-treated.

Again, the irritation sends messages to the brain. The conscious section of the brain is asleep, but the subconscious part is stirred into action.

So a crazy adventure dream begins!

Sometimes it's only a bubble of air trying to escape from your tummy that starts it off.

Some folk have what I call explosion nightmares.

You feel as if your head and whole body were bursting asunder. You're the target for a cannon or runaway train.

This kind of nightmare is easily explained.

Here again your breathing has been restricted in some way. The body convulses in a mighty effort to get air.

What about nightmares in which you're always falling? They are mostly caused by the actual sensation of falling or slipping. Perhaps you're too near the edge of the bed. Or the bedclothes are slipping off.

Or in turning over, you don't "grip" the bed (this happens when the sheets are new and shiny).

How long does a nightmare really last?

Only a couple of minutes at most. And it comes on as you begin to waken, or as you begin to fall asleep.

The person who doesn't get nightmares is the man who goes off to sleep quickly and wakens quickly.

Dreadful dreams, even if they recur, do not harm the health. Neither do they indicate illness of body or mind.

Worry doesn't bring nightmares. Neither does overwork. They may cause dreams – but not violent ones.

Rage complexes, unpleasant childhood memories, long forgotten primeval instincts can sometimes be responsible.

But next time you dream you're being chased by a Zulu warrior with a seven-foot spear – the cause is more likely to be something like a breadcrumb in your bed!

Best Thing To Take Last Thing At Night

June 25, 1950

I MET a patient last Thursday morning. He was a pleased as Punch – with me, as well as himself!

"Man, I had a grand sleep last night – the best I've had for a fortnight," he said.

My cure for his sleeplessness was simple. Previously he'd been trying to doze off by counting sheep. I told him to count his breaths instead. Trying to visualise sheep needs mental concentration. It actually kept him awake.

It's little things like this that make all the difference between a healthy, dreamless sleep and that awful twisting and tossing.

One of the best nightcaps is to relive in your mind the most pleasant holiday you've had, starting from the time you set off.

One of my patients had a grand holiday – when the sun shone all week, and the children were as happy as crickets.

Now, if he can't get to sleep, he starts (in his mind's eye) at the railway station. "And I've never yet got past the first day on the beach," he tells me.

Believe it or not, cold feet keep a lot of us awake in summer as well as in winter. The reason is wet and cold socks, due to perspiration.

Try a little exercise just before going to bed. This speeds up the circulation and warms the feet naturally.

Sometimes we're no sooner between the sheets than we get palpitations or are bothered with flatulence. The slightest tummy upset keeps us awake.

Here's how to beat it. Sip very hot water slowly. Do cycling exercises for one minute. Suck a peppermint or soda mint.

What if you waken in the early hours with indigestion?

As good a palliative as any is a glass of warm milk and a nibble at a biscuit. Don't take a laxative. That might well make matters worse. Take the laxative in the morning.

And coughing at night can be subdued by a hot drink of any kind. A spoonful of glycerine or honey eases the throat. If you do need a cough mixture, add about a wine-glassful of water to it. But don't get out of bed for the hot water. Keep a Thermos at the bedside.

If you're kept awake by cramp, a teaspoonful of milk of magnesia often works wonders before bed. If cramp does come on, twenty or thirty drops of sal volatile* in a wineglass of cold or hot water are excellent. The affected muscle eases off very quickly.

Another anti-cramp tip. After your bedtime bath, rub the affected part towards the heart with a rough towel.

A woman patient was worried about headaches at night. She told me she was taking aspirins "and they're not doing me any good," she said.

"Did you crush the aspirins?" I asked her. That was the trouble. She didn't. Aspirins taken in daytime get shifted around the stomach. At night they lie in one spot in the tummy and may irritate the lining.

Result – more headaches, less sleep. But if you crush them this doesn't happen.

Some people get a stuffy nose whenever they get into bed, though they don't have a cold. If you suffer from this, ask your doc if benadryl capsules would help in your case.

Always remember – sound sleep is one of the best health givers. So it's worth paying attention to the little things that give you sound sleep.

A scented solution of ammonium carbonate in alcohol that was sometimes used as smelling salts

It's Often A Bad Sign If You Snore

April 1, 1956

THERE'S no time like spring for a check-up on your general health.

Once you're aware you're not at your best, the battle is half won.

Here are some tests to see how you measure up.

Test No. 1.

Look at the back of your hands. Do the veins stand out unduly?

If they do, then it's likely you're off colour. Your circulation could be improved.

And it's time you gave your lungs exercise.

Good walks in the open air and moderate exercise can make these veins subside a bit for the average person.

Test No. 2.

Bend slowly down towards your toes, but don't strain to get right down. Then come up fairly quickly. If you see stars with bright lights when you come up, that's a warning. Your digestion is under par – and your tummy needs toning up.

There's no miraculous tonic for this. But a little change in your diet helps. Take greens, fruits, milk – and chew each mouthful twenty times at least.

How's your muscle tone? Just look in the mirror and see. If there are new grooves at the side of your mouth and perhaps extra wrinkles on the forehead, the chances are that all over your muscles have lost their oomph.

You can make another check-up in front of the mirror. Rumple your hair, then brush it back into place. When there's no sheen it means the body reserves are so low they can't spare any nourishment for the hair.

And when the hair is disobedient and lies "any old how", that's a sign you're under par.

You need body-building food, like cod liver oil.

If you look into the mirror and say – "Goodness me but I'm looking awfully old" – don't think that's the permanent truth. It's more likely the old look means you need a tonic.

Another sure test of fitness comes in the wee small hours.

Round about this month you may find you're being wakened by noises that don't usually disturb you – a passing car, ticking of the clock, rattling window.

That can indicate oxygen starvation – you're not getting enough spring fresh air.

Try a night or two with cotton wool in your ears. We all have a mechanism for closing down the system for sleep. But when we're not up to scratch this mechanism doesn't work so well!

Here's a test for the husband and wife.

Has your husband – or wife – started to snore? If so, this is one fitness test you've failed. Your muscles are flabby and the lungs aren't being used enough.

Snoring begins when you lie on your back – and you lie on your back because your muscles object to any other position.

A sick person lies on his back, but a fit person lies on his side!

Shallow breathing is another reason for beginning the snoring habit. The mouth opens in an attempt to get extra air.

A sure general check-up is – how do you feel at about two in the afternoon? A man came to me last week complaining of sleepiness. He wondered if there was anything seriously wrong. "No, no", I told him. "Afternoon sleepiness is common in spring".

The cure is easy, but slow. Go to bed an hour earlier, eat a little less and take a morning laxative.

What about your weight? When you notice your weight is going down a little, begin taking a tonic. Loss of weight in spring is a sign you need one.

A lot of folk come to me in spring about their eyes. In most cases there's not much wrong with their eyes. The trouble is due to their general condition.

Half an hour with a good book can test your fitness. If you can keep reading without changing the angle of the book, you're well above average spring health.

If we're well up in years, we've got to hold the page further away – and that's a sign not only of reduced fitness, but of weakening of the focusing power of the eyes.

One last test.

Are you flat in the back? You're a lucky person if you are, for you're fitter than most at this time of year. A flat back generally indicates better than average breathing, better than average oxygen intake.

And that means better than average blood.

If You Find That You Wake Up At Three Or Four In The Morning

November 30, 1958

THERE'S nothing more annoying than to waken up in the middle of the night. Especially if you can't get back to sleep again.

But in 99 cases out of 100, there's no reason why you shouldn't drop off again.

The great thing is not to imagine all sorts of things. Usually it's worry and being anxious that keeps us awake.

In natural sleep there are two occasions when sleep is shallow and you're apt to waken.

The first is around 3 and 4 a.m. The second is when it's time to get up.

If you waken about 3 a.m., the first thing to remember is – don't open your eyes. If you do, you're likely to stay awake.

That's because the conscious brain switches on.

People who take sleeping tablets shouldn't waken at 3 a.m. At that time they're in the deepest sleep of the night. So, if you do ever waken then after taking sleeping tablets, don't get up. You're liable to an accident, for you're at your dopiest.

What are the things that make you waken at the wrong time?

An unexplained noise. A squeak of a floorboard. A rattling window. Steps in the street. When this happens, you should get up. Investigate the noise. Put your mind at rest.

Unless you do, you'll take ages to settle.

For even if the noise doesn't recur, your brain is waiting for it, the ear is cocked – although you don't realise all this is going on.

Sweating is often the cause of broken sleep.

It's alarming, and we're apt to think we're in for a bout of flu. That's seldom, if ever, the case.

Usually all that's happened is a change in the outside temperature. The heat in the bed builds up until you break into a sweat.

This is the least important reason for waking in the middle of the night.

A dry mouth is another thing that's sure to waken you. Yet you can get back to sleep – in one movement. Simply roll over off your back and close your mouth. You've been breathing through your mouth, and the air has dried things up.

If the dryness is really bad, a sip of water is all that's needed.

Everybody knows a heavy meal is bad for sleep. But did you know that no supper can be just as bad for some folk?

It's always a good thing to have a biscuit and glass of milk for supper. Otherwise, hunger pangs can waken you – usually about 5 a.m.

Indigestion, wind, stomach or bowel upsets can break a good sleep. Here, warm water is the answer.

But there's something else you can do. When the tummy pain is above the waist – sit up in bed. Two minutes can work wonders.

If the pain is below the waist, then get up and walk about the room for a little, so long as you don't wake anyone else.

Cramp, tingling pains, a leg or arm gone dead – all are caused by over-tiredness or undue pressure on one place.

Rubbing for cramp is important – the quicker and harder the better. Often it's the calf muscle that knots up. The remedy is to rise, put the heel on cold lino – and press hard. Of course, rub too.

One of the most alarming things to waken with is a choking sensation.

Well, that choking is a compliment to yourself. You're a nose breather. The nose has become blocked, and it's still trying to take in air with the mouth closed.

But of all the sleep disturbers, worry, self-reproach, apprehension, and mental strain are the ones that can harm health.

It can be so bad that even when you're apparently sleeping, the worry can be going on – only wakening you occasionally. If worry wakens you, your whole sleep suffers – and, in the long run, so does your general health.

Comes home and falls asleep in his armchair every night

September 7, 1958 — **Every night when my husband comes home from work he has his tea then sits down in his armchair and falls asleep. I find this very annoying, but he says it's good for him. Is he right?**

No. Too many husbands have this bad habit. It's bad because it means sleeping in an unnatural position. Also, it means he doesn't sleep so soundly at night. He shouldn't have a big meal when he comes in. At that time, his stomach is tired whether he's been doing manual or office work. A cup of tea and a "bite" are enough just then. Next, a wash and clean up. And the heavy meal an hour, to an hour and a half, later. The tummy — indeed the whole body — are fresher by that time.

April 2, 1950 — **What's the right side to sleep on?**
Sleep on the side you find most comfortable. You probably change sides ten to twenty times during the night, anyway.

March 1, 1953 — **I only fall asleep lying on my stomach. Is this harmful?**
No, apart from the very remote risk of smothering yourself in too soft a pillow. Probably you roll over on your side during sleep and are safe.

February 2, 1958 — **At night in bed, when dozing off, I keep "jumping" for no apparent reason. What's the cause of this?**
Many folk do this, especially if a little overtired. A hot foot bath and hot, milky drink before retiring may prevent it.

October 9, 1955 — **When I go to bed, I can't sleep for cold, no matter how many clothes I wear. Is there a remedy? I'm 32.**
A brisk walk, followed by a mustard foot bath, just before going to bed. Make sure neither bed nor pyjamas are damp.

May 7, 1950 — **What's a good test that you're getting a sound sleep?**
You should fall asleep within five minutes of going to bed. If you're still awake after half an hour, then it's 10 to 1 you're not going to sleep deeply. You shouldn't wake up until minutes before you mean to get up — and you should wake up voluntarily. Finally, the state of the bedclothes will let know see if you've tossed about too much during the night.

November 14, 1954 — **Is it a good thing to take a big meal last thing before going to bed?**
Generally speaking no. But it's largely a matter of habit. If it IS taken, breakfast should be extremely light.

April 5, 1953 — **Whenever I close my eyes in bed my mind goes into a whirl. What's the remedy?**

Relax all your muscles and compose yourself for sleep. Recalling happy past days is often a help.

September 20, 1959 — **I'm female (17). For three months I've been finding it difficult to concentrate. At times I just want to go to bed and fall asleep. My hands perspire a lot.**

Changes of mood and an unsettled temperament are common in late teens, but must not be yielded to. I think you are just a bit too emotional.

March 2, 1952 — **I've nine hours' sleep each night. Would it be detrimental to my health to cut it down to seven hours? I'm 34.**

Too drastic. Try cutting down by one hour at first and see how you do for six or eight weeks. After that you could try 7½ hours, but not less.

December 23, 1951 — **I am 63 and in excellent health, except that every so often I get an attack of sleeplessness. I can lie all night without closing an eye. I lead rather a dull life. Would it help if I had more interests?**

Yes. I think it would. If you worked away at something that interests you, you'd get healthily tired and your sleeplessness would probably disappear.

January 26, 1958 — **For two months I've been dreaming every night. Sometimes I've to wake up my husband as I'm scared after dreaming that one of my friends has died. What's the remedy? I'm 24.**

Treatment, if you've nose or throat trouble, or indigestion. Otherwise a simple sedative at bedtime.

October 16, 1955 — **I usually go to bed about 10.30 p.m. and sleep till about 2 a.m. I waken then and cannot get back to sleep. Yet when I rise at 8 a.m. I still feel tired. I'm 45. What do you recommend?**

Have a little hot milk in a thermos by your bedside, drink this at 2 a.m. Take, at the same time, a couple of aspirins if the warm milk alone doesn't do the trick.

March 23, 1952 — **When my husband is sleeping his breathing is very short and quick, and his heart thumps alarmingly. What do you advise?**

If he wakes refreshed, doesn't complain about a bad night, and is well in daytime, all should be well. If not, he should see his doc.

September 1, 1955 — **I'm serving in the R.A.F. The boys in the billet say I often talk in my sleep. Can I do anything to stop this?**

Talking in one's sleep is usually associated with dreaming. Avoid large late meals or indigestible food before bed. And see that your part of the billet is well ventilated.

— Chapter 9 —

Think Yourself Well Again

M ENTAL health was regarded very differently in the 1950s, in comparison with these early decades of the 21st Century. It was a taboo subject. Terms like "nervous breakdowns" were used, as if "nerves" could be fractured and the problem was a physical ailment like a broken arm or sore toe.

And there are direct links drawn here to "nerves" leading to chest troubles, liver ailments and heart problems. There is even a suggestion that "winter blues" is a special kind of indigestion.

Reading between the lines, warnings of the dangers of "melancholy", "suppressed emotion" and "monotony" are euphemistic ways of describing depression.

The suggested remedies — a good cup of hot tea, a dose of salts, double helpings of castor oil — are physical attempts at cures for non-physical problems which had deeper and highly complex causes. The homespun remedies might, of course, affect brain chemistry to a degree but were more probably of limited value.

We have made steps forward in the treatment of mental health, but there are clearly further measures yet to be taken, breakthroughs still to be made. A reader looking back on us (as we look back on the 1950s) would probably smile at our simple ways.

It is a difficult area in which to accurately make a diagnosis and more complicated still when looking for a complete cure. So the "just buck yourself up" message in most of the recommendations given here may not have helped much.

But perhaps the therapy of an understanding, sympathetic ear, and an acknowledgment of the problem, went some way towards helping.

Are You Working On Only Half A Brain?

May 22, 1955

"DOCTOR, why do some folk always seem to be chock-full of vitality, and I don't seem to have an ounce of it?"

A patient asked me this on Thursday.

Now, it's true that many of us lack vitality. And often the reason is a strange one.

My patient was well fed. She enjoyed a healthy home, plenty of fresh air, good food. Yet she felt listless and out of sorts.

All because of monotony!

A colleague of mine says monotony is the greatest killer of our age. And, in a way, he's not far wrong.

If you lead too monotonous a life, there's no doubt that:- you'll have less resistance to colds, flu, tonsillitis, or any infection that's going. Your digestion will also be poorer. You're more liable to heart trouble and thrombosis. And you'll age more quickly – and probably die several years before you should.

So you see it's vital that we snap out of monotony.

This is doubly important where food is concerned. If the stomach is getting the same kind of food day after day, the digestive juices get used to it. They're no longer jogged into action. And so digestion suffers.

A long period of monotonous diet can land you with a lazy pancreas.

Then the liver will suffer. And when that happens, your whole system becomes half-poisoned. A good liver is essential to vitality.

In theory it should be possible to live entirely on porridge, milk, and treacle. But in practice you'd waste away!

All because of the monotony.

If you can beat monotony, not only will your digestion improve. Every single cell in your system will work better – glands, nerves, muscles.

The most dangerous monotony I know is the one that will hit the middle-aged person living alone.

They live the same old routine, with nobody to speak to, no urge to snap out of it.

All this means the victim is living with what you might call half a brain – the half that deals with automatic things like heart action, &c., and semi-automatic actions like walking and putting the kettle on.

Now the thing we call vitality is really nervous energy which is stored in the other half of the brain like a battery. We've simply got to keep charging this battery.

All very well, you'll say, but how is it to be done?

Well, it's as simple as this. Be lively in your thinking. Be interested. Be curious. If you're not, your nervous energy will leak away pretty much in the same way as a car battery loses energy when the car's lying idle in a garage.

Patients tell me that their loss of pep has caused loss of interest in anything. But the reverse is the case. It's the loss of interest that causes the loss of nervous energy.

Many people who are NOT living alone are also using only half their brains. One day is too much like another with them. They don't meet enough people. They don't speak to enough people. There's nothing more ageing than the same deadly routine day after day.

A special warning to all you men thinking of retiring.

For goodness sake, don't retire unless you've something in view that will really occupy the half of the brain we're talking about. It's slow suicide to retire to nothing but monotony.

It surprises many that Mr So-And-So died only 18 months after he retired. It doesn't surprise me. Monotony (living on half a brain) lowers resistance and tends to bring on 1) chest troubles and 2) heart ailments.

You don't need to be a highbrow. Just take an interest in what's going on around you. Keep your mind alive. Add to your nervous energy.

All of us can add to our energy just by change. Go to work by a different road. Grow something new in the garden – something you've never grown before, something that will tickle your curiosity.

Play your golf on a new course occasionally.

As for the housewives – change your furniture around. Switch the curtains if you can. Get your husband to distemper the bathroom a different colour.

Most important, go away for an occasional weekend. What a tonic a change of scene can be.

Another thing. Don't agree with everything your husband says.

Better to have an occasional argument than boredom. Speak about something NOT connected with housework or the children.

In short, don't live on half a brain!

THE MODERN VIEW, BY DR LYNDA

VITALITY is the state of being strong and active — having energy. It's the life force which is inherent in wellbeing and health. Lack of vitality results in fatigue, lack of enjoyment, and old-fashioned melancholia.

Living half a life, working on half a brain?...not sure the 1950s Doc got his neurophysiology right here. Neither am I convinced that monotony itself can bring on all the ails he mentions. But fatigue, indifference and low mood may follow.

I'm pretty sure his patient is depressed, as the causes of these sort of symptoms are usually psychological rather than physical and linked to anxiety, low mood and an accumulation of stresses.

And yes, people are more likely to have heart trouble if they are depressed. But it works both ways – people with heart disease are at risk of developing a depressive illness or low mood.

Common lifestyle habits brought upon by low moods, e.g. obesity, poor diet, excess alcohol consumption, smoking and a sedentary lifestyle, are similar to risk factors for heart disease.

And viral illness can certainly lead to depression. Post-viral depression is a well-known consequence of a flu-like illness. But there is little current conclusive evidence that patients with depression have a higher risk of flu and colds.

As for the monotonous diet, it may well lack a variety of nutrients and minerals and vitamins, but I'm pretty certain you could survive on porridge, milk and treacle.

Low mood often leads to either overeating or loss of appetite, resulting in obesity related illnesses like diabetes or irritable bowel syndrome. Poor eating results in nutritional deficiencies.

That said, I loved his philosophy for beating the blues: be lively in your thinking, be interested, be curious, speak to people, change your routine, take an interest in what's going on around you, keep your mind alive, grow something different, change your curtains, go away for the weekend.

Variety is, indeed, the spice of life.

Having a positive outlook does seem to be an adjunct to good health, though it's difficult to prove. Perhaps negativity just makes it seem worse.

My own philosophy: take a leaf out of the 1950s Doc's book here. Be passionate and curious about life. Keep active and interested in the world about you. Try new things and you'll get more out of life.

I'm pretty sure that the answer to low mood and mild depression in many cases today doesn't come out of a bottle of tablets but would be better served with a listening ear, friendship and a push to get out there and live life instead of dwelling on the negatives.

And I love his last bit of advice — don't agree with everything your partner says. The making up is fun!

Three Warnings We Should Never Ignore

October 4, 1953

THERE'S a lot of nonsense talked about nervous breakdowns. It's true, a complete collapse is most distressing, and needs at least six months' rest and six months' sympathetic treatment from relatives, doctor and friends.

But it's also true that every victim gets at least three warnings.

And the doctor has three chances to prevent the final breakdown.

One in ten of us is susceptible to neurosis that can lead to collapse. Eight are under the risk – although more remote. That leaves only one person in the ten who is proof against nervous breakdown.

Sounds serious, doesn't it? But never forget that only one person in a thousand ever reaches the breakdown stage.

Everyone is wise to recognise the first symptom. We lose the ability to do our work smoothly and quickly. We get dithery and het-up. We jump from one decision to another. Even our speech gets dithery. Too many "buts", "ahs", "well, what I really mean is", as if we couldn't make up our mind what we want to say.

A housewife finds she loses all method in doing the housework.

The second stage in a nervous breakdown is forgetfulness. Inattention. Pessimism. Afraid of the worst. More mistakes in the daily round.

Stage No. 3. Chronic depression. A vague feeling of unhappiness that can't be lifted.

Stage No. 4. Complete collapse.

A victim usually consults the doctor halfway through stage one. He complains of palpitation and pulse racing. Perhaps he sweats too much. He may even start blushing. Headaches and slight dizziness can also worry him. This is the time to start the cure. If not, he'll eventually feel squeamish; suffer from diarrhoea, bladder trouble. He may even develop nail biting, or blinking eyes.

The physical signs of the final breakdown are utter exhaustion, plus dread of carrying out the simplest task.

Who are the types most likely to suffer?

Well, first of all, there's Mr Go-Ahead. He's got to the top of the ladder very quickly, by hard work, higher than average intelligence. He's come from humble circumstances.

But he still secretly can't believe he deserves it. At the back of his mind there's a fear his success is only temporary.

Now, unless he gets it into his head that he is well thought of, that nobody is jealous and ready to step into his shoes, Mr Go-Ahead risks a breakdown – although he can take 20 years to reach the crisis stage.

Second type is Mr Ordinary, who has landed for a responsible job. He's been made a foreman. He's not too intelligent. He has to strain to hold down the job. Unless he does something, he'll break down.

He can't keep it off for more than five years.

His cure is simple but drastic. He should ask the boss to relieve him of his responsibility. He'll lose in his pay packet, but it's cheap at the price.

Quickest breakdown happens to Mr or Mrs Thin-Skin. An irritating neighbour or workmate gets under the skin. The constant irritation can cause a breakdown in less than six months.

If you can't make the best of a neighbour, ask the council for a shift. Get an exchange of house. Until then, avoid the person at all cost. Don't argue. Don't speak unless you have to!

And now for Mr or Mrs Restless. Their trouble is a needless waste of energy. It's rush and excitement with nothing at the end of the day to show for it. They feel they must keep on the move, mentally as well as physically.

Here the cure is difficult. One way is to ration your entertainment. Change to gardening or an easy hobby. You can waste energy for ten years, but you'll eventually burn yourself out physically and mentally.

Another unfortunate is Mr Brooder. He's had a big disappointment in his job or socially. He's afraid of another big disappointment. In his case there's a distinct possibility of a breakdown in twelve months.

But let me repeat. Few people ever reach the breakdown stage. And it is very easy to pull yourself up at the first stage, and snap out of it.

THE MODERN VIEW, BY DR LYNDA

ANXIETY and depression are bread-and-butter stuff for me as a GP, and this chapter made me wonder if, since the 1950s, we have moved on much at all in our attitude and understanding of mental illness.

There is, indeed, a lot of nonsense talked about nervous breakdowns and the stigma and attitude of people today are sometimes even less sympathetic and supportive than you would imagine even from the profession itself.

How does the busy GP with a 10-minute slot deal with the exhausted, weeping woman in front of him/her when they have a queue of people at the door? I'm afraid many just do blood tests, which might compound the issue by increasing anxiety, and, when they come back normal, reassure the patient there's no serious physical cause of their problem.

The 1950s Doc describes a number of symptoms and signs which are as true now as they were then: palpitations, fatigue, headache, dizziness, inexplicable bowel and bladder symptoms, inattention and lack of motivation.

Causes are generally due to life stresses. These include: work pressure, financial uncertainty, bullying, marital stress and relationship breakdown, bereavement, lack of supportive networks and loneliness, illegal drug use, and poverty. Often several causes combine to create untold distress.

There were no real drug treatments for depression until the 1960s.

Potent sedatives (with horrendous side-effects), electroconvulsive treatment, and long-term stays in institutions were, fortunately, reserved for the very severe and thankfully are no longer used.

The family practitioner was left with lifestyle change and support, along with an array of herbal tonics and concoctions, to meet the problem.

Nowadays, there is a vast array of medications which can treat the symptoms of depression and anxiety. But they don't address the cause, so should be used in conjunction with lifestyle change, talking therapies and counselling.

Indeed, some people (and some doctors) head straight for the tablets and use them as a sticking plaster to cover up the problem.

Tablets can help "get your head in a better place" and more able to deal with the issues, but unless the underlying cause is tackled, recurrence and chronic misery ensues.

The 1950s Doc's description of the types of people who will suffer from depression are OK as they go, but don't be fooled — everyone is at risk and none of us knows when life will deal out a bad hand and we'll require support and treatment for one of the commonest and most debilitating illnesses.

It worries me that so many, especially young people, end up on long-term medication to treat a social disease. Popping in to see a friend and taking them for a coffee or offering them a hand of friendship, a bit of company and a hug, might be more appropriate in helping them cope with life's troubles.

The Simplest And Best Cure Of All
February 5, 1956

A WOMAN in her early thirties got a shock when she came to see me last week. Her vitality was low. She picked up one trouble after another. Her heart was unsteady. She was anxious for a cure – like a tonic, or vitamins, or sunray treatment.

But she wasn't prepared for the cure that I prescribed – HARD WORK!

Yes, I strongly advised her to take a job that would keep her busy. "It'll make a new woman of you", I told her.

Did you know that about 60 per cent of our ailments begin with the mind, and that about half of these are directly due to the fact that a lot of us don't work hard enough?

It's a medical fact that man is born to work. For hard work brings our most health-giving asset – satisfaction.

It not only gives our system rhythm, but it also keeps the balance between brain and brawn.

Just as important, it oils the link-up between nerves and muscles. If we don't enjoy our work and get real satisfaction from it, we're prey to an awful lot of trouble.

A good day's work is one of the secrets of a good-going, steady heart. And it makes us far less likely to develop low blood pressure – or the opposite, high blood pressure. My records prove it.

It's amazing how often, when I examine a man who's worked hard all his life, I find his heart is sound as a bell.

Watch two men doing a job. One works away steadily. The other loafs about. It's the loafer who's most tired at the end of the day.

What's more, he's bound to pay for it in the long run. When we don't work, the brain becomes like a nagging woman. It nags the heart. It nags the nerves. It nags the tummy.

The inner conflict affects the normal working of the heart, and blood pressure. It has almost the same damaging effect as worry.

The folk who don't have this inner conflict generally have tons of vitality. They're the happy people who come home at tea-time with the satisfaction of having done a decent day's work.

Do you know the healthiest time of the year for most of my women patients? Spring-cleaning time! They're so busy – and so pleased with the job they've done – their whole system gets a chance to function properly.

Anyone threatened with nerves, or even a complete breakdown, can't do better than busy themselves on a job. There's nothing worse for the nerves than having nothing to do.

The hard worker has two more advantages over the lazy lad. He resists infection twice as well. Any employer will tell you it's the hard workers who are last to go down with flu. Again, that's because of their vitality.

Hard workers also stand up to pain better, because their nerves are not so touchy.

Please don't think all this applies only to people who work with their hands. It goes for clerks and other brain workers.

But in their case, the dangers are even greater. Here's why. When time drags with them, there's no muscular outlet. Their brain and nervous system are under strain.

One word of warning, though. The hard worker has at least one weakness. He's usually too quick to get back to work after an illness. The main risk with that isn't a chill but heart strain.

When you've been in bed for, say, a fortnight, you know how weak your legs feel when you get up. Well, your heart is a muscle, too – and it's just as weak.

So all hard workers must resist the desire to get back – until their doctor gives the word.

The big danger about hard work is when you're working against time, and the work is unsuccessful.

This combination is so wearing, it can break a man in six months.

P.S. – The fitter and stronger you are, or the brainier you are, the more important it is for your health that you work hard. You're like an expensive car – your performance is potentially greater. And, naturally, your "engine" is never happier than when it's running at a good, steady speed.

THE MODERN VIEW, BY DR LYNDA

HARD work and routine — absolute essentials! The 1950s Doc was pretty close to the mark in this one.

We all have a circadian cycle where our internal clock regulates our biological processes, including brain activity, hormone production, cell regeneration and loads of other functions.

It works on a night and day principle. Without this, our sleep becomes disordered and eventually results in mental and physical ill health.

Hard work and employment bring a load of health benefits and satisfaction. It maintains our circadian, or system rhythm, as the 1950s Doc calls it.

It gives us self-esteem and a purpose. It increases our physical exercise, our life satisfaction and vitality and, as an added perk, gives us more money to spend on things we enjoy.

But you do need to enjoy your job. He's right when saying: "if we don't enjoy our work and get satisfaction from it we are prey to an awful lot of trouble". I often liken a person's job to a marriage. You spend a long part of your day doing it, so as well as being productive for your boss or the company you work for there has to be some gains for you too.

You have to enjoy your time at work or else the stresses begin to accumulate and eventually cause problems. You have to work at this sometimes, though, and remain interested.

If the job is monotonous or boring then find a way of making it pleasurable, perhaps by enjoying the company of the people you work with or the people you deal with.

It can be fraught with problems like bullying, too much work, not enough time, too much pressure, poor relationships and all that can lead to stress and anxiety and depression. Time out and talking can get you back at it for a while but, ultimately, decisions need to be made on whether to continue or change.

People off work with depression and stress need to get into a routine quickly. Sitting at home focusing on the negatives, isolating themselves from people, comfort eating, poor food choices and alcohol and smoking make life worse.

Routines help to restore the balance to the circadian cycle and natural rhythm, Get up in the morning, go for a walk or a cycle — exercise stimulates a variety of hormones and endorphins to help lift mood and it gets you out again.

Meet other people — we are social beings and need each other. If someone is talking to you then you are not dwelling on your own issues and you may discover a solution to your own problems by having a wee blether with a friend.

Watch what you eat as it can affect mood, weight and self-esteem.

And alcohol is a depressant — need I say more.

Even tackling little jobs and seeing them finished gives you a feeling of satisfaction and a lift when they're done.

Too much work has its issues too. There needs to be a work-life balance. So if you feel there is too much to do and you have no time for friends and family and no time for self-care it's time to stop and reassess.

Why More Folk Are Getting High Blood Pressure

April 15, 1956

WE'RE working shorter hours. We've far more leisure. We're enjoying longer holidays. We've never been more comfortable.

And yet – more and more of the patients I see every day are being hit by high blood pressure!

Today there are 50 per cent more cases than in our father's day.

Why on earth should this be? Well, let me say right away this increase doesn't surprise me in the least. It looks like getting worse, if anything.

You see, high blood pressure is brought on mainly by: 1) prolonged emotional upset; 2) too much excitement; 3) feeding the stomach too quickly; 4) getting off your mark too quickly after the main meal. And we must admit it – that's just the kind of life many of us are leading nowadays.

Let's have a look at one of my patients. He's typical of what's going on. He bought a second-hand car, which he couldn't really afford. He's living up to his income and a bit beyond.

Can you wonder that he developed H.B.P? He was under constant financial strain, and consequently under constant mental strain. He was living in one big crisis.

And there's nothing worse for blood pressure. We're all able to deal with a temporary crisis – but when the crisis goes on and on, we suffer.

Suppose you suddenly come face to face with a bull. Your glands force out a mixture that gives strength to the muscles and increases the power of the heart. You're able to run faster than you ever thought possible. Even your digestion stops to allow for extra energy.

Once you're safe from the bull the gland control shuts off the mixtures. You flop down on the grass and go limp. The heart goes back to normal rhythm and you're none the worse.

But folk with H.B.P. never get relief. The "bull" is after them day in, day out. And what happens is this. The gland control goes haywire. Their system is constantly flooded with a mixture (such as adrenaline) that keeps them up to "high doh".

An easy victim is the man or woman who works hard during the day – and wants to be in the swim in the evening too.

If you've a hard, responsible job, don't become an official of an organisation. Not even in your own church! It's not good for your blood pressure to bear one responsibility during the day and another during the evening. Particularly if you have to join in a fair amount of argument.

Don't get the idea that hard work is bad. Nothing could be less true. But hard work demands the relief of a dozy, quiet evening.

On the other hand, I believe lack of hard work during the day is one of the causes of the increase in H.B.P.

Maybe some folk think it's smart to dodge their responsibilities. But no matter how thick-skinned they are, there's a feeling of dissatisfaction.

This demands relief in pleasure at night. Result? They're inclined to burn the candle at both ends.

What about the mother who works during the day?

That's not necessarily bad for her blood pressure. It all depends on what the extra money is for. If it's to clothe the children or put them through an academy, then the deep satisfaction she gets relaxes the system.

But if it's sheer greed for "extras", then she's not doing her blood pressure any good.

Next, I would very much like to mention this. The old-fashioned Sunday was a relief, not only to the soul, but also to the body. We were really relaxed then. In these days we didn't need to rush all over the place trying to get the utmost out of life – and never finding much at all.

Lose your religious belief and I'm absolutely certain you'll wear yourself out searching for an alternative.

TV sets, Continental holidays, smashing weekends, cars, motor bikes, rounds of golf on Sunday – they're poor substitutes for morning service, a nap after Sunday dinner and an evening walk with the family.

What can we do about H.B.P? Well, remember it's not so much a disease as the result of your way of life. I can give injections to lower the pressure, but this works only for an hour, or perhaps a day. The real cure is to change the way you live.

H.B.P. need not be serious. It needn't make you an invalid for the rest of your life. Change your ways and live a **MODERATE** life. Surely that's not a hardship?

The cure can well be sure and lasting.

There are many **POSSIBLE** signs of H.B.P. But here is a symptom you must not ignore. It's a feeling of extreme tiredness, **PLUS** tension.

When you're tired, yet still tight in the muscles and nerves, then H.B.P. may well be the cause. Appearances are no guide – you can be pale, purple, fat, thin. Your veins can stick out around your neck. These are not sure signs of H.B.P. It's the tired, tense feeling.

And the remedy is – go easier.

What Sort Of Hangover Do You Get?

December 15, 1957

ARE you all set for a good time at Christmas and New Year? I hope so! Because if you are, my waiting-room will be pretty well empty.

It isn't only that folk are too busy to "feel" ill. Our health on the whole improves. Blood pressure, arteries, heart troubles, sleeplessness, nervousness, all these improve at this time of year.

They are what I can tension troubles. For 40-odd weeks of the year, hundreds of folk live at full stretch.

But in the next three weeks, the couldn't-care-less-let's-enjoy-ourselves attitude is the best medicine in the world for them.

You see, half of good health comes from the brain. At Christmas the brain gets a rest from worry – or it should.

The folk who benefit most are those who've been hard at it all year – especially the ones with responsibility.

It's amazing what this relief from tension does. You can have less sleep – yet you'll sleep more soundly. You may eat more – and that includes black bun, &c., - yet your tummy will cope with it amazingly well.

You may tire yourself out – yet the after-effects aren't nearly so bad as you'd expect normally.

You may drink a little more than you should – yet the hangover is surprisingly mild.

Of course, nobody can go over the score and get away with it.

Just one word for the housewife. Don't tire yourself out beforehand. By all means tidy the house for New Year, but don't let it be a labour.

"Ah, that's all very well", you may say. "But what about that morning-after feeling?"

Forget it. We all have our own kind of hangover.

But it isn't a cause for alarm.

All that's happened is that a few poisons have got into the bloodstream.

Here's how to get over them pretty quickly: -

A headache. If it's dull and deep, overeating is the likely reason. A glass of plain, hot water, a dose of salts and a few hours of fasting will clear the bloodstream.

A splitting headache. It's usually caused by alcohol poisons. Don't believe a word of that old "cure" they call "a hair of the dog that bit you". Nothing could be worse. Take plenty of fresh air and a couple of aspirins.

And don't forget hot water. Drink a good pint of it. Better still, add fruit juice. Take some oranges or grapefruit. Any of the citrus fruits are splendid for alcoholic headaches.

The washed-out feeling. You've no headache, but you feel like a wet rag. For this hangover there's nothing worse than a long lie.

The trouble is easy to diagnose. You're full of stale air. It's in your lungs and blood. So get out of bed, go out for a good walk. Come back to a hot bath. And to finish off the perfect cure, have a sleep in the afternoon.

The eyes hangover is very common. The eyes are burning, the eyeballs may ache, or the eyelids itch. And, of course, there's a feeling of being dead beat.

This one's due to nicotine. Too much smoking and being too long in a room where the air is thick.

Bathe the eyes in a pint of tepid water, with a pinch of salt added. Then have an hour of good, fresh air.

A stuffy nose. A few late nights are apt to bring this on. A hot footbath, a cosy bed, and a cool bedroom are better than any nose drops. Plus, of course, good fresh air.

The shivery hangover. You waken up and think you've landed for a chill. It's tempting to stay indoors. Don't. Get out into the open air and the shivers will disappear.

You'll have noticed how often fresh air is the cure.

Believe me, it does wonders at Christmas. Fresh air and exercise burn up the food inside us and produce heat and energy.

And if you've been drinking you'll get the harmful effects out of your bloodstream more quickly.

First-footing is a splendid idea for that reason. But your travels should be done on foot. If you first-foot by car you won't have such a happy time.

Noises That Can Easily Get On Our Nerves

April 13, 1958

YOU come home from the office or the workshop dead beat. You flop into the armchair and tell your wife – "It's been an exhausting day".

Yet, if you think back, you haven't done so very much strenuous work. You then think that, actually, you haven't even had a great deal of worry, either. Why, then, had the day taken so much out of you?

Something's been getting on your nerves.

It needn't even be a big thing. Perhaps it was the workmate beside you with a continual sniffling of his nose. That continual sniffle can, by the end of the day, pull you right down.

Any nerves strain is tiring, and noise is very hard on most systems. The odd thing is that one noise may drive you up the wall, and yet not even be noticed by somebody else.

Your ear may have a different tone sense from mine. So, you see, noises can affect us to different degrees.

But, generally speaking, never thole screeching, wailing, or rattling noises.

These make most nerves squirm.

They exhaust you in two ways. The noise alarms the brain. Tension is set up in every muscle of the body. The brain then gets wise to the false S O S and tries to shut out the alarm messages. So the brain gets sorely overworked.

Suppose you're lying in bed at night and you hear a door rattle. It rattles again. By now I'll guarantee you're all keyed up waiting for the third rattle. You try to ignore the noise. And even though the door continues to rattle, you do fall asleep.

Next morning you can't possibly be as fresh as you should.

All through your sleep, part of your brain and many of your muscles have been on the qui vive for the rattle. So save your energy and stop any noise that's upsetting.

But what if you can't do anything about the noise? A pneumatic drill outside the house, for instance.

The next best thing is to occupy your mind. Start on a job. Set your mind working on something so it won't have time to notice the other noise.

To merely sit still makes the irritation a hundred times worse.

We all get spells when things wear our nerves more than usual. That can be a warning to take things easier.

Unsuspected exhaustion shows itself when you're easily irritated. It could also be a hint to cut the cigarettes down from 25 to 15 a day. Too much nicotine for your particularly run-down system makes the nerves far too sensitive.

Too much alcohol can bring about the same kind of trigger reaction.

A course of vitamin tablets does help you to get over this spell. And porridge, wholemeal bread, eggs, liver – add a little of these to your menu every day.

Now, what about your own special weak spot?

I know one patient who can't bear to see anybody pluck threads out of their clothes.

Another can't stand dogs . . . just because "they get on her nerves".

If anything odd like this gets on your nerves, don't get ideas that you yourself are odd. It's a throwback to your earlier years. Something terrified you away back, and the fear is still there.

We've all got a weakness in this way.

Much more serious is your situation when it is other people who are getting on your nerves. Continual nerve strain of this sort can harm in two ways.

1. Blood pressure soars up. In the long run you're the easiest victim of heart trouble, thrombosis, hardened arteries, or a stroke. You lose any good nature you had, and develop into the bad-tempered type of person that no one likes.

2. Or the opposite happens. The blood pressure falls. You lose all your confidence. Your energy drains away. You are always tired. You're not enthusiastic about anything.

In short, if you let people get on your nerves over a long period, it'll spoil your whole life.

Your energy either builds up inside you like a dam, or drains away in an alarming way.

Believe Me, You'll Be A New Man In No Time

November 28, 1954

THERE'S an epidemic on the rampage just now – and it's most difficult to cure. It's the winter blues!

And it can be much more serious than you imagine.

There are four stages –

No. 1 **A feeling of tire**.

No. 2 **Sulkiness**.

No. 3 **A spell of depression**.

Unless you do something by the time stage No. 3 arrives, you seriously risk stage No. 4 **A low state of health all through the winter**.

You can beat the winter blues in many ways.

First of all, ask yourself, "Are there any aches?"

If the answer is yes, then your blues may be a mild dose of flu – not enough to be noticed. I see lots of cases like this. The answer is easy – a full 24 hours in bed!

No aches? Then how about your appetite? If it's jaded, then the villain is your liver.

Your depression is nothing more than a special kind of indigestion. Start the day with a good-sized glass of hot water. Or suck a lemon and try half a grapefruit.

And remember, the most important course of your lunch these days is the first – a good soup which isn't fatty. No fatty meat in it, but a good marrow bone and vegetables.

A good dose of salts is another very good thing these days. In fact, this is the time to give yourself a good clean-out with a double-your-usual dose of castor oil. Once only, though, because it's quite drastic.

The reason for all this is that our cleaning system is below par. The liver is clogging up, and the filtering of poisons isn't quite as effective as it should be.

When this happens the brain is first affected. That is why, if you have a try at some of the cures I mention here, then you'll be amazed at the difference in morale that they will quickly afford you!

A bout of the dumps affects some folk differently. It's their nerves that are jaded. They become irritable or sulky.

Old folk, youngsters, bachelors, spinsters – they're all likely to be victims.

Well, there is something for this type of blues – vitamin B! We don't really know why or how, but vitamin B is a godsend to them.

You can buy vitamin B preparations from the chemist – or the grocers for that matter.

Happy, too, is the housewife who has a good stock of blackcurrant juice in the house.

And get out the jam you made in the summer.

One warning about food, though.

When you're in the dumps, it's easy to make the mistake of having a fancy meal just to brighten yourself up.

Don't do it!

Your depression will be all the deeper next day.

Go in for simple foods. Nothing rich. Nothing greasy. No "fries". A good cup of hot tea is an ideal pick-me up. Make it as hot as you can sip it.

And take plenty sugar (if you can get your hands on it) that's an essential when you're "low".

Eat a fair amount of sweeties. Best are barley sugar, plain boilings, home-made tablet or toffee. Not chocolate!

All of us suffer at times from weather blues.

There's no escape from horribly depressing weather. When the air and the very ground are soaking, the first victim will be the mind.

There's a good reason for this – oxygen starvation. Our lungs get an overdose of wet air. The inner air passages are filmed with wet. The area for fresh air entering is reduced.

All this means the blood is poorer, the circulation slower.

For some of us, a straight aspirin can work miracles – especially if we're not in the habit of taking them.

A really first-class cure takes only two seconds.

Plunge the face and hands into cold water – cold enough to make you gasp aloud.

A hot bath is also good, but the cold plunge is really better.

These all seem little things, but together they can make a difference to fighting off the Winter Blues.

The One Thing That Will Double Your Chances Of Dodging This Flu

February 1, 1953

EVERY second person is asking me – how can I best avoid the flu?

My first answer always is – the less you think about the flu, the less chance you have of catching it.

Let me explain. Dad goes to work one morning. Two of his colleagues are missing. They've got flu.

Automatically dad thinks "Goodness, I wonder if I'll be next?" Quite unconsciously, he's afraid. Fear affects the action of the heart. This affects the blood supply. Circulation to the nose and throat are upset. The throat dries up. The nose feels stuffed. Resistance in this danger area falls.

And that's just the chance the flu germ has been waiting for. It pounces – and dad's off work.

Now see the difference with mother. She nurses him. On top of that, she's got a family to look after, meals to cook, and a house to run. She hasn't time to worry about whether or not she'll take flu. And nine times out of ten she doesn't – simply because she had no fear of it.

Doctors are the same. They have no fear of flu. They don't worry about it. It's one reason why you seldom hear of a doctor going down with flu, no matter how many patients he sees.

Now here are some facts that will help to kill that fear.

First – everyone has some immunity to flu. If you had it last year, you're less likely to take it this year. Your last dose built a kind of resistance in your system – almost like vaccination.

The same applies if you managed to get through a flu epidemic, with sufferers all around you, without taking it yourself.

Your immunity to the germ increased during that period, and you've a better chance of fighting if off this time.

Figures show that, even in the big epidemics, only one person in every five takes flu.

A major part of your resistance to flu depends on your general fitness.

So avoid getting thoroughly tired out. That's when resistance is at its lowest ebb.

If flu strikes in office, factory or house, start cutting down your activities. Mum could cut out that session of darning or mending. The younger folk might cut a dance or a visit to the cinema.

With this time saved, go earlier to bed. Avoid long periods without food. You've more chance of catching flu on an empty tummy because the blood supply to nose and throat is poor.

At the same time, don't indulge in huge feeds. This takes extra blood to the tummy, again impairing the supply to the danger area.

Air the bedrooms longer than usual. That's where germs linger. An hour at least with open windows and bedding thrown right back (depending on the weather) should do the trick.

When and if flu does strike, a simple antiseptic spray is a good thing. Not often – once a day is enough – all around the room where flu victims have been.

If you want to take medicines, then cod liver oil and fresh fruit are the best combination against flu.

Now, a note to housewives.

Germs live in dust. Damp your dusters when dusting the house. Damp floors before sweeping, and carpets before beating.

Don't flap sheets and blankets when making the beds – except out of doors.

Don't visit folk who have the flu for at least three days. After that it's usually safe enough.

But I must emphasise this. All these precautions are excellent things only when they go to build your morale.

The moment you start worrying whether you're taking enough cod liver oil or keeping down enough dust – you might as well quit.

No matter what you do, fear of flu is the real enemy.

Husband's misconduct with a girl in his office

September 29, 1957 — **I feel I am on the verge of a nervous breakdown. It's all caused by my husband's misconduct with a girl in his office. This happened some months ago, but I seem to be getting more depressed as time goes on. We have three children at school. I feel I am neglecting them. I just feel like sitting and crying all day and all night. I have no one of my own to turn to. Is there anything I can take for my nerves? It's all right to say just snap out of it — but I've tried.**

Time, patience and sympathetic understanding are all needed. Do your daily duties to the best of your ability and have an occasional heart-to-heart with your doctor and minister. Remember, your children depend on you.

January 15, 1956 — **Ever since a man I knew threw himself off a bridge close to my house, I've suffered nerves. I heard him shout, and the splash. My thoughts always seem to go back to the bridge.**

It's natural for such a tragedy to impress itself on your memory. But it will fade steadily if you fill your mind with thoughts of happier events which have occurred since then or are still in the future.

February 24, 1952 — **What's the best method to induce relaxation to relieve nervous tension? The tension causes my face to become hot and interferes with the normal rhythm of the heart.**

To have a relaxed body, you need a relaxed mind. If you go on worrying about these more or less trivial symptoms, you'll attain neither. Your doc might well prescribe something to help until you learn how to relax.

November 28, 1954 — **Can anything be done to relieve noises (chiefly music) in the head?**

A little almond oil, or glycerine, dropped into the ears at bedtime helps by keeping the eardrums supple.

February 10, 1952 — **For 18 months I've suffered from nausea. It used to come on if I started up suddenly and did heavy work. Now it's almost constant. Sometimes it's so bad my head swims. Six years ago I had a shadow on the lung. Constant X-raying has always been negative since.**

Your trouble is no doubt due to anxiety and continued worry about your illness. Be thankful the shadow didn't become a reality. Readjust your attitude to life, make your thoughts cheery and these unpleasant symptoms will disappear.

October 28, 1951 — **About 18 months ago I visited a mental hospital with a friend. Ever since, I've been haunted by an awful depression about it. How can I stop worrying?**

Try to realise that mental sickness is nothing more than another form of illness. Most of the people you saw are probably fit and well by now. Any illness is depressing, and there's no reason why mental sickness should be more depressing than any other.

May 19, 1957 — **I'm not long out of hospital after treatment for an irregular heartbeat. Now I can't keep my temper. I "fly" at my husband if he says the least thing to me. I'd like to be gentle and kind, but something always starts my temper.**

Time and patience, and an oft-repeated promise to do better, will do the trick in time. Try to think of your husband and your friends, instead of yourself.

May 5, 1957 — **Can a victim of alcoholism cure himself?**

Yes, if he has determination and a real desire to be cured. Sympathetic help from a near friend is invaluable, of course.

October 13, 1957 — **Can you tell me how to build up a good nervous system? I've been bothered with nerves and depression for years. I'm a woman (55).**

This is a matter of your environment and way of life as much as your general health. Far too many people nowadays grouse and are envious instead of counting their blessings and being contented.

July 10, 1955 — **I'm a woman. How can I have an examination by my doc if I've no-one to accompany me?**

Most family doctors get over this difficulty tactfully and with ease. Write to your doc about it, and he may fix up an appointment.

March 31, 1957 — **Can you suggest a remedy for an O.A.P. who is troubled with dreams at night appertaining to his former work? Can constipation have anything to do with it?**

A very mild sleeping tablet (or mixture) may be required to do the trick. Keep your bowels regular, but don't overdo medicine or take too strong laxatives.

June 9, 1957 — **I'm 33 and have always been a rather nervous type. Recently, I've had spells of heart beating rapidly for a few seconds, followed by a queer trembling sensation throughout. I've been staying indoors quite a lot and smoking sometimes 25 to 30 cigarettes a day.**

I think you're developing "smoker's heart". Cut out tobacco entirely and get out as much as possible.

— Chapter 10 —

A Martyr To Indigestion

THE causes and remedies for digestion problems deserve a chapter of their own — patients of the 1950s weren't finished with their food, and didn't stop writing to the Doc about it, just because they'd swallowed it!

You don't hear as much these days, about stomach ulcers, probably because (as Dr Lynda explains) treatment for them has greatly progressed.

But not long ago stomach ulcers were the height of fashion. People who worried got them, people under pressure got them. Having one was almost a badge of honour, given to mark the fact that you held down a difficult or responsible job.

So digestion, and remedies for indigestion, were important in the 1950s.

A fruit juice 10 minutes before eating was advised, and hot baths were good. But scones after 6pm, TV dinners, and even looking at large portions of food, were bad.

Then, when you reached the age of 60, you had to start throwing away kitchen utensils.

And constipation was always a worry, so there were a lot of laxatives taken.

There were also a lot of home-spun remedies that (might have) helped, such as apples roasted in front of a coal fire, a teaspoon of hot butter, and orange peel.

Swallowing these, it was claimed, would "keep you regular" .

It Isn't Just What You Eat That Goes For The Tummy

April 4, 1954

THERE'S a new sickness on the go just now. The patient feels no pain. There's no diarrhoea, no temperature. But the stomach rejects all food.

I call it "spring clean sickness".

What's happened is that all the smells of spring cleaning have scunnered the stomach. Those who suffer most are the folk who sit down and eat in a room that's being cleaned.

It's just one of the unusual things that can put the tummy off.

Why, I'm sometimes asked, do our health and our pep vary so much from day to day?

Ask your tummy!

It's the most temperamental organ we have. Even a wrong thought can upset it. So can fatigue.

You can upset it, too, if you wade into a big meal when you're really very hungry. That can make you sick. At best, you'll feel below par for twenty-four hours.

The sensible thing is to take a little drink at least ten minutes before the meal.

But remember – not milk! Fruit juice or a cup of tea is best.

It's the same when you're excessively tired – physically or mentally. Rest for 15 minutes before you have a meal. And start the meal with a piece of crisp, unbuttered toast.

Hundreds of families, I'm sure, would enjoy better digestion if mother didn't put the whole dish on the table! For even the appearance of lots of food on the table can put the tummy off. Far better if the helpings are ladled out on to plates in the kitchen and then brought through to the dining-room.

Don't think that's fussing. It's just common-sense. The tummy likes small helpings best.

And always use this method when feeding invalids. It can really help their recovery.

And here's a warning to folk with a television set. There's such a thing as TV indigestion. You're just asking for it if you rush and get the supper ready in the middle of a programme – and eat the supper while watching the rest of the show.

It can cause indigestion and broken sleep. Certainly you're not getting the best from your food.

One sure sign of the tummy being "off" is a blown-up feeling for a whole day. Usually this is caused by taking too much liquid with our meals. An extra cup of tea, perhaps.

The cure for this is simple. Keep off foods until the blown-up feeling is gone.

Drink tea alone and it passes through the tummy in five minutes. Take too much tea with food, and the liquid is mixed up with the solids and can't get out freely. The tummy rebels against it.

More people get indigestion at tea-time than at any other meal. That's because we're losing the habit of "high tea".

A man comes to the surgery complaining of indigestion and flatulence during the evening.

I usually find he eats far too much bread and scones about six o'clock because he's not having a fork and knife dish to tea.

In other words, he's getting too much starch.

Here's a first-class way to help your digestion at tea-time. Make a point of having a bit of cheese with your bread. Spread the bread with jam by all means, but in addition ALWAYS have margarine or butter. That makes the perfect balance.

What about lunch-time?

Well, if you like suet pudding, remember it's silly to take chops or fatty beef for the middle course. This combination is perhaps the hardest of all on the tummy.

THE MODERN VIEW, BY DR LYNDA

A COUPLE of new "Docisms" here — spring clean sickness and TV indigestion — neither of which I can find much basis for. Sorry 1950s Doc.

In fact I struggled to find much sense at all in this article.

Tummy upsets in this country are usually caused by viruses, food bacteria, toxins and drugs. They usually cause a short-lived vomiting and diarrhoeal illness. Viruses are usually spread by contact with contaminated food and contact with infected individuals.

Most outbreaks of viral gastroenteritis occur during the winter months, from November to April, and are usually due to the rotavirus and norovirus. So perhaps he could be forgiven for associating it with spring cleaning.

Food poisoning caused by salmonella and campylobacter is usually due to poor food hygiene and under-cooking and has nothing to do with drinking tea with meals!

Occasionally, poisons and toxins found in seafood can be the source, and some drugs like antibiotics, antacids, laxatives and chemotherapy can also be blamed.

When it comes to chronic diarrhoeal and digestive problems, bread and starch can cause problems but only if you have a reaction to gluten, a dietary protein found in cereal, called coeliac disease. It isn't a true allergy to the gluten but a problem with the immune system which sees the gluten as a threat to the body and attacks it, setting up an irritation in the small bowel or intestine which disrupts the body's ability to absorb nutrients for food.

The body isn't then able to digest food properly, causing diarrhoea, tummy pain and bloatedness.

It's not clear yet what actually causes the body to do this, but it often runs in families and may be linked to gastroenteritis in early childhood.

The Doc was a wee bit out on his transit times too. Normally a cup of tea will take about 40-50 mins for 70-80% of it to go through the stomach. Most meals take 4-5 hours to leave the stomach and 30-40 hours to exit at the other end.

He was nearly right, too, with his wrong thoughts causing problems.

A single wrong thought in itself won't do much but chronic stress and high anxiety do result in tummy problems and irritable bowels.

But what use unbuttered toast and always having cheese and butter with your bread is I've no idea, and I'm sure the "tea-jennies" of this world won't agree with the sins of taking an extra cuppa with a meal!

It's So Easy To Ruin Your Tummy

October 28, 1956

ONE in every five of us ruins his stomach. One in every two ill-uses his stomach. And can you guess the reason?

Not, as so many think, because we eat the wrong food. We abuse our stomachs in five different ways, and the No. 1 cause is WORRY.

Our digestion works automatically. If you let it get on with the job without interference, you could eat like a horse right into the nineties.

Yet today I have patient after patient plagued with a bad stomach – and they're still in their middle fifties.

All because their brain interferes with digestion.

You're asking for tummy trouble if you're worried or pressed for time and eat against the clock – if you're in a bad temper – or if you're more interested in reading the newspaper than in what's going into your mouth.

These are the habits which give you an over-active stomach. They increase the flow of "acids" in the stomach and irritate the lining.

True, the stomach recovers quickly, but in the long run you're bound to get chronic inflammation.

And, after that, one of two things is almost certain to happen.

No. 1 is an ulcer. Nobody really knows the main cause of an ulcer, but we've found out that worry is always present.

This is followed by a trouble almost as serious. By the time you reach fifty the glands producing the juices pack up. Instead of an over-active stomach you now have the reverse.

The stomach goes stagnant, digestion is slow, and there's loss of appetite. You lose weight, and for the rest of your life you're likely to be bloodless.

The **No. 2** most common abuse is smoking on an empty stomach.

When we inhale, some smoke goes down into the stomach. If it's empty, the lining is exposed to the irritation. As a defence, the lining exudes mucus and the smoker develops chronic stomach catarrh.

I find that when a patient gives up smoking, it's his stomach that feels the benefit, even more than his lungs.

One hint – never smoke a cigarette too far down. The last inch is "wet". If this nicotine juice gets into the stomach, it's really being abused.

Pipe smokers, too, are wise to be careful about a "wet" smoke towards the end of their pipe.

No. 3 abuse is two tiny meals and a big one every day. So avoid extremes in eating, and try to have all three meals moderate in size.

The tummy is the size of a grapefruit, but it can blow up to the size of a football!

The big meal habit eventually reduces the stomach's elasticity, and it loses its power to shrink. So it stays big. A big, flabby stomach is impossible to cure. You're doomed to indigestion.

Abuse **No. 4** is hard bits of food that irritate the stomach and overwork the acids.

Swallow a hard little potato chip whole – and you'd be amazed at the trouble it causes. That chip lies at the foot of the stomach and rubs against the lining. Acids have a job to break it down.

The ideal is to chew every mouthful twenty times. The minimum is ten times.

You should chew most headache and rheumatic tablets for the same

reason. A headache tablet can literally burn the stomach if it lies there in one piece. It will make marks that may never heal.

Enemy **No. 5** is heat.

The man or woman who likes things piping hot is asking for chronic indigestion in middle age.

The stomach is more tender than the throat. The first drop of tea that's too hot sears the stomach lining.

Above all, never do this on an empty stomach.

Alcohol is also too "hot" for anybody before a meal. Many a working chap has his nip before he goes home for tea. Good luck to him – he maybe needs it. But after years of this he'll likely run into some trouble with his stomach.

Bad teeth are dangerous to the stomach, too. The tummy gets irritating poisons from them. This can not only cause indigestion, but possibly ulcers.

So there you are.

Remember, it's irritation that ruins the stomach, not food. Eat anything you like – but never worry about your stomach. Don't even think of it. All you need do is to go easy on highly-seasoned foods. Not too much salt, vinegar, pepper, mustard, &c.

Chew your food well – and enjoy it!

THE MODERN VIEW, BY DR LYNDA

THE 1950s Doc was right, getting peptic or gastric complaints is not because we eat the wrong food.

It's true that some foods may give you indigestion but there is no substantial evidence that ulcers are caused by food at all.

Ulcers today are caused mainly by a bug, helicobacter pylori, and drugs — usually anti-inflammatories like ibuprofen.

Even as far back as 1906 bugs were found in the stomachs of people with gastric ulcers but it wasn't until the 1980s that the link between helicobacter pylori and ulcers was confirmed and current treatments revolutionised ulcer care.

Smoking makes it more likely that you will develop an ulcer because it affects the protective mucosal lining of the stomach, making it more difficult to heal. Smoking also affects the way food goes through the system. Smokers appear to be at higher risk of becoming affected with helicobacter, whether they smoke on an empty or full stomach.

There is also no evidence that stress and worry causes ulcers — unless that stress causes you to smoke, drink alcohol or abuse anti-inflammatory drugs. But stress might have an effect on your tummy in other ways, like irritable bowel.

The second trouble is the gland producing juices "packing up". I think what he means here is gastric atrophy, which is a process of chronic inflammation of the mucous lining, usually due to infection with helicobacter or an autoimmune response which results in malabsorption of vitamin b12 and does indeed cause pernicious anaemia.

The trouble these days is that anyone with upper digestive problems ends up on a class of drugs known as protein pump inhibitors, which reduce the amount of gastric acid secretion in the stomach and are used in treating ulcers and indigestion.

They are also used to protect the stomach when anti-inflammatory drugs are used in the treatment of arthritis and other inflammatory problems.

Chronic lack of stomach acid, due to these drugs or gastric atrophy, has been linked to gastric cancer. So, as usual, there is a downside to the long-term use of these drugs.

They can also cause osteoporosis (bone thinning) and diarrhoea.

As for the rest of the Doc's advice here, I'm not sure it would make much difference whether you chew your food twenty times or ten, and hard food will be broken down regardless in a healthy stomach.

And there is no evidence of hot tea drinkers, those who smoke cigarettes too far down, or those who drink alcohol, having more chance of cancer, either.

One Thing I Want You All To Do On The Day You Reach The Age Of Sixty

March 16, 1958

ON the day you reach 60, I want you all to go into your kitchen and do something quite drastic – throw your frying-pan in the bin.

Believe me, you'll be all the better without it.

If you use the frying pan too much, it's a menace to health.

And the older you are, the greater the danger.

After 40, you shouldn't use it more than once a day. After reaching the age of 60, cut out fries completely.

If you eat too many fries after the age of 40 then you double your risk of getting an ulcer.

Of every 100 patients with ulcers, nearly 99 of them have admitted they were "daft" on fried foods.

It causes 50 per cent of all flatulence.

And any man or woman who practically lives out of a frying-pan will grow old quicker than they should.

Maybe you think I'm too hard on the frying-pan.

Not really. What I'm saying is – for goodness sake don't allow the frying-pan to be too hard on you.

This is most important for anybody who doesn't earn his living by sheer muscle.

A labourer can maybe get away with it – but never a man who is an office worker.

Even if you're one of the lucky ones with a first-class digestion, fries at every meal will bring you down eventually. You'll be tired, you'll have headaches, and it's not unlikely that you'll finish up a bad-tempered old man.

Now, why should all this be? Well, as soon as you fry an egg, or chips, a harmful chemical change takes place in the frying fats.

The food also suffers.

Valuable vitamins are lost – vitamins that give you a good skin and build up resistance.

Worse still, all fries irritate the stomach, and it'll have practically nothing to do with that fried egg. The egg is passed on to the duodenum, which, in turn, is irritated.

That's why duodenal ulcers are so common.

Hard, fat-covered food strains the liver, too. Over several years of ill-treatment, the liver toughens up. Part of it may stop working.

Fortunately, the liver is big. We can live with only half of it working.

But fried-food addicts can, in time, go over the safety margin. Then the effect is the same as with years of hard whisky drinking.

And there's a risk of headaches, lack of energy, dullness in thinking.

But we haven't completed the vicious circle.

A poor liver means the arteries suffer. Poisons get into the walls of blood vessels.

So, before we realise it, the arteries are hardening. And with this comes the danger of a stroke in late middle-age.

"But, doctor, there's nothing tastier", you say.

Well, if you must have a fry, the best time is at tea-time – never at lunch. You're more likely to rest after tea.

Fried bacon is good and does no harm. Only remember this – fry it in its own fat.

Don't fry eggs along with bacon, rather poach them. For few of us can fry an egg properly.

As for these eggs that are fried hard round the edges, they're really sore on the digestion.

Cheese and meat lose a lot of vitamins when fried.

And, please, never fry anything twice. No tummy can stand that. If you must have chips – do them in deep fat. "Boil" them in fat. They're a lot better for you.

Lastly, here's a warning sign that may help you in time.

If you ever feel that only fried things are tasty enough for you – take the hint! Cut them down.

Better still, cut them out.

You maybe won't thank me for that advice now, but you'll bless me in ten years' time. I guarantee that!

There's Nothing Quite So Good For You As A Bit Of Chicken

December 28, 1958

OF all the good things we eat at Christmas and New Year, by far the best is – chicken.

Have a bit of chicken before you go first-footing, or to a dance. You'll last the pace better than on any other single item of food.

It not only gives quick energy, but more staying power, ounce for ounce, than even sirloin of beef.

Why is chicken so good?

Because the bird was meant to fly, so bone and flesh are light. And it beats other birds because it lives a "sheltered" life. Ducks, &c., need oil and fat for waterproofing. Some birds need fat and grease for warmth. Chicken is different.

When you've got a chicken for dinner, here are a few tips:

Give granny the breast.

Let the children have the legs.

Mum and dad should take the wings.

The breast is the most easily digested meal we know. Old folk can take it without any qualms. It's short-fibred, and very easily broken down in the mouth.

Even if granny has only one tooth in her head, that's enough!

The legs are the most nutritious. Ideal for growing children. If anything, the legs are the hardest part of the bird to digest, though still easier than other meats.

Young stomachs can easily deal with them.

The wings are the in-between parts. Good food value, and good for digestion.

I don't care what kind of stomach you have, chicken won't do it any harm. It's the one meat that's definitely non-irritating to the tummy. Even folk with ulcers aren't upset.

Some people have an easily irritated bowel (colitis). Most meats are taboo to them – but not chicken.

So don't just have it for Christmas and New Year. Try to take it off and on all through 1959.

In fact, I'd strongly advise chicken fairly regularly in certain circumstances.

Growing children thrive on it. It's a great body-builder. It gives them a stamina that could stay with them all their lives.

When invalids are getting over a bad illness, the system cries out for strength. But poor digestion perhaps can't cope with red meat. Then chicken's the answer.

A small hospital, with say, 30 beds, uses half a dozen birds a day. So you see, you're on to a good thing.

Lots of us haven't as long for lunch as we'd like. That's bound to play havoc with our digestion, occasionally.

So, the next time your tummy is out of sorts, plump for chicken as the main dish.

Folk inclined to gobble lunch can't do better either. Neither can the worker who lives far from his job.

Chicken has another advantage. It's one of the meats that's just as tasty when cold. Most other meats have to be reheated. That can lead to trouble for poor digestions.

And of all the types of soup mother can make, none has so much value as chicken soup.

The reason is that the good comes easily out of the bones.

You'll find a little fat on the top of the soup, but it's easily skimmed off. After that, the soup's perfect. The less fat on the chicken, the better the buy. That's as good a way of judging as any.

What should we take along with chicken? Ordinary vegetables, or try a vegetable salad when having cold chicken.

And don't get the idea that chicken is only good for the old, the ailing and youngsters.

If you're under par, chicken will give you a big lift in a week. But if you're hale and hearty – and you've a good tummy – you'll get even more value out of chicken.

Now don't say, "Oh, that's all very well, but look at the price".

Compared with beef, &c., chicken isn't as expensive as you'd imagine. It's light-boned, so you get good value for weight.

Every year, more and more people are going in for a chicken on the table. This year the record was broken – 7 lb. per head of the whole population.

A Lot Depends On Where You're Brought Up

August 19, 1951

A NEW patient came to me on Thursday. As he sat down I asked him if he came from country stock.

He was astonished to hear this. "Why, yes", he said. "But I came to the town nearly 20 years ago. How did you guess?"

It's something I can always tell.

In this case, it was his breathing that gave the game away.

He used a quarter more lung power than city-bred folk.

And he used the lower part of his lungs – the most important part.

Nearly all people born and bred in the town breathe "high" in the chest. This inadequate breathing may cause many illnesses – chest troubles, ulcers, indigestion. It may even be a cause of coronary thrombosis.

This is only one reason why the countryman is twice as tough as his townie brother.

There are many others. And townies can copy a lot of them.

Just watch the countryman. See how he takes a longer stride. That's a splendid thing. Half our ills come from the stomach, and if you walk from the hips, the abdominal muscles are "worked" with every step.

Digestion is improved. There's less constipation and self-poisoning.

I find the countryman can often work much harder and longer than the town man. He doesn't tire nearly so easily.

Why is this? One big reason is that he gets up at the time Nature intended us all to get up – at daybreak.

If we lie beyond that time, our natural rhythm is broken. Most town folk break the rhythm every day. They lose the freshening stimulus of sunlight and early air (the finest of the day).

The best hours for sleep are those before midnight. Early bedders always have more pep.

Here again the country folk have the advantage.

Another thing. A first-class sleep depends on quiet. Did you know that many folk in the cities have never had a 100 per cent. sleep in their lives? That's because an eighth part of their system works all night to resist the town noises.

Some of us can't do much about it, but if at all possible, sleep at the back of the house – not in a room facing the street.

Another cause of tiredness common to townspeople is poor eyesight and hearing.

The countryman develops "long sight". His sense of hearing is finer. So is his sense of smell, which helps him to enjoy his food.

"That's just his luck", you may say. But if we in the town take the trouble, we can get the same benefits, even if it's in small doses.

Take even half a day in the country. It has more value than a tonic bottle for a week.

For, if our grandparents or great-grandparents were country stock, we still retain the basis of all these advantages. They're latent in our system. And even a half day in the country will make them active again.

Most of us had forebears who lived in the country.

And what a delight countrymen are when it comes to temper! They aren't as emotional or so easily upset as town people.

Flying off the handle is bad for the brain, nerves and heart.

So most of us in the towns could do with a real country even temper.

Lastly, we should all make a point of walking at least a mile a day, and doing it on country roads if at all possible. Hard streets prevent that spring in the step you get in the country.

It's The Easiest Cure For Such A Lot Of Things

June 17, 1951

A PATIENT complained to me of indigestion last week. When I advised her to take more baths, she looked rather taken aback.

But hot baths are often one of the best cures for temporary indigestion.

The water warms the feet, and this removes chill from the blood circulating to the tummy, which is often the cause of indigestion.

At the same time the heat soothes the muscles of the tummy and bowels. The muscles (surface and inner) relax – and away goes the pain.

We're too apt to regard a bath simply as a cleanser. It can do a lot more than just clean. It can relieve headaches, nerves, constipation, sore throat, husky voice, sleeplessness, rheumatic pains and over-tire.

And there are a number of other things that are better done in a bath than elsewhere.

A warm bath nearly always gets rid of an ordinary headache.

But the bath must never be too hot or too cool. "Almost hot" is best. Then the body is surrounded by heat, but the head is clear. So the blood is drawn away from the head to the body.

The cure is particularly effective if the headache is caused by over-tire or worry.

In the same way, I've even known a hot bath to cure toothache.

A pleasantly warm bath is ideal for soothing nerves – especially if you add a small handful of washing soda crystals. These give the water a silky texture, and as we move about, the water laps all around giving a massaging effect.

The nerves get sleepy and are less trigger-like.

Quarter of an hour is a fair time for a nerve bath. The massaging effect of the water on the muscles is also one of the best things for constipation.

I met Mr B. last Wednesday. He was husky-voiced, and had a sore, raw throat. "Go home and have an almost hot bath", I told him.

The secret here is that you inhale the steam.

The nose and throat get a clean-out. The throat relaxes. The phlegm comes away from the nose.

And, after all, it's far more comfortable to inhale in a bath than to stand over a basin with a towel over your head.

Exercises are often recommended for asthma and bronchitis. They ease the chest muscles. But patients sometimes complain to me that the exercises tire them out.

This is when the warm bath does the trick. Exercises are easily done in water, because it needs less effort to move the body there.

The bath is the best place for women to shampoo their hair. It's twice as good as done over the sink, and not half as tiring. You see, the value of a shampoo is in the rinsing – and you can do that much better in a bath.

Finally, here are some don'ts about having a bath:-

Never shave when having a bath. I know quite a number of men do this, but there's a tendency for the razor to slip.

In no circumstances use electrical appliances.

Never smoke in a bath. I know a lot of people who don't enjoy a bath unless they have a cigarette at the same time, but the effect is altogether too soothing and I've known a man fall asleep in his bath just because of this.

There Are Four Good Cures For Constipation

October 25, 1953

THE curse of constipation. Yes, that's exactly what "not being regular" is to thousands of folk.

But thousands of others have found a way to beat it – and some have sent us their hints.

Here they are – and what the doc thinks of them.

One in five says, "Drink a glass of warm water before breakfast every morning". Some drink the water last thing at night. Some like it cold, others as hot as they can stand it.

Number two cure in popularity – treacle.

You can dissolve some in a glass of hot water, or in milk. Pour it on your porridge, or on brown bread, or take it with baking soda, or just itself off a spoon. Dozens of readers swear by it.

The rest of the cures ranged from Danish blue cheese to two pints of beer a day!

Here are some:

A lady from Bishop Auckland minces 2 ounces each of dates, figs, prunes and raisins, adds 2 ounces of powdered senna, 6 ounces of glycerine, and takes a little each night. A Falkirk reader roasts a large apple at the fire for two hours and eats it at bedtime.

Two Glasgow folk rely on apples, too. One simmers apple peel in water and drinks the fluid. The other cuts a slice of an apple, allows it to turn brown overnight, scrapes off the brown part in the morning and eats it.

A Halifax reader cuts an orange up very small – including the peel – and eats it during the day. She believes the oil in the orange skin does the trick.

Vegetables have their supporters, too.

"C.L., Glasgow", says – "My unfailing cure is plain-boiled beetroot, eaten without vinegar".

Another reader says – "Ask any farmer how valuable turnip is in keeping his cattle healthy – and try it yourself".

A lot of folk work on the assumption that if machines need oiling – so do human beings.

Olive oil is the most popular lubricator. A little on a spoon each day seems to work wonders.

From a reader in Morpeth – Take a teaspoonful of warm butter each morning before breakfast.

Montrose – Dissolve a dessertspoonful of honey in a glass of hot milk last thing at night.

Broxburn – Stand with arms outstretched at shoulder height, bend as far as possible to your right, then to the left, ten times each way. Do this last thing at night, first thing in the morning.

North Shields – Sprinkle a cupful of dried fruit with brown sugar, cover with vinegar, soak for 24 hours, drink the syrup and eat the fruit regularly.

And to finish with, one that isn't nearly so daft as it seems, from Caldercruix – Buy a dog. Take it for a three-mile hike every day before breakfast – and ten miles on Sunday.

The Doc. says –

I certainly agree that water – particularly warm water – is one of the best things to cure constipation.

The cause of the trouble is often insufficient fluids in the body.

Most can be cured by increasing the amount of water you drink. A glass of WARM water first thing in the morning has a double benefit. It provides the extra fluid – and it starts off the action of the bowel.

After the water, the cure I like best is fruit. It can bring three things the body needs to function correctly – water, bulk, and laxative juices.

The fruits which have the best laxative effects are figs and prunes.

Vegetables have no laxative juices – but their bulk and water can be helpful for some folk.

One point about eating skins and peels. They are an irritant. If that's what you're needing, they may do the trick. But you must be careful not to overdo the irritation.

You may get indigestion or colic.

One trouble with water is that it tends to pass through too quickly. So I like the suggestion of taking porridge, linseed and dried fruit. All these soak up water as they swell, and hold on to it.

The husks and little rough bits in these things also stimulate the bowel. This can be particularly good for young folk.

The various oils are good. Exercise is valuable, too. Often, constipation is simply tiredness.

The four things which do most to cure constipation are, in order of importance:–

1. habit.
2. water.
3. fruit and vegetables.
4. exercise.

A common leg problem for women who are plump

March 8, 1959 — **For the past year, clusters of tiny red veins have been appearing just above my knees, and are spreading. Are they broken veins, or are they a sign of poor circulation? I'm female (28).**

These are common in women who are plump. They are dilated capillaries, perhaps associated with some sluggishness of circulation in the deeper veins of the thighs.

October 23, 1955 — **I've high blood pressure and am 16 lb. overweight. Would sago, semolina, peasmeal or oatmeal cooked in water with a little salt be too fattening for me?**

You require to cut down your diet all round, and in particular to avoid sugar, starchy foods and seasonings.

April 1, 1951 — **There's a craze for slimming and keeping your weight down. What about putting weight on?**

Best methods are extra rest, peace of mind and an extra pint of milk a day.

March 12, 1950 — **I have suffered since 1943 with swollen ankles. Age 49. Weight 10 st. 9 lb. I get plenty rest. My heart is OK and the swollen ankles aren't due to dropsy, kidneys or rheumatism. Is there any other cause?**

The likeliest remaining cause is varicose veins. If the leg is fat, these may not be visible.

July 10, 1955 — **My daughter (16) has discoloured legs – large bluish patches. She's 5 ft. 10 inches and weighs 12 stone.**

She's too heavy for her age, and may have a sluggish gland somewhere. Take her to see your doc.

March 25, 1956 — **I've been putting on a lot of weight and was advised by a friend to take two teaspoonfuls of vinegar after each meal. Would this be helpful — or safe — as I also am anaemic?**

It might be effective in getting down your weight, by irritating the stomach and hindering digestion. But it certainly wouldn't be safe. Discipline yourself to eat much less.

February 2, 1958 — **In an article, you once said a 24-hour starvation once in a while is wonderful for health. Does that mean no liquids, such as tea, fruit juices, clear soups &c.?**

No. At least two pints of fluids would be needed.

April 29, 1956 — **I'm overweight and have been instructed to go on a diet, with an occasional enema. Do these enemas assist in getting my weight down?**

Only indirectly, by helping the bowel action. Don't become dependent on the enemas by overuse of them.

February 12, 1950 — **Why is it that young people nowadays seem to be growing "up" but not "out"? They're taller than ever before — but they don't have the width to carry with it.**

It's probably because they're getting lots of things that make for growth (milk, &c.), but not enough of the body-builders (meat, eggs, butter, &c.).

August 25, 1957 — **I'm a woman (32) with four children. I've a very flabby tummy, but exercise like "cycling in the air" is not helping.**

You probably have enough physical exercise in looking after the house and family. Special exercises would only tire you more. Get a suitable supporting corset and lie down each afternoon for an hour.

May 20, 1951 — **My daughter has lost a lot of weight lately. This especially shows in her neck. Can you suggest how to fatten her up?**

An unexplained loss of weight is not to be taken lightly. It should be investigated by your doctor. Meantime, try regular hours, a little extra sleep, and plenty of milk.

August 23, 1953 — **My husband died from T.B. Recently I've become breathless, but I'm also rather fat. Would I be getting thin if I'd contracted T.B.? I'm 42.**

Not necessarily, at least not till the disease is well established. Your overweight is responsible for the breathlessness, in my opinion. Diet strictly.

July 21, 1957 — **I take three cold baths a week. I am told by a friend this should only be done by people who are slimming. Is this so? I am very slim, and only take the baths because I find them refreshing.**

No. These have no noticeable effect in reducing weight. Continue them, for the summer at least.

August 6, 1950 — **My weight has gone from 11 st. to 11 st. 10 lb. in six months. I can't diet, since I work in a hotel and must eat what I'm given. Would anti-fat tablets help?**

They might. But best of all would be to cut down the amount you eat by 25 per cent. You don't have to eat all of what you're given.

August 24, 1958 — **I'm a girl (13), underweight and very small. I also have frightening dreams. Could this have anything to do with my weight?**

Your dreams may well be caused by subconscious worry about your size.

— Chapter 11 —

Prevention Is Better Than Cure

A PARAFFIN wax hot bath might not be often prescribed by doctors of today. And you might cast a sceptical eye upon the various "tonics" (drugs in bottled form) recommended in this chapter as preventative medicinc.

But the perils of having "a thoughtless husband" are surely there for all to see. And getting to bed early to avoid the flu sounds like it would help, although the health benefits of sitting in the back row at church might need a bit of explanation.

But there is good, sensible, down-to-earth advice here too. The Doc of the mid-20th Century might not have had the benefit of the extra 60 years of research that modern medics have, but he was no fool.

So if he tells you to sprinkle cold water on your Adam's Apple, morning and night, you should do exactly that. And are you sure you are walking the right way?

A Little Thought Can Save Your Wife No End Of Trouble

February 5, 1950

INTO my surgery on Thursday came a married woman just into her forties. She's fifty per cent bloodless. She's had colds, eye trouble, and headaches, this winter.

"Just one thing after another," she told me.

Well, I put half the blame on a thoughtless husband.

His wife is what everybody calls a grand housewife and mother. She'll tackle anything at any time. A grand spirit indeed. But her husband shouldn't let her do it.

One of the commonest afflictions from which housewives suffer is back ache. Yet too often the husband thoughtlessly aggravates the strain.

He comes in, gets his tea, and plunks himself down in his armchair. He's there for the evening.

Meantime, his wife brings his pipe, the paper, his slippers. She gets up to switch on the wireless or "turn it up".

She answers the door. She puts on the kettle for supper.

Now, she has been bending up and down all day, probably more than her husband.

In each case the body requires a rest – but hers isn't getting it.

Some husbands even let their wives take off their boots. Another bend, another strain for tired back muscles.

Yet if his wife asked such a husband to take off her shoes, he'd think she was daft.

The need for rest in the evening is so important for a woman that I say to every husband – Don't let your wife do any housework or odd jobs in the evening. (Jobs like jam-making, for instance.)

Tell her she needs the rest. And see she gets it.

At bedtime, don't keep on chatting to the wife. A woman needs more sleep than a man, and these hours before midnight are most important.

And, for any sake, don't rake up things that she has forgotten to do. Nothing upsets a woman's sleep so much as grumbling before she falls over.

Other don'ts that will save your wife a lot of nervous strain are:- Don't leave her to spank a strong-minded child. You're stronger, more controlled, and not so liable to be left a "bag of nerves".

Don't leave her to have a row with a tradesman or argue with the folk next door about the mess their cat is making. A man's make-up is better fitted for unpleasant tasks.

I had a patient who was nervy for weeks and off her food because of a stairhead row.

Don't keep her waiting at meal-times, especially dinner. As the minutes go past she sees the food spoiling – all her work going for nothing.

Spoiled food's bad for you. But the strain is far worse on her.

On the other hand, nothing boosts a woman's morale more than sitting down, even once a week, to a meal she hasn't cooked, or seen until it's on her plate.

So don't let her make the breakfast on Sunday. You do it.

Don't let her carry on when she's fluey. Every week I'm called to wives who kept going too long and are now faced with months of ill health – bloodlessness, bronchitis, even pneumonia.

The same with convalescence. I've never known a woman who wasn't on her feet before her time. "But, doctor, I'm not going outside." That's the excuse.

And that's the reason for so much continued ill-health. By staying indoors, the patient loses the tonic of fresh air, of meeting people.

And at the same time she's carrying on the housework when she shouldn't.

Talking about going "out". How do you walk with your wife? It's far too common to see a husband one pace ahead. He forces her to match his pace instead of keeping to hers.

And don't run ahead to tell a bus conductor to wait till your wife arrives. It might look you're being very chivalrous, but it's bad for your wife.

Yes, husband can help their wives a lot – if they take a little thought. Even in little things like answering the door.

THE MODERN VIEW, BY DR LYNDA

I QUITE agree, a little thought can save your wife no end of trouble. But not quite in the way the 1950s Doc suggests.

Anaemia (bloodlessness) is usually due to heavy periods in women and the wife obviously hasn't been wearing her string vest (see The Clothes We Wore, page 267) to ward off the cold and chills.

Some things don't change, though. How many men still come in and plonk themselves in a comfy chair in front of the TV! Though my other half had better not start asking for a pipe, his paper and his slippers or he might find himself wearing them on his head!

These days, relationships and marriages are more equal and those scenarios are unusual as women are, in many cases, the main or only wage earner. So men have to muck in with household chores, child care and sorting out the neighbours and their cats . . . should they need sorted out!

And yet relationships are still unequal in many ways. Many of the people I see in my surgery who are distressed, upset and depressed have relationship issues at the heart of their troubles.

Couples have forgotten to think of how the other feels and consider each other. They've been complacent in looking after each other and forget humans need affection and compassion and tolerance to survive.

Selfishness and laziness destroy it.

Yes …. it's nice to sit down in front of the TV after work but surely it's nicer to snuggle up with the other half to watch that movie, sharing the chores beforehand and a bag of treats afterwards.

Sharing life's bad moments and tribulations makes you closer, and when the good times come it multiplies the bonds between you.

My mother used to say "No one's died o' stoor yet", so occasionally make time for each other, forget the housework and spend time doing things you enjoy together.

The 1950s Doc was right about something else too. He was right about getting out in the fresh air when you are convalescing and meeting people. It's a great tonic because we are gregarious creatures by nature and need company to thrive.

Yes, a little thought can make our lives a lot better, and make them much happier and more enjoyable.

Is Your Adam's Apple Tender?

December 27, 1959

"IS there any secret to beat colds and flu, now that winter's on us"? I was asked that question the other day.

Here is the answer:- Look after your throat. Believe me, it's the best friend you have!

Did you know that from your throat comes – 50 per cent of all colds. 50 per cent of all rheumatism. 75 per cent of all gland troubles. 20 per cent of all deafness. 25 per cent of earache, running ears, mastoids, &c.

And this may also surprise you – if you're bloodless, if you're chronically depressed, it may well be that your throat's to blame.

Take, for instance, that "fluey" cold which is rampant just now. If you want to dodge it – or minimise it – you should be very throat-conscious.

The first danger sign is a dryness of the throat. Press gently with the thumbs on both sides of the Adam's apple. Tender to the touch? Then your throat needs help.

That rawness and tenderness is a sign there's a big battle going on. And the germs are winning.

So right away, the answer is: a couple of aspirins. Crush them, swallow them dry and wash down with a hot drink. Then get yourself off to bed – and the battle's practically won.

Now here's how to be good to your throat.

Never go to bed with a dry throat. If it feels dry, go out and take a five-minute walk. That induces mucus to flow again – and this protects the throat lining and helps to kill germs.

Very often a dry throat is a sign that the body is crying out for fluid. Not just a cupful, but a good couple of pints.

The quickest way to get a bad cold is to "hawk" the throat – to force out phlegm by deliberate coughing! It tears the lining, weakens the germ defences – and accelerates the trouble. Next day you're almost sure to wake up stuffed with cold.

If you feel you must clear your throat, there are only two sensible ways to try it. The first is to cough gently. If that doesn't do the trick, take six deep breaths. But remember to breathe IN through the nose and OUT through the mouth.

The worst thing you can do to your throat is to breathe in by the mouth.

Of course, some folk have a "weak" throat.

Well, here's how to strengthen it. Morning and night sprinkle cold water round the Adam's apple.

Another great help is to paint the throat. But the painting must be done when the throat's at its best – not when it's infected.

And nobody should wear a scarf as a habit – that's bad for the throat. A scarf is meant to keep the body warm, not to protect the neck!

Now here's a warning if you've a sore throat and feel shivery – you've got flu.

Headaches and temperature usually indicate tonsillitis. Laryngitis isn't so serious. Your throat's sore when you speak. The pain is fairly far down. There's less headache and temperature.

Anybody with a sore throat should talk less. If you've laryngitis – keep silent.

What's the remedy when your throat's acutely affected? Look out an old sock and an old hankie. Wring out the hankie in cold water, wrap it round your neck and cover with the old sock. That helps as well as anything.

Another thing. Keep a kettle on the boil in the sick-room. The steam moistens the air – and that's a tremendous benefit.

In really bad cases you can get penicillin injections, though most cases can be cleared up with M. & B.

Yes, it's the easiest thing in the world to be good to your throat. In winter it's the most important thing you can do.

A Wonderful New Treatment

February 3, 1957

IT'S a wonderful thing for me to be able to say to patients gravely ill – "Ten years ago – even two years ago – your number would have been up. But today we'll be able to pull you through".

For it's amazing how, since 1947, we've discovered new treatments, techniques and drugs that are proving all the difference between life and death.

A middle-aged man came to me with artery trouble. He was threatened with clotting in a vital spot. There the artery was in bad shape. He needed a replacement! Yes, a new bit of artery.

Now, a piece of bad artery can be removed and a healthy piece stitched in its place. Today we can use plastic for arteries, too.

Sometimes an artery is ruptured or weakened. Ten years ago the patient risked sudden collapse.

Now we can fit a plastic sleeve over the artery. The weak section is strengthened – and the patient given new life.

A vital clue in the diagnosis of heart trouble is a sample drop of blood from the heart.

Only recently has this been possible, and in a wonderful way. A long, flexible "needle" is slipped inside a vein at the elbow. Slowly the needle is pushed along inside the vein, up the arm, round the shoulder, across the chest – and into the very heart itself!

The needle tip is watched all the way. When the heart is reached, a tiny sample of blood is taken. And from what we learn from that drop of blood, we can start the correct cure.

For this you can thank one of the bravest doctors in history – he first tried it on himself.

In the next year or two we will certainly have achieved a great victory over polio. We won't, perhaps, be able to stamp it out altogether. But we'll be able to prevent the paralysis that goes with one of the three types.

Up till now, radium was the only radio-active substance available for treating certain troubles. It was used locally on the skin surface, or inserted in needles.

Now, radio-active substances – isotopes – can be sent round the body in the blood stream and the doctor can watch their progress.

This is a great help in diagnosing trouble and sometimes in treating difficult cases.

For instance, in bladder trouble, some leading surgeons fill tiny balloons with isotopes, insert them inside the bladder, and leave them to do their healing work.

These new ways are of tremendous benefit in healing tumours and blood conditions.

A patient of mine, a middle-aged woman, was cured not long ago by an operation that used to be impossible.

A new breathing machine took over the job of her lungs. The surgeon was able to do his work unhampered by the rise and fall of the chest.

We can even introduce oxygen into the blood stream itself. In other words, the patient breathes without lungs.

The flow of the blood, too, can be directed, and the circulation forced to by-pass, temporarily, a trouble spot which is being dealt with. This "traffic cop" method can be a life-saver for folk with thrombosis.

Before the 1940s many a patient died because they couldn't stand up to an operation.

Nobody need fear an operation nowadays. I've seen a patient who needed a completely new supply of blood – and he got it.

For years, this was too tricky for surgeons. Now new blood is introduced as the old blood is drawn off.

I know it's fairly common to read of folk who collapse in the street and later die of shock. But what of the victims who don't die? Often they end their lives paralysed down one side.

Still, there's hope today. We've found it's sometimes possible to remove the clot from the blood vessel leading to the brain. I've had a patient like that, and the paralysis was cleared away.

It's the same with clots in the legs. At one time, gangrene was inevitable. But a patient can sometimes be saved from that now.

Remember, the new treatments I've mentioned are possible only in certain conditions.

But it's heartening to know that, all in all, our chances of pulling through a serious illness today are a lot higher than they were even ten years ago.

Hot Stuff!
September 16, 1956

A LOT of folk could save themselves trouble and pain – if only they appreciated the value of heat.

Now's the time when heat and warmth, correctly used, can help to keep us well through the winter.

Heat is not only a preventer of trouble, it's an important part of just about every cure I can think of.

It speeds up the circulation and draws blood to the part of the body that's in trouble. It soothes jangled nerves. It speeds up germ-fighting agents all over our system. It eases joints and muscles that have been made stiff.

Heat is a must in curing or easing troubles like lumbago, rheumatism, neuralgia, neuritis, toothache, earache, pleurisy, sore throats, boils, strains and common aches.

But remember, there's a different treatment for all of them. The secret is in knowing the right one to use.

Take the case of a man who came to my surgery last week.

He is in his 50s and was just getting over a dose of flu. But he complained of tiredness and suggested it might be because he couldn't stand up to illness the way he used to. I discovered his tiredness was due to the wrong use of heat.

When he felt the flu coming on, he had gone to bed with an extra blanket. When the flu really set in, he piled on more blankets. That was his mistake.

His body had already sent up its own temperature to fight the flu. So, instead of helping, the extra blankets made his body work harder and left him washed out.

Inflammations are best helped by poultices and fomentations. For rheumatic pains – hot baths work wonders.

If you've rheumatism in hands or feet – a hot paraffin wax bath is about the best thing. Dip the affected parts in the bath for as long as you can thole – and continue the bathing daily until the pain has gone.

It's surprising how few people know how to get the best out of a hot water bottle.

They stick their feet on it, and because their soles are nearly burned off, they imagine that the heat must be rushing all through their body. This is not so.

Your feet can be burning while your chest is still cold. So the best place to put the bottle is near the body.

Let its heat radiate through the blankets and in turn, warm you all over. Electric blankets and heating pads are first class.

What about strains? A crick in the neck, staved thumb, twisted ankle or wrist and pulled muscles can all be eased by heat if correctly applied.

Electrical treatment (at a clinic) or massage are the best things. Electrical treatment sends currents deep into the body. At the correct level they make heat and so supply an inside cure.

Massage is really a form of heat treatment, too. It's not just a question of the strained or twisted muscles being soothed by the movement of the hands and the circulation set coursing.

The friction of the hands on the body sets up heat that helps the cure.

If you're using a liniment, embrocation or cream for massage, remember those with a little heat of their own are often best. A tingling, stinging feeling afterwards is a sign that it's doing its job.

I'm a great believer in hot drinks, too. Every morning I have a drink of hot water from a vacuum flask at my bedside. It does a power of good to almost every part of the body and helps to prevent winter troubles like flu and sore throats.

Two parts of the body need special heat treatment.

First, the eye.

If you have a stye or inflammation there, it's no good sitting in front of the fire. The heat is too drying. But as the eye is difficult to bathe, try this method.

Tie a piece of white lint round the head of a wooden spoon, dip it in hot water and hold the back of the spoon against the eye. When the lint cools, dip it in again, and so on. After about 15 minutes, you'll feel the pain ease.

If you keep up the bathing, it should cure the trouble completely.

Next, the finger.

A poisoned finger can be about the most painful thing I know. If you're not careful, wrong treatment can make it twice as bad!

Get a basin of hot water – as hot as you can bear – and plunge the whole hand in over the wrist.

Keep it there for half an hour, adding hot water from time to time. If that doesn't ease the pain, see your doctor at once. Never dip the finger in on its own.

Yes, I have great faith in heat. So had our grannies – and time has shown how right they were.

There's Nothing So Good For So Many Ills

November 16, 1958

HAVE you any liquid gold in the house? You should have. That's what the ancient Greeks called olive oil. It certainly justifies that name – especially in winter.

There's not one other thing in the medicine cabinet so important for so many things.

If you're bothered with chest colds in winter, olive oil does you the world of good. Rub your chest with it before you go out in the morning. The oil soaks into the skin, and gives an extra layer of warmth.

If your winter weak spot is the small of the back, a rub here in the morning can help.

Chronic bronchitis is a curse to old folk. And olive oil, for that reason, is their best friend.

We all have extra aches and pains in winter. The joints "freeze up". Rubbing sore joints usually takes out the ache. But next time, do it with olive oil. It's the best for all-round value. You get a gentle rub. There's no smell.

Here's a tip for anybody laid up in winter. Rub the heels, elbows and buttocks with olive oil. You won't get bed sores, or bed soreness.

Can you guess what the most common thing that annoys old folk is? It's itching. Well, olive oil is often the answer.

The day you start getting the pension is the day when you're wise to start to rub the skin with a little "liquid gold". It's safe, and keeps the skin wonderfully supple and healthy.

Now for the mothers.

Maybe little Bobby isn't thriving as he should be. Do what granny did. Feed Bobby through the skin, for that's what olive oil does.

Just watch the difference by January. He'll look healthier, and his resistance to colds is built up.

Did you know olive oil is good for sore feet where there's a lot of hard skin? Every night soak cotton wool in the oil and wrap it round the feet with a bandage. In about ten days the hardness will go – and you'll have comfortable feet again.

Many of us, particularly after we're 55, are worried about hard wax in the ears. A little oil helps to soften the wax. But don't have the oil too warm. Olive oil holds heat in a remarkable way. That's why, when you use a poultice, you should smear the area with olive oil first.

The advantages are trebled.

(1) The oil holds the heat of the poultice.

(2) The skin is protected from scalding.

(3) It's easy to pull off a dressing when oil is on the skin.

This kind of accident happens all too often. A child pulls a kettle of boiling water off the stove or a cup of hot tea off the table.

Remember olive oil.

Pour it over the burn to cover the area. It won't cure the burn. But it eases the pain in the emergency.

It's not ideal – but it's safe.

Ladies will be interested to know that olive oil helps to improve skinny arms and bony elbows. It even helps to take out wrinkles. Put it on at bedtime, especially in cold weather. Cracked lips, chafed cheeks, frostbitten ears – olive oil is at your service.

Your stomach, too, likes olive oil. It's soothing – and a laxative.

If ever you've a long spell of indigestion, one teaspoonful before each meal can make all the difference. Indeed, it can prevent hours of pain for anybody with an ulcer.

Heartburn yields to olive oil remarkably, so does "wind". The liver and gall bladder both get a tonic from olive oil.

So much so that regular little doses can help to get little gallstones on their way – and so save you from the surgeon's knife.

Of course, for each of these troubles, it is possible to get a more specialised remedy. But nothing else is so good for so many things as olive oil.

And it is so safe, too.

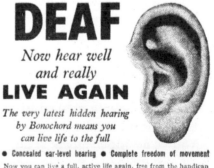

If You Want A Quick Cure — Here Goes

July 10, 1955

MOST of us have spells of tiredness. Usually they're (1) in the morning when you wake up and feel "awful", or (2) when you've come home in the evening saying, "I'm dead beat tonight".

Next time you're tired one way or the other, don't indulge in self-pity.

You can do a lot to produce new energy in a safe and simple way. For morning tiredness, take a quick hot bath. Three minutes is ample. Your circulation is sluggish. The hot water gets the blood moving.

But you're not right for the day unless you pour a cupful of cold water down your back and another down your chest.

That takes the place of a cold spray. It drives the blood inwards, away from the skin. Your system is "shocked" into action in a mild sort of way.

Instead of tea for breakfast, take coffee. One cup of strong coffee should give you slight stimulation for three or four hours.

Now, what about 6 p.m. tiredness?

There's nothing better than sitting with the feet up for half an hour. In semi-darkness, if you can. This will slacken off the nerves as well as the muscles.

Also take a big, hot, sweet drink. It must be sipped. Pouring down the throat is no good. By sipping, your tummy lining is able to absorb all the energy.

These are among my favourite quick remedies.

Here are some others.

You've a sudden attack of indigestion. The safest quick remedy is hot water at both ends. Sit with your feet in a basin of hot water. At the same time, sip a glass of hot water.

You see, the footbath warms the blood on its way past the outside of the tummy. And the hot water warms the inside.

Please try this before powders, &c. And miss the next meal.

Sleeplessness? You're twisting and tossing in the middle of the night.

Get up. Walk about the house in your slippers and pyjamas. Don't put on clothes.

In most cases, the trouble is wind. And movement shifts it. It may well be, too, that the rhythm of the system has been upset. The little bit of exercise will readjust this.

Then there's the opposite.

Around 2 p.m. some of us tend to feel sleepy. Suck a barley sugar and glucose sweet. The energy will be absorbed in two minutes. The sleepiness will go.

I'm often asked – oftener than you'd realise – "What's a quick remedy for a fit of the blues"?

Well, for women I think there's nothing better than a good cry – then a cup of tea. Then you must have company. You can never fight depression on your own.

And for men there's nothing better than a good laugh!

For all of us there's one sure cure. Go out and watch children at play.

But don't try to cure the blues with alcohol. This will only make you worse. It may lead to a real breakdown if your depression is serious.

What about nervousness at the big occasion – like a speech or examination?

Well, here I may be able to help you, provided the occasion justifies it, of course.

I can give you a pill that will give confidence and shoo every butterfly away from your tummy.

Aspirin helps in a lesser degree. For ordinary headaches, you can't be too quick with an aspirin. One within two minutes will do far more good than four after an hour.

Everybody, especially in hot weather, should carry a few aspirins.

If you develop a headache indoors, go to the window and take ten slow, deep breaths. Then back to the kitchen for a cup of fresh, hot tea.

You'll be surprised how this "cure" really works.

Another cure – take off your shoes. This helps to bring the blood away from the brain.

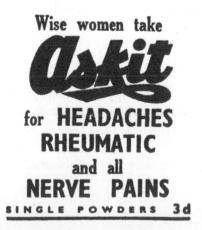

Get Up Off Your Beam End

August 2, 1959

ASK ten folk you know this question – Do you walk to your work – or do you sit in a bus, train or tram?

It's almost certain nine out of the ten do their travelling sitting. TV, cinema, scooters, more cars, more office jobs, more leisure, all add up to one thing – nowadays we all sit far too much.

And that does more harm than you think. So much so, we've now proved that folk who sit about too much are far more likely to attacks of coronary thrombosis. Fat gets right into the arteries, increasing tremendously the blood's tendency to clot.

Beware this inner fat!

Let's have a look at some of the patients under my care.

There's Mr B. His trouble is bad indigestion. There's little wrong with his tummy, except for one thing. There's fat lying round it.

The tummy isn't able to expand and contract because of the fat. Tablets and powders help, but there's no real cure unless that fat is exercised away.

Then there's Mrs X. She's breathless at the slightest effort.

Yet her heart isn't too bad. But lying round her lungs is a restricting layer of fat. They can't breathe out and in properly when the need arises.

Mr Mac is worse off. He's almost an invalid, though still in his 50s. He, too, is breathless. But a little extra effort makes him really ill. He has to shuffle along.

Inner fat has worked right into his big heart muscle.

And inner fat is becoming far more common than it used to be because of this combination of circumstances – we've more food than ever we had.

We've more leisure, too, so we sit too much. You can't possibly be at your best if you spend half your life in a chair.

Apart from inner fat, you're more liable to arthritis in the back. And your muscles can waste away due to lack of exercise.

Even more surprising is the effect on the brain. The whole system is slowed down. Your very thinking becomes sluggish.

Next time you're sitting in front of the TV and feel jaded – try this. Get up and go round the block for a walk.

And suppose you're sitting at a desk, and making heavy weather of your job.

Get up. Take a short walk.

When you get back to your seat you'll probably be more able to master that problem.

There's one proper way to sit in a chair. Sit right at the back of the chair. If it's straight-backed, so much the better.

When you sit up straight your tummy hasn't the chance of sagging forward. The muscles there are doing their job.

Sit on the edge of your chair and see what happens. The back curves and the tummy bunches up. The position couldn't be worse.

If you have to sit up in bed, don't use an extra pillow for your shoulders.

Double it and fit it into the hollow of the back. It's more comfortable.

And if you feel you must have a rest during the day, a chair is the last place to take it.

Never fall asleep in a chair. The legs are hanging down, the circulation angle is bad. The blood tends to be sluggish round the ankles.

For proper rest, the feet should be level with the heart. That helps to give an easier blood flow right round the system.

So let's make it a rule – now. The less we sit the better.

Are You Using Your Legs Properly?

March 24, 1957

ONE of the worst things that has happened to us in the last 40 years is that we've lost the habit of walking.

Most folk think it terrible if they miss a bus and have to walk a mile. Unless we change this outlook, we're likely to land in all sorts of trouble.

For instance, an all too common complaint today is sleeplessness. Yet our grandfathers slept like tops. Do you know why? They had the habit of "taking a turn" before bedtime. That's better than tablets.

After a ten-minute evening walk, your system is all set for sleep. The muscles are oiled and supple. This lets you relax in bed in a way that's impossible if you go straight upstairs from the fireside.

A walk also stops the brain racing on. A too-active mind has too much blood. This keeps you from sleeping. But a walk evens up the blood flow.

When we sit about at night, the circulation gets short-circuited. There's precious little blood movement, particularly in the legs. That's why we have cold feet in bed. A brisk walk can prevent this.

Many of us are harassed by our jobs. We look for tablets, tonics, &c., to keep us going. Take my word for it; a walk in the evening does more than anything to give you physical and mental stamina for the next day.

Office workers especially will be far better at their job – and enjoy it more – if they take an evening walk.

You can also "walk" your stomach into first-class fettle. Walking sends plenty of blood to the stomach, liver and bowels. These organs need extra blood to do their job efficiently.

But there's another advantage – a good walk is a kind of massage for the stomach. The muscles are toned up. As muscles play an important part in digestion and elimination, walking is probably the safest and most natural way to beat constipation.

Once you get over the 30 mark, walking is one of the surest ways of keeping a healthy chest.

Too many folk let their lungs go rusty. From morning till night their breathing is shallow. Only a quarter of their lung capacity is turned over at each breath. Walking increases that turn-over greatly and helps to keep you free from chest colds, bronchitis – even T.B.

And, because walking gets plenty of oxygen into the lungs, it's a grand safeguard against bloodlessness.

Pimples and blotches, too, will disappear after a course of regular walks. First there's the tonic effect of the air on the skin.

More important is that invisible perspiration on the face is dried up as you go.

There are between 200 and 300 sets of muscles in our system. Walking exercises all of them, even in the eyes and ears.

Being out in the open exercises eye muscles that are unused at work – the muscles for seeing distant things.

The air on our ears improves the muscles that control the opening and shutting mechanism. The softer country colours soothe the brain through the eyes. Country noises are like balm to a brain which has been jarred by the noises of typewriters or pneumatic drills.

A walk in the park gives the nerves a chance to recover from overwork and slight inflammation after a worrying day.

Now for how to walk. Yes, the right way can be developed. Simply lengthen your stride as far as you can without feeling strained or becoming breathless.

Walk from the hips. The thighs have to swing – that's important. The folk who get too fat are generally those who walk from the knees.

And don't walk fast. The slower speed allows free-swinging of the arms. This in turn helps chest and lungs. You can smile at the ploughman's walk. But his digestion and lungs are usually good and his nervous system sound. You can, in some measure, enjoy these things, too.

Most of us wear too many clothes when we walk. A muffler and gloves are ample protection.

Walk in all weathers if you like. It's not harmful – so long as you don't stand about. Chesty folk, however, should avoid foggy weather, and high winds are not advisable for "hearty" folk.

The beauty of walking is that it's the one exercise all of us can take to some degree. After all, what were we given legs for? Be a walker and you'll be livelier at 80 than many another person is at 60.

How can you cure a black eye if you can't get steak?

The DOC REPLIES

March 5, 1950 — **What's the best cure for a black eye — bearing in mind we can't get steak?**
Steak has no special properties in the treatment of a black eye. There's nothing to beat a piece of cotton wool soaked in cold water. Apply it regularly for an hour immediately after the bump to the eye is received.

December 28, 1958 — **Could a man (40) going bald, but with no apparent disease, infect younger members of the family if they use his comb?**
Ordinary baldness of early (or late) middle age is quite non-infectious. But every person should have his (or her) own brush and comb. Both should be washed at least once a month.

March 24, 1957 — **Do children really get growing pains — or is that an old wives' tale?**
In a sense, it's quite true that they do. During rapid growth, and especially when teeth are also being "cut", muscles, tendons and joints are easily overstrained and ache with unsuspected tire.

January 6, 1952 — **My sister sighs a lot during the day. Her friends tell her that every time she sighs she loses ½ oz. of blood. Is this true?**
No blood can be lost in this way. Sometimes sighing is a bad habit. More often, like yawning, it's the result of mild poisoning of the blood, due, for instance, to lack of oxygen, tiredness, or alcohol.

May 26, 1957 — **Is it helpful to anyone with high blood pressure to become a blood donor?**
It might well give great temporary benefit. Last century, blood-letting was the main treatment and often did a lot of good.

January 22, 1950 — **I used to complain a lot about tiredness, but recently have thrown it completely off. My wife says it's because I have changed to leather-soled shoes instead of rubber. Is this likely? I walk a lot.**
A lot of people have this idea about rubber soles, but they're wrong. The leather sole certainly gives a crisper, smarter step, but medically there's nothing to choose between the two.

November 6, 1955 — **I've had a bad thumb hack for over two years. What's the cure?**
An old-fashioned one (and highly successful) is to fill the crack with melted cobbler's wax, and bandage. Repeat the wax until healed.

January 8, 1956 — **Are carrots, eaten raw, good for eyesight? If not, what good do they contain?**

They appear to sharpen the eyesight for night time (and almost dark conditions anywhere). They also contain useful salts and vitamins, and in small quantities, well chewed, stimulate the flow of digestive juices.

June 16, 1957 — **Is turpentine dangerous as a remedy for worms?**

Yes. The dose must be carefully regulated and controlled by a doctor in charge of the case. There are, however, more modern, safer remedies.

May 1, 1955 — **Has a man one rib less than a woman?**
No. Both have 12 pairs.

April 2, 1950 — **Is it true that sniffing the fumes from a tar boiler helps to cure a cold?**

A lot of people think this — but they're wrong. The effects are more likely to do harm. People suffering from asthma or bronchitis often get an attack after one or two whiffs from these fumes.

January 12, 1958 — **My young married sister is going to a party. As she is expecting a baby, I've told her to be very careful about what she drinks. She told me I listen to too many old wives' tales. Am I right or wrong?**

Excess of any sort is unwise for a person in her condition. Were she to drink a lot or eat greedily, she might harm herself or her baby. But, with a little sense and self-denial she can still enjoy parties quite safely.

July 16, 1950 — **When one of my work-mates requested the loan of a gold wedding ring to rub on a stye on her eye, I nearly flopped. Is it a cure?**

No, it's a superstition with no foundation to it.

July 28, 1957 — **Has X-ray treatment a beneficial effect on acne? Is it able to cure it, or at least, greatly reduce it?**

Such treatment has a vogue from time to time, but most doctors avoid it because of possible dangers or complications. Simpler treatment, if persevered in, will usually cure.

February 1, 1959 — **Would a person sitting alongside a TV set (not viewing) have their health impaired?**

Not if the set is properly made and in good working order.

June 2, 1957 — **One day recently I had toothache, and stuffed a fairly large piece of cotton wool into the hole where the filling had been. But I swallowed the cotton wool with some food. Is there any danger?**

Not the slightest. But get the tooth re-stopped at once, or the decay may spread rapidly.

— Chapter 12 —

Things A Doc Can Tell – Just By Looking At You

IS there a circle round the coloured part of your eye? Do you have bright red cheeks? Do you have spoon-shaped fingernails? Have you been handling chrysanthemums or daffodils?

Most scarily of all, do you see coloured rings round whatever you are looking at — because if so, you must see your doctor within an hour!

Frankly, some of what is said here is quite frightening.

If the state of your health is writ large on your face or in your fingernails, then the ailment you have is surely so obvious, and serious, that you need radical treatment, and urgently.

You would be forgiven if, after you read this chapter, you have a long hard look in the mirror...although spare a thought for what looking in a mirror says about your ambition!

Little Things That Tell Me Such A Lot
May 10, 1959

YOU'RE sitting in the doctor's waiting-room. The door opens – and it's your turn. You get ready to tell the doctor what's wrong with you.

Well, this may surprise you. Before you've taken the few steps into the surgery, the doctor is likely to know already!

A glance at a patient can show one of several little signs that the doctor doesn't like to see.

For instance, I can look at a man and tell him right away it's time he relaxed.

One warning signal is on the temple, or down one side of the neck. It's a prominent blood vessel – and it's throbbing. Ever so slightly – but it's evident.

It's a sign the arteries are hardening. Also the beginning of high blood pressure (if that doesn't already exist).

That throbbing blood vessel is the red light to stop worrying, stop running for a bus and stop "hearty" eating.

You've to stop trying hard to beat the other fellow – whether at bowls or in business. Hard competition can now be dangerous. Not only that, it's time to make sure you never wear tight clothes, particularly on hot summer days.

High colour in the cheeks can be a very good – or a very bad – sign.

If you're feeling well, then you are well.

But bright red cheeks, plus breathlessness can indicate that the heart isn't too sound. Here again a slower tempo in the way you live is called for.

Bluish lips, too, demand a quiet life. It's almost certain the heart has difficulty pumping the blood around the system. And that means an all-over shortage of oxygen.

To all of us there comes a time when we've got to face the facts – we're not as young as we'd like to think.

There are two signs of this – both in the eyes.

No. 1 is red blotches on the whites. That means thickening of the arteries – not due to ill-health, but just to your years.

No. 2 is a circle round the coloured part of the eye. Once that appears, you can't escape the fact that old age is on you. So slow down accordingly.

It doesn't take me two seconds to see if you're a bit bloodless. Your fingernails tell the tale.

Spoon-shaped nails – hollowed instead of curving outwards – are sure to indicate poor blood.

Brittle nails with ridges like corrugations down them tell the same story. You need good food, like meat, plenty of brown bread, milk, corned beef.

A pale face? It tells me very little. But pale lips tell much.

Here, again, it's the blood that needs an iron tonic. And getting that tonic out of a bottle isn't enough. You've to change your diet slightly after finishing the bottle.

Now, we all know about swelling of the neck – that indicates thyroid trouble.

Here's the other side of the story. A man came to my surgery complaining of tiredness, restlessness and mental weariness. He looked tense and taut and his eyeballs were a bit prominent and staring.

Yet simple treatment did the trick.

And the remedy was all due to a new drug that gives better results than we've ever been able to achieve.

P.S. Have a look at your fingernails. Any white spots? If so, start eating a little cheese, sardines, trifle, pork, haricot beans, dried figs. You're short of calcium. And that can mean chilblains in winter, unless you do something about it from now on.

THE MODERN VIEW, BY DR LYNDA

THE 1950s Doc was quite right — you can tell a lot before a person sits in front of you in the surgery.

That's why we still get up and call our patients from the waiting room and is what worries me when we do modern consulting by telephone rather than seeing people in the consultation room.

You can watch the way they get up and walk into the room. Did they get out of the seat easily? Are they limping? Facial expressions, mood and demeanour say a lot and a few questions later should see a good practitioner well on the way to diagnosis.

Around 90% of diagnosis should be made on history and observation and, in the main, examinations should be mainly confirmatory. Eyes, lips, cheeks and hands are what are on show in the consulting room without removing any clothes and tell us a lot about lots of different diseases.

Paleness of complexion is deceptive and objective but combined with pallor of the inside of the lower lids, pale nails, cracking of the sides of the mouth (angular stomatitis) and nails which are spooned and ridged are all signs of anaemia.

Blue lips and nails are signs of heart and lung disease due to a lack of oxygen circulating round.

Nails are an incredible source of information on your health. Beau's lines (horizontal lines) are due to periods of altered growth due to illness. "Spooning" (koilonychia) and longitudinal ridges can be signs of iron deficiency. Yellowing nails can be due to smoking or fungal infection. Pitted nails are usually due to psoriasis, though white spots are nothing to do with calcium and are nothing to worry about.

Heart and lung problems cause "clubbing" (a roundness of the end fingertips), splinter haemorrhages (like splinters under the nail) and blueness of the fingertips. The list could go on!

Interestingly, the description of underactive thyroidism was true and treatment was revolutionised in the 1950s with the start of levothyroxine treatment which continues today. I assume this is the "new drug" the 1950s Doc mentions.

One thing that I disagree with is the idea of slowing down with age. Exercise at any stage of age or illness is a good thing, so don't slow down...keep it up!

Some Signs We Can't Afford To Ignore
November 4, 1951

A VERY worried woman came to me last Wednesday. "This morning I started seeing a speck float across my eyes", she said. She thought something drastic had happened to her sight.

I asked her to try to focus on the speck and "hold" it. The patient said she couldn't. The speck always dodged away. I was able to tell her nothing had gone wrong with her eyesight.

What are these specks a sign of, then? If you can't "hold" them, the trouble can be one of three things. You're liverish. Or you've had too much brain fog recently. Or you've been worrying too much. The body gives all sorts of little signs like this when things go wrong.

Often they aren't things you'd go to the Doc about. But it'll pay you to do something about them.

Strange though it seems, over-worry can show itself in a bad smell.

Only you yourself are conscious of it. It comes from a combination of mouth secretion and stomach upsets. It's a sign you should ease up. At other times, a bad smell may be due to inflammation of the cheek bones.

But don't worry if you lose your sense of smell altogether. It's only a harmless accompaniment or aftermath of a cold or flu.

You may think baggy eyes are due to over-smoking or under-sleeping. That may be so. But if you aren't over-smoking or under-sleeping, it may be a sign of kidney trouble. And that definitely needs a check-up.

If you see double for a second or two, it may be due to late nights. But if not, you'll be wise to have it investigated – even if it only happens once.

If you're young or middle-aged, pay attention to noises in the ear. They can be due to stuffy rooms or a slight gas leak over a long period – or even to taking too many aspirins! There's no need for old folk to worry about them. They're due to changes in the circulation – quite harmless.

Shortness of breath is a warning sign, although 19 folk out of 20 are wrong when they think it means heart trouble. It's more often a sign that you eat too big meals, drink too much fluid, get over-excited, have mild asthma, or don't take enough exercise.

I had one man recently complaining of breathlessness. He asked if he should ease up a bit. I told him he needed more exercise – not less. Like an awful lot of us, he was simply out of condition.

A twitching eyelid or ankle muscle is often a sign of over-work, worry or excitement. It'll disappear when the cause is removed.

Does the ball of your foot ever ache after a longish walk? It's a sign the arch is over-strained. See to it, it's the easiest thing in the world to correct.

An odd dizzy turn is usually a simple warning from the tummy. If it's really a bad spell, you're liverish. Starvation for a day and a laxative often put you right.

Then there are those bouts of clumsiness, when you knock over cups of tea at the table and find you're all thumbs. That's a sign of over-tire. It upsets our co-ordination. Rest is the cure.

And, lastly, one more sign you're slipping up – if you don't look in the mirror more than once a day. It indicates lack of ambition both as regards health and pleasure, and your job. Keep looking in the mirror. You'll be healthier because you'll naturally take care of yourself.

THE MODERN VIEW, BY DR LYNDA

SEEMS to me that this chapter could be entitled "Some signs we SHOULD ignore"! Floaters, loss of smell, noises in the ears, visual disturbances...

But was the 1950s Doc right?

"Floaters" are shadowy shapes drifting in your field of vision. Usually they are due to the gel in the eye drying out a little with age and are, indeed, harmless most of the time. But if they suddenly appear with vision loss and flashing lights or disturbance in the field of vision then it could mean something more serious so need to be seen by your optician or doctor urgently.

Occasionally they can be caused by inflammation or haemorrhage or retinal detachments or tears, but again they usually have pain or loss of vision. Floaters on they own usually require no treatment. They are certainly not signs of being "liverish" (a term that was used to describe nausea and queasiness with gastric or digestion) or brain fog (a term I checked in an old home doctor book describing mental strain due to overindulgence in food, alcohol, drugs and sexual abuses!)

Sudden change or loss of vision is nearly always serious and should be looked at quickly. It is commonly due to migraine but serious causes such as stroke, tumours and retinal problems need to be dealt with quickly as they are potentially treatable and need fast action to get the best outcomes.

Loss of smell not so. It's usually a short-lived complication of colds, as the 1950s Doc says, though a bad smell is usually dental problems or acid reflux.

Breathlessness is a common complaint and we do tend to get less and less exercise as we get older and often it can be due to being out of condition. But in older people in particular a sudden change or recent onset of breathlessness can indicate heart or lung disease. Needs checked out.

Dizziness, again, is something you shouldn't ignore as it can be due to a host of problems — some serious and lasting and some short-lived and self-limiting — but definitely worth getting checked. It is usually not due to the tummy and I'd certainly not advise starvation and laxatives!

But I do love his last sign — not looking in the mirror more than once a day indicates a lack of ambition. He might be right there!

What Your Mouth Says About You

August 3, 1958

A MIDDLE-AGED man
came to see me last week.
He complained of a pain in
his back. He thought he'd been
lifting something heavy and had
strained himself.

He'd strained himself all right. But
he wouldn't have had a sore back if his
teeth had been in good order!

One look at his mouth told me he had
an abscess at a tooth.

The poison was getting into the blood. When his back muscles were
stretched they became inflamed by the poison.

That's just one of the many troubles that begin in the mouth.

A quarter of all the cases of sciatica I see are the result of abscesses at
the roots of the teeth. These can also lead to hardening of the arteries,
lumbago, even arthritis.

The mouth is one of the doctor's best guides when examining a
patient. With one quick look he can tell by your tongue if your tummy's
upset or you're constipated. He can spot if you're anaemic or if you've
kidney trouble.

If you're a heavy smoker or drinker, your tongue and gums give the
show away. Your mouth can even show if you had certain infectious
diseases early in life.

Nine out of ten tummy troubles start in the mouth.

Maybe we don't have to chew every mouthful 32 times. Our food
nowadays is more tender than in granny's time. But don't forget that
even milk pudding and porridge need one or two chews if the digestion
is to do its work properly.

The saliva, which is so necessary to good digestion, is pumped out by
the action of the jaws.

No chewing – no saliva!

One young man I visited had flu for the third time this year. It
turned out that when he has a sore throat he sucked penicillin lozenges
one after the other until his throat was better.

Maybe his throat was OK, but he'd reduced his resistance to zero.

You see, in killing off the harmful germs in his mouth, he'd destroyed the friendly ones as well. So when flu germs came along they had a clear road into his system, with nothing to fight them.

Here's a tip when you brush your teeth.

Rinse your mouth out thoroughly with water afterwards. You don't kill all the germs, but you give them a setback. And the helpful germs are there to fight any infection that comes along.

Real tonsillitis is another story. You must kill all of the tonsil germs. Otherwise they may develop into chronic tonsillitis.

It sometimes happens that the throat gets better, and the patient stops taking his medicine too soon.

The germs, instead of being completely killed, are driven into the heart of the tonsil. There may be no pain, swelling or inflammation. But chronic tonsillitis can cause recurring colds, indigestion, even rheumatism and heart trouble.

At this time of year, you often hear of cases of food poisoning.

A common cause is the unhygienic way some food is handled. For instance, you see a shop assistant licking her finger to separate paper bags. Then she picks up some food.

She's perfectly healthy. Her hands are spotlessly clean. But she may have germs in her mouth to which she has developed immunity.

The customer may not be so lucky. Those germs are new to him – so down he goes with food poisoning.

If You've Been Handling Chrysanthemums, Don't Touch Your Eyes

November 2, 1958

IF ever you have a vague feeling that something isn't quite right with your health – have a look at your eyes.

Your peepers can tell you a lot.

A middle-aged, but healthy, woman came to see me last week. She couldn't pinpoint her trouble. It was a vague feeling of unfitness.

One look at her eyes put me on the track right away. They were bulging. I suspected she had a slight heart strain. Subsequent tests proved me right.

When the eyes bulge there's strain on the system somewhere. The two places likely to be affected are:

(1) the heart.

(2) nervous system.

If you're past the 40 mark, you shouldn't ignore pouchy eyes.

It's wise to see the doctor. If the pouchiness disappears during the day, it could well be kidney trouble. But if the eyes get pouchy as the day wears on, the chances are there's nothing seriously wrong. You're simply overtired.

There's one colour in the whites of the eyes we all want to avoid – yellow.

When the liver is upset, it tints the white yellow. Either that or you're heading for gallstones. So, get treatment early.

By far the most serious sign in the eyes, however, is the sunken look.

When, over a month or two, the eyes seem to go back into their sockets, it's high time you had a check-up.

You see, behind each eye is a little pad of fat. Often, when any wasting disease is developing, these pads of fat disappear.

Of course, that's only over a period.

The eyes can sink overnight after a dance that lasts into the small hours. Then it's simply overtire, lack of sleep and loss of fluid from excessive perspiration.

Old folk particularly should watch their eyes for the sunken look.

It's strangely tragic, but many old folk, even today, die of malnutrition. They're not able to prepare wholesome food. They live on tea and bread. And it's seen in their eyes.

Now let's have a look at some of the kinds of eyes you can waken up with:–

Gritty Eyes – the trouble could be dust. More likely, however, there's a germ at work. When the eyes feel irritated, don't wash the actual eyes. Bathe the outside of them with warm water. Apply with a good-sized bit of cotton wool.

I'm sure this does more good for all types of irritation. More important, there's no danger of damage.

Bloodshot eyes – red streaks running through the white look awful. Well, it's not as bad as it looks. It's fumes off tobacco or a fug that does this – or lack of sleep. That's all.

Pink Eyes – instead of a clear white, the colour is an all-over pink. This indicates you've had too much alcohol or the beginning of conjunctivitis.

Swollen eyes – you're allergic to something. The sap from chrysanthemums is particularly hard on the eyes. So is the juice from the stems of daffodils in the spring.

So if you handle these flowers, keep your hands away from your eyes until you have had a chance to thoroughly wash them in hot soapy water.

One swollen eyelid is more bother. It's a sign you need a tonic.

What about your vision?

Well, you can see stars without getting alarmed. Specks, dots, &c., aren't so bad as they look – except in two cases.

No. 1 is when you have a headache, feel sick and see coloured rings round whatever you're looking at. See the doctor within an hour, for your sight is in danger.

No. 2 is just as important. The edge of a black curtain comes across your vision.

Part of what you're looking at is blacked out. This may last only ten minutes, but have it seen to at once.

Have You Noticed Anything Different About Yourself Recently?

December 7, 1958

IT happens eventually to all of us. We look in the mirror one morning, and notice for the first time a change in our appearance.

Or, worse still, the woman next door tells us!

Before you run for the doctor, let's have a look at changes that can well happen to us.

Bulging veins head the list. It suddenly strikes you that the veins on the back of your hands are sticking out. Don't imagine you're heading for trouble like high blood pressure. After 40, this change is of no importance.

But bulging veins down the side of your neck is a change that isn't good.

It could be a sign your heart isn't as fit as it should be. It's maybe being asked to do too much. Be on the safe side and see your doctor.

Have a look at your temples.

Do the blood vessels there stick out, and it's the first time you've noticed it?

If so, whether it's worth bothering about depends on two things – your age and weight.

Underweight and over 40, these prominent blood vessels can be ignored. But if you're overweight and under 40, then a check-up isn't a waste of time. It could be an early sign of rising blood pressure.

Thin, spidery veins may start to show up on your face.

Naturally you're a bit worried. But need only be concerned about your appearance – not about your health. These veins don't indicate anything wrong. It's the same when they appear on the thighs.

It's not so likely you'll ever have enlarged veins showing up on your tummy. But if this does happen, get advice at once. There may be a blockage of the blood flow around the liver.

When veins begin to show up on the legs, these will never cure by themselves.

Elastic stockings are needed, or better still, an operation. Do exactly as the doctor advises, or you'll have aching legs all your life, and the trouble will get worse.

At one stage of your life you're bound to see a change in your fingers.

They become knobbly at the joints. This can happen any time after 40. One thought that hits folk is "Goodness, I'll be heading for rheumatoid arthritis".

Of course, we're all more liable to rheumatic pains in the joints as we get older. But this indication of rheumatics isn't important.

And it's not the kind that spreads to other joints.

But swelling from the last joint of the fingers to the nails is something to see to. Particularly for those who always have chest colds in winter. These swollen fingertips are a warning to seek help from the doctor. They're a sign that the chest isn't up to par.

When you're aware that your lips or the edges of your ears are pale, that's the time to think of a tonic.

Blue lips, on the other hand, may be a sign of poor blood flow – possibly a tired heart.

What if your nose is slowly taking on a red hue? Is it the heart? The trouble is likelier to be a continual irritation of the stomach.

There could be a second reason – you have been through a long spell of nervous tension.

Some folk change their complexion. Perhaps to a brick red. This could be high blood pressure or plain indigestion over a long period. Or it's just hereditary.

Constant swollen ankles and puffy eyes are due to the same thing – a lazy kidney.

Now here's a change that occasionally worries the ladies. Their face gradually becomes coarse and heavy.

Often the reason is the passing years.

But in a few cases the doctor can give the ladies back their good looks. That's when the reason is thyroid gland upset. A simple course of thyroid extract can work wonders.

Last, there's one change we must never ignore – when the face slowly becomes "small".

The quicker you see about it the better. For it might indicate an onset of a wasting disease.

Little Habits That I Always Look For

January 20, 1952

ALWAYS, before I start my evening surgery, I take a peep into the waiting room.

That's because many folk have little habits which give a lot away.

For instance, if I see a man drumming with his fingers on the arm of a chair, I know it's a danger sign. That drumming man might be heading for a nervous breakdown.

Once a man came to me about quite a different trouble – indigestion. But I noticed his habit of drumming his fingers. As a result I was able to nip the trouble in the bud, and he avoided what might have been a serious breakdown.

Often I see a man pacing back and forth while others sit still. Besides knowing he's an impatient type, subject to blood pressure, I also know he may not be getting enough exercise.

This often happens with people who have office jobs.

One evening, several months ago, I had such a man in the surgery. I found he had high blood pressure. I prescribed for it – and included a lot of country walking in the "cure".

Last week he was back for a periodic check-up. I noticed the restless pacing had gone. And – yes, you've guessed it – the blood pressure wasn't nearly so high.

Then there's the type that's continually stretching.

It's a fairly safe bet he has an office job, too, or at any rate, one that takes a lot of mental effort.

You see, when you've a thinking job the brain gets a bit more than its proper share of blood. The rest of the body is neglected. Stretching the muscles is an attempt to restore the balance of circulation – and a reminder you have to do something about it.

The lips give a lot away.

Pale lips are one of the first signs of tiredness or shock. Blue lips can mean heart trouble coming on (although they may only mean a cold, so don't let this alarm you).

When I see a patient with pursed lips, I treat him gently.

He's either a quick tempered sort of chap and liable to flare up, or he's under some manner of strain at work or at home. Either way, he's a potential thrombosis case.

Some of these signs you can recognise yourself.

If you look in the mirror and see that one of your eyes is bigger than the other, it's a sure sign of over-tire.

And if you see someone whose eyelids flicker, something's worrying him. This often happens if you're not on top of your job, or worried and anxious about something.

The state of the eyes can give away several things.

A girl came to me in an awful state the other day. Her eyelids were badly swollen.

"My mother's worried in case it's my kidneys", she said.

I gave her a thorough examination. No kidney trouble.

Then I asked her "Have you changed your make-up recently"? Yes, she had – and that's what made her eyelids swell.

Another patient with swollen eyelids had been growing daffodils and tulips in a bowl, and got too near them. He was allergic to these flowers.

We all know the finger-nail biter. That's just uncontrolled nerves.

But I meet quite a few people who bite the skin at the side of the nails. I find they're people who have plenty of go in them, but have to conquer shyness before they can get going.

And the voice can tell me a lot. Often it indicates asthma, chest trouble, &c.

The other day I was called in to see a young lad in bed with a cold. His mother told me she'd seen his nostrils quivering and didn't like it.

She was quite right. If a patient's nostrils quiver when he has a cold, it often means a bad chest cold is on the way or even pneumonia. In this case, I was able to stop anything serious.

Finally, here's a point I'd like to stress.

The untidy, couldn't-care-less man is the one most likely to catch cold and flu, and get attacks of boils.

Untidy dress makes for untidy health.

So be tidy at all times!

Do my false teeth give me flatulence?

August 30, 1953 — **My mouth and throat always feel dry and I'm troubled with flatulence. Could plastic teeth be to blame?**

Plastic teeth may cause this. Check up whether the condition dates from the time you got your teeth. But two more likely causes are indigestion and a blocked nose (causing mouth breathing).

December 16, 1956 — **I'm 18 but my teeth are heavily filled. I know I can't hope to keep them much longer, but I don't like the idea of a full set of dentures. Can at least a few teeth be put into the gum without a plate?**

No. Some sort of frame or plate is necessary to give satisfactory mastication. Your dentist will keep you right.

April 9, 1950 — **My three-and-a-half-year-old daughter grinds her teeth at intervals during the night. As she sleeps in the same room as my wife and me, our sleep is constantly interrupted. Is there a remedy?**

Better have the child examined by your doctor. Grinding may be due to adenoids or a bad tooth. If it turns out to be only a habit, she'll grow out of it. Meantime, make her sleep in another room, if possible.

June 15, 1952 — **Are there any tablets to prevent teeth decaying?**

Yes, vitamin tablets, particularly "C." Fresh fruit is best, not only for the vitamins, but the chewing and fruit juices are extraordinarily good for preventing decay (e.g. a good, firm apple).

November 6, 1955 — **I'll have to visit a dentist soon, and I'm terrified to go. Is there anything I can take to calm me?**

Two aspirins or compound codeine tablets would help. But a stronger and more suitable dose could be had from your doctor or dentist, if you were frank about your fears.

October 28, 1951 — **Is it a good thing to rinse out the mouth with whisky after having teeth out?**

It doesn't do any harm. The alcohol sterilises the mouth. But you'd be better with a recommended mouthwash.

March 17, 1957 — **My daughter (12) has only 16 teeth and has only room for four more to come through.**

As she grows older her jaws will lengthen, and perhaps give plenty of room for adult teeth. Ask your dentist about her teeth, however.

January 27, 1957 — **After having a tooth removed, I bled excessively for four days and had a fainting turn. Later, I couldn't get my tonsils out because I'm apparently a bleeder. Now I've another bad tooth to come out. What can I do to avoid the previous effects?**

Certain substances can be tried (by injection) to hasten clotting of the blood. The usual procedure is a consultation between doctor and dentist.

February 26, 1956 — **What's the longest period one can be put under dental gas?**

It depends on various things, but could extend to an hour or more.

June 30, 1957 — **I'm having 16 teeth out with gas. My fiancé has offered to take me afterwards to my home – about 80 miles away – on his motor cycle. Would this be quite safe?**

It would be most unwise, in my opinion, even in good weather. At least 24 hours' rest is desirable after such extensive extraction.

September 22, 1957 — **Since I came to Cyprus with the Army I've started to lisp certain letters. This seems to be getting worse. I've a big space between my teeth. (I'm 20).**

By taking pains you can improve your diction yourself. If it's possible for a dentist to improve your "bite" and tooth arrangement, that will also help your speaking.

August 24, 1958 — **My dentist told me my gums were receding. Is there any way receding gums can be checked?**

Regular gentle massage of the gums with tooth paste may improve them. Ageing gums always recede a bit.

October 22, 1950 — **The muscles of my upper lip have fallen in through waiting a long time for false teeth. I have now got the false teeth but they make no difference. Is there anything I can do about it?**

You should get your dentist to adjust your teeth to give more support to the lips.

June 3, 1951 — **Would it be safe for a man of 76, told by his doctor that his heart was good and blood pressure normal, to have all his teeth extracted by gas?**

Yes, but it would be best to have it done in your own house, for you should lie down for two hours immediately afterwards.

February 25, 1951 — **I've been troubled for many years with flatulence. At times it restricts breathing. Please say what foods not to take**

See your teeth are in order. Decayed food can cause flatulence. Don't take fluids with meals, take them between meals.

— Chapter 13 —

The Clothes We Wore

STRING vests are the best garments ever invented — a universal "truth" (according to The 1950s Doc) proved by the fact that polar explorers and Commandos wore them.

On the other hand, you should never wear wellies when it isn't raining.

And there is a significant, indeed historic, judgment delivered in this chapter.

Many an argument has been had between mother and child over the years about whether you will, or won't, be more susceptible to catching a cold if you go outdoors without wrapping up properly.

"But a cold is a virus, Mum, it doesn't matter whether I wear a balaclava, it won't stop me getting a cold", says the child.

"None of your nonsense, put on a scarf as well," replies Mum.

So who is right? Can you get a cold from being cold?

The definitive answer to this age-old battle is provided over the page.

There's Nothing Like A String Vest To Keep Out The Cold

September 28, 1958

UP!

DOWN!

I'LL tell you in one sentence how to be hardier and healthier this winter. Don't smother your skin.

Ventilation, all the way from toe to head, is your best defence in any weather – even if it's freezing cold outside.

If you can keep a layer of air round your skin, you won't catch chills readily. You'll be better able to resist all the germs that laid you low last year.

Underwear that clings to you is asking for trouble. Underwear that hangs loose and is springy is just the ticket.

Good woollens are all right, but even more important is an open weave.

This open-mesh underwear is wonderful. Athletes, commandos, and polar explorers swear by it.

For the menfolk, the best buy is the string vest.

It doesn't keep you exceptionally warm. It keeps you just right. You'll never overheat.

And it's overheating that causes 75 per cent of all winter colds.

A string vest keeps the shirt off the skin. Sweat gets a chance to dry off you by evaporating. And there's a good layer of air circulating all round.

The body works best if it's kept at even temperature.

String vests (or open-mesh material) allow just that. All the family can wear them, except perhaps grandma and granddad.

Here's another tip. Choose a shirt that's springy.

A good woollen one is first-class. It absorbs cold sweat and still stays clear of the skin – especially at the important point, the small of the back.

It's the same with socks. I prefer the 5-ply home kind. The knit is open, the space allows air in, and this is what takes the sweat away from the feet.

Leather shoes are good, too, because leather can "breathe".

Many winter colds come from cold feet. But it's not the cold weather that does that. It's the sweat going cold on you. Heat simply oozes away at your feet.

Rubber boots, leather coats, rubber raincoats – they're all splendid for keeping out the rain. But they shouldn't really be worn when it's not raining.

Otherwise they cause and keep in sweat, which can chill the body.

Folk sometimes ask me why a cold, or flu, comes on after a chill. It's just that when the body's chilled, your defences are chilled.

The germs that were already there get a chance to get going.

Not only that, the nerves that take orders from the brain to deal with cold or germs are chilled, too. They're too slow to act.

The small of the back and the feet are the two dangerous spots for cold sweat and chilling.

Even your gloves are better to be woolly.

And fur-lined boots can be surprisingly cold if there's sweating.

Wear braces instead of a belt in cold weather, to let the hot air rise and get away.

It's a surprising fact that all stale air is cold.

When it's exceptionally cold, a woollen scarf is a grand thing. It warms up the big

high fashion in

Lily *shoes*

SWAN SONG
The new 'A' line court in
Black suede with a little
illusion heel
49/11

arteries to the brain. But remember to whip off the scarf when you feel too hot.

Keeping out cold is not so good as building up your own warmth. So wash yourself often in cold weather. It tones up the skin.

Change to the skin at bedtime. Never go to bed in your under things.

Don't drop clothes on the floor either. But, also, don't fold them neatly in a pile. Hang them on the chair to give them a chance to get "unflattened".

Only on foggy, damp days should you fold them, then put them under the quilt to avoid night damp.

Keep the "spring" in everything you wear. Then you'll have the all-important layer of air all round your body.

THE MODERN VIEW, BY DR LYNDA

UNTIL fairly recently, it was thought that we got more colds and infections in winter because we were more likely to be inside in crowded rooms with central heating and recycled air in cold weather.

But there are recent studies which show that lowering the temperature in the nose down to 33C reduces the immune response and, coupled with the fact that the rhinovirus (which causes colds) replicates more readily in slightly cooler temperatures, does lend credence to the old wives' tale of keeping warm to avoid catching a cold.

Not sure about the 1950s Doc's clothing angle though. True, having a layer of warm air next to the skin will keep you warmer, and woolly garments will indeed trap more warm air.

But I'm not convinced about the value of string vests or clinging underwear. And as for the belt-versus-braces angle....really?

A scarf is a grand thing to keep you cosy, but not sure it warms the arteries to the brain!

I'm surprised the 1950s Doc didn't mention a woolly hat, as most heat loss is through the head so a hat will help reduce this in cold weather.

The washing in cold water I can see no benefit of. And going to bed with your knickers on surely won't increase your risk of colds.

I did wonder about throwing your clothes on the floor, but you have to remember that they had no central heating or double glazing and the rooms would be damp and cold in winter, so taking them to bed under the bedclothes might make sure they weren't damp and cold for the morning.

It's All Because Of This Extraordinary Weather!

December 6, 1953

I SAW an Oriental poppy in full bloom last week. "And what the heck", you may well ask, "has that got to do with a Doc article?"

I'll tell you.

The Oriental poppy, you see, normally blooms at only one time of year – early June.

Yet here it is blooming away miles out of season – and all because of the queer weather we've been having.

Well, just as flowers are stimulated into unusual activity by the weather, so are germs.

They love mild, damp weather. The net result is that in my surgery just now I've more cases of sore throats, colds, influenza colds, lumbago, diarrhoea, boils, muscular rheumatism, and "wabbit" feeling than I've had for years.

Many of us, by behaving foolishly, are laying ourselves open to attack by these more vigorous germs.

I have an old patient, Mr L., who, until three weeks ago, was my pride and joy. Though he's no spring chicken, he was as fit as a fiddle.

He watched his diet, took plenty of exercise and dressed sensibly for the weather.

Right now he's in bed with an influenzal cold and lumbago! The reason? He was so deceived by the seemingly grand weather that he went out without enough clothes on.

This combination of cold and muscular rheumatism has been commoner this year than ever before. We are being attacked by two germs at once – another sign of how fit the germs are!

And those of us who have tried to take too much advantage of the weather by wearing too little have fallen victim to the double attack.

At the other extreme are people who are ill because they've been wearing too much.

What should we do, then? Dress for the weather from day to day, so that we're warm – but not too warm.

A common bad habit just now is wearing the same clothes too long. Because we feel it's coming on to winter we tend to change less often.

That's bad. Underclothing which has been worn too long is usually damp. It may not feel it, but it is.

You'll have noticed how kitchen salt collects damp. There's a lot of salt in perspiration, so it collects damp, too.

So the next time you feel chilly in this sort of weather, don't just put on a scarf or an extra sweater. Change your underclothes!

You know, this weather could be a golden opportunity for us to store up health for the winter. It's a great opportunity for exercise – and exercise outdoors.

The tiredness that's so common just now is sometimes a direct result of the weather.

Mr S. was tired. I soon found out why. He was sleeping badly – because he was working by the calendar. So he had extra blankets on his bed – and he kept his windows shut.

But temperatures at nights this year have been ten to fifteen degrees above normal, and there's been precious little rime.

No wonder Mr S. couldn't sleep!

Mr J. felt worn out. A look at him told me why. He was suffering from a crop of pimples and boils. The perspiration caused by the stickiness in the air, plus dirt and dust which wasn't being "washed" away by rains, were causing them. He needed to wash and bath more often.

But perhaps the strangest effect of all is that many of us have been walking about with flu and don't know it!

It isn't a bad dose, but it's there, just the same – and the more people walk about with flu, the more get it.

If the weather was colder the flu might be more severe, but there'd be less of it.

Who are the people most likely to be affected by this weather? There are four main groups:-

1. The very young – babies up to six months.

2. The very old – the over 70s.

3. People who are rheumaticky or come from families with rheumaticky tendencies.

4. "Chesty" folk.

If you're in one of these groups, for goodness sake get out at night for a brisk walk, eat fruit and watch your dress.

And one last thing. Do take the weather from day to day.

The time when we could expect certain weather at certain times of the year is gone. Make up your mind what to wear when you get up in the morning by looking out of the window – not at the calendar!

Slush Is The Killer
December 30, 1956

WHEN you go out on a bitter morning, with a biting wind driving into your face, how do you wear your scarf?

Do you wind it round your neck and let the ends hang?

If you do, change right now. Wear your scarf the old-fashioned way – once round the neck and cross the ends over the chest. That'll save you a lot of ill-health.

One of our most vulnerable spots is the bony part of the chest, about six inches below the chin. It's there you have very little flesh for protection against chilling.

And that's the spot where your windpipe comes nearest to the surface. If you let the bitter wind get at that area, you're wide open to bronchial colds, bronchitis, laryngitis, &c.

You're also open to that exhausting, hacking cough that's so common just now.

A biting wind fills my surgery more than any other kind of weather (except slush).

It's the weather that lays folk low with pleurisy. Cold winds get at your sides, chilling the "envelope" which holds the lungs.

Next, you can't get enough air through the nose, because the inside has swelled. So you breathe through the mouth.

This means that the air you take in isn't warmed.

The double chilling retards the blood-flow round the lungs. Germs get a chance to collect. The envelope gets irritated then inflamed. Pleurisy has struck!

Anybody who isn't up to par should never be out longer than half an hour in such weather. Don't think you're safe even with the wind at your back. The main risk with it is lumbago.

Slush is the worst weather. Nobody is tough enough to stand for long in slush.

Even walking in it is bad. The strongest of us can get catarrh, headaches, indigestion. Slush chills the blood at the feet. This cold blood returns to the heart and passes the stomach on its way.

That explains the indigestion, the constipation.

Stand in slush, and almost immediately you'll feel a stuffiness in the nose. For there's a link up from feet to head.

Anybody not quite up to the mark is liable to heart strain, bronchitis – even T.B. Indeed, slush is our winter enemy No. 1 because it weakens the resistance of us all.

Changeable weather is rheumatic weather.

It's then that bones ache and joints swell. That happens because quickly-changing temperature, plus the change from dry to damp atmosphere, upsets the body's thermostat.

So, in a way, the body chills itself.

If you've a weakness to fibrositis, the muscles are poisoned. In neuritis and sciatica, it's the nerves. In arthritis, it's joint pads and linings.

One thing you mustn't do in changeable weather is sit about on damp days.

You're better to stand in the bus than sit down on a wet seat.

Better still – walk!

If anything, sciatica and haemorrhoids are the risks in changeable weather for anybody over forty. If they're not in top form, five minutes sitting on a cold, damp seat can do the damage.

A spell of unseasonable mild weather is the time for coughs and colds.

Germs get a chance to multiply. Nobody feels like risking going out without their winter woollies, overcoat, &c. So we're overheated – and perspiration goes cold on us. We get chilled.

What can we do, then?

Nothing much, I'm afraid, except be aware of the danger when the weather gets suddenly mild – and take things a bit easier.

Clear, frosty weather, with a bit of mid-day sun is our best friend in winter. We should all get out and about then. It's a real tonic, and can give us the invigorating health that even summer can't beat.

Why Most Women Are More Alive Than Their Men

May 19, 1957

IT'S amazing, isn't it, how a woman can do a two-hour washing – and ten minutes later walk out of the house as fresh as paint.

Yes, women are away ahead of men in the secret of freshening up when they're tired.

And don't think they only LOOK alive. They are! Do you know why? It's because they wear lighter and looser clothes. They wash oftener. They use perfume – a fine freshener if used behind the ears.

They brush and comb their hair oftener. They put on new make-up.

But the main secret is one that all men should copy. Women change their clothes oftener! That's the best way of freshening up.

A clean shift right to the skin is a tonic to your blood flow. The cool air on your skin drives the blood inwards.

And once fresh clothes are on, the blood bounces back to the outer veins. This washes away poisons that have been lying around the muscles. So your aches and pains disappear. You'll also have a feeling of "lightness".

When we're tired, we swell up slightly. Our clothes are tighter and we're under pressure. But after changing into fresh clothes, the swelling in the blood vessels goes down, and the pressure lifts. We feel like walking on air.

While you're at it, wiggle your toes. That's where the hold-up in our circulation is likely to be worst. It's furthest from the heart, so it's the feet that are first to swell.

Wiggling the toes sets the blood going again at its normal rate.

And if you've time, wash your feet with warm water. Never use cold. If you do, the aches and pains will return worse than ever after a quarter of an hour. With fresh socks and different shoes, your feet get their healthy share of blood, and the swelling goes down.

Next, the best way to freshen up the brain.

You can do this in two ways – with water, and a brush or comb. Dab your forehead or splash your face with cold water. It's almost certain that in 60 seconds you'll feel bright enough mentally to tackle any problem.

The cold water drives the blood away from the surface into the brain. Then, when you've dried yourself, the blood flows back with extra force.

This peps up the circulation. The brain gets fresh blood. Poisons that have been lying in the brain are washed on their way.

In some cases this can cure a headache caused by overwork.

Brushing or combing the hair helps in much the same way. It improves the flow of blood from the brain to each tiny hair.

Here's a freshener for the nervous type, or anybody who's had a harassing day. Dab cold water on the eyes, then simply close them for a little. But first place a little cotton wool into the ears. Again, the cold water brings fresh blood to the eyes. Closing them gives the nerves around the brain a rest.

The cotton wool shuts out noise. Silence is a wonderful relief to nerves.

On a really hot day nothing steadies the heart so much as dipping the wrists into cold water.

Next, sip ice-cold water. Take a long time over it. This slows down and steadies the heart. But on no account gulp down cold water on a hot day, or when you're tired. You can upset the heart quite seriously.

Did you know you aren't so likely to feel tired in summer if you've plenty of saliva in your mouth?

So, if you've got a hot throat, give your teeth an extra brushing. This stimulates the gums and gets the saliva going.

Finish off with another grand freshener – a gargle. All you need is a teaspoonful of peroxide of hydrogen in a cup of warm water. Remember, a fresh mouth means you'll be fresh all over.

These are the quick ways to freshen up. But don't forget they only stave off tiredness. They aren't a lasting cure. For when we're tired, we must realise that rest and sleep are what the body is really crying out for.

You can keep going if you have to, but make three hours the limit of your extra effort.

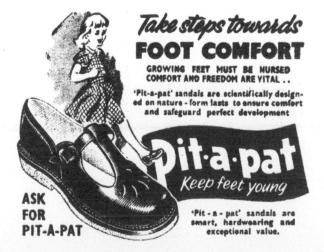

Let's Have A Word About Your Underwear

April 3, 1955

NINE times out of ten, when I ask a man to strip, I can't help thinking – "My goodness, what a silly way to save money!"

He may be wearing a £15 suit, a two-guinea shirt – and a rag of an undervest.

The dearest items of clothing should be – your shoes and your socks.

And, third – underwear.

The kind of underwear you have means far more in health than you realise.

It can prevent half the rheumatism, sciatica, fibrositis, chills, &c. that plague us. Not only that. Poor underwear causes tiredness, loss of pep, and progressively poor circulation.

Try this test right now. Take one of your undervests or pants in your hand and crush hard. Now open your hand quickly. If the garment doesn't spring out, it's worse than useless.

Give it to your wife to cut up for dusters.

Good woollen underwear takes a lot of beating.

Reason is this – your vests or pants should not cling to the skin. Wool doesn't do that. It's curly and each tiny fibre has a "tread" on it like a motor tyre.

Our skin then gets a chance to breathe. There's an all-important layer of air round the body.

Plain cotton can only take one damping from body perspiration. An open weave can take two dampings. But wool can take three or four dampings and you won't feel chilled.

Thanks to the natural mesh of wool, the dampness is absorbed like blotting-paper.

Our skin is always trying to get rid of four items:–

1. The surface layer of dead skin.
2. Sweat and vapour and dust.
3. Poisons.
4. Salt.

Wool accepts all these. The skin stays fresh. The kidneys work better. The circulation is at its best.

But see what happens when your underwear can't absorb the debris. The material clings to the skin. The debris chokes up the pores. Your system is poisoned, suffocated. No wonder you feel off-colour both mentally and physically!

Wool is particularly valuable at this time of year, when the temperature is cold in the morning, warm at mid-day and cold again after half-past seven at night.

Only good underwear can adjust itself to these changes!

You won't like this – but it's so true. Underwear is "finished" long before the tears and holes appear.

Once it flattens down and loses elasticity – you really should discard.

Once a vest "closes up", it becomes almost waterproof. The sweat can't get away from the skin – and you're bound to feel chilled.

I like wool and silk mixture. Nylon and such fabrics – well, do have these in open mesh. That's the secret.

How do you tuck in your shirt, under the pants or over?

Most men tuck the wrong way – the shirt inside the pants. You'll feel colder in winter and warmer in summer if you do this. You lose the absorbing value of the underwear.

And, while on this point, let's pay a big compliment to the Americans. They go in for the best under-garment of all – the undervest and pants combined. We might sneer at their "combinations". But for health and pep they're by far the best!

Long sleeves, half sleeves, no sleeves? Long pants, short pants?

I plunk for half sleeves. Long sleeves are only necessary for older folk.

No sleeves have this disadvantage – all the skin "debris" which is continually coming off the body is left to lie on the upper arms.

The shoulders are apt to get clogged because there's no proper material there to absorb the dirt. Long pants are bad for circulation, except a) in severe weather or b) old folk whose circulation is already poor.

In spring, change your underwear at least twice a week.

In summer, every second day.

Otherwise you'll be liable to chills and fatigue.

And one way to save on underwear. Don't go to bed in them. Tossing in your sleep wears out vests and pants tremendously.

Apart from that, your underwear needs a rest every night to allow the fibres to rise.

The Best Pills To Keep Out The Cold

January 31, 1954

WE'RE a shivery lot these days, aren't we? But, honestly, need we feel the cold quite so much?

Four out of five of us could harden ourselves a lot better against this Arctic weather.

The first step is to eat certain kinds of food that do their greatest good in winter. Don't turn up your nose, for instance, if the butcher offers you mutton chops! He's doing you a good turn.

Ask for streaky bacon at the grocer.

"Squander" half a crown at the chemist on cod liver oil, halibut oil, or olive oil to take internally.

If anyone in the family feels the cold terribly, let him or her have more than his share of milk, butter and cheese.

And let everybody get plenty of broth made with not-too-lean boiling beef.

You see a lot of folk have the wrong idea. They think overcoats, &c., make them warm. That's not strictly true. Overcoats only keep in the heat.

And every manjack of us has to produce his own heat.

"Inside" heat is the objective, and one thing that produces it is animal fat. Some tummies don't take kindly to fatty meats, I know. But we have a pretty wide choice.

Of all the fats, halibut oil and olive oil are most easily turned into heat. You can even get these in capsule form, and they do a world of good.

One word of warning – don't overdo it to the extent that you upset the stomach. Good digestion is of first importance in keeping warm. A poor stomach means less heat is produced. And for goodness sake, don't overeat!

Don't take too many laxatives either. Then tend to reduce body heat. Fatigue, too, is inclined to make us cold – and it's twice as bad if you're mentally overtired.

A man who works with his brawn loses heat naturally. But some of the heat is restored by the exercise.

The clerk or boss isn't so lucky. The brain uses up body heat at just as fast a rate, but there's no compensation. All the heat has gone for good.

That's why adding up figures, or worrying about some problem, will make you really shiver!

What about sleep? Get to bed a bit earlier if you can.

A late night means you'll feel colder next day. You've been using up too much energy and body heat.

Far too many homes hang on to blankets that are useless. It's false economy to keep bedclothes when the good has gone out of them.

If you're cold in bed, put on something round the neck and shoulders. The warmer you feel through the night, the warmer you'll feel next day.

One final word for the menfolk. Short underpants these days are just asking for it. There's far too big an "escape route" for heat.

Don't think you're hardy when you boast – "I've never worn long drawers in my life!" Be sensible. Close the gap in really bitter weather.

Another thing. Don't wear ankle socks. Long ones are invaluable, even long stockings.

An excitable man who's worried about his hair

March 30, 1952 — **My hair's thinning at the crown. As I'm an excitable man, is it due to nerves? Any cure?**

It's not due to your excitability. There's no recognised cause. Some people tend to develop this early, some late. Massaging and brushing help to slow the process.

September 16, 1956 — **I am 66 and have been troubled for a while with an itch round my thighs after I get to bed at night.**

Keep a careful look out for thread worms, which commonly cause such discomfort. If none are present, have a warm hip bath before retiring, and then apply a little calamine cream.

October 31, 1954 — **Would you recommend a bald man to wear a wig?**

No, unless it is for business reasons to improve his appearance or to hide his age.

December 31, 1950 — **Is it possible to get the shape of a nose changed by plastic surgery, without leaving noticeable scars or marks?**

Yes, it's possible, but if it isn't necessary for health reasons I doubt if a surgeon could find time to do it. It would cost up to 100 guineas.

March 4, 1956 — **I've a large number of moles, some fairly big, on my face. They seem to grow bigger every day. Is there any way of getting rid of them? I'm a schoolgirl (16).**

If they're growing you must see a skin specialist at once. I fancy you're merely becoming more conscious of them. Generally speaking, moles are best not interfered with, apart from judicious use of harmless cosmetics.

November 7, 1954 — **I'm only 22 but my hair is going grey and thin. Can scurf cause this?**

To some extent, but it's more important to realise that the scurf as well as the hair condition may be due to general debility, or fast living. Adjust these, if necessary with the help of your doc.

January 27, 1952 — **I am a youth of 19 and have a very thick growth of hair all over my body. Is this natural? Is it possible for the hairs to be removed?**

This is natural with many people, particularly those of vigorous constitution. Don't give it a second thought. Nothing can be done to get rid of it, even if it were desirable.

March 3, 1957 — **At neck and underarm, I have tags of skin on a stalk. Friction from clothes is causing one to become tender and red. I'm 60.**

See your doc about these. He may snip them off, or tie them with suitable ligatures so that they ultimately shrivel and drop off.

November 6, 1955 — **What can I do to prevent or cure cold sores in winter? I'm very subject to them.**

This is simple herpes, due to a virus which lives permanently in the skin, and is activated by a cold or fever. Dab at once with methylated spirits when you feel the first prickling burning sensation, which heralds an attack.

April 1, 1951 — **My fingers are badly stained with nicotine. How can I get rid of it?**

You can reduce it by not smoking in a close atmosphere, and by not smoking your cigarettes so far down. It won't scrub off.

April 8, 1951 — **What causes a red-blue complexion?**

It can be caused by a variety of things – indigestion, over-eating, over-drinking, bad circulation, blood pressure, &c. You must find the cause, and then eradicate that.

November 7, 1954 — **Since I had my hair permed 10 years ago it has been breaking at the ends and getting shorter. My eyebrows have also come out.**

Some fault in your general health accounts for this, not the perming.

May 2, 1954 — **My face is covered with freckles. Is it inadvisable to try to remove them?**

Yes. They're nature's protection against harmful light rays.

February 2, 1958 — **Does washing the hair daily have any adverse effect on it?**

Not if the soap is thoroughly rinsed out, and the hair well dried by brisk rubbing with a clean towel. A little hair dressing may be needed daily.

May 13, 1956 — **My skin around neck and eyes is badly wrinkled. As I'm not yet 50, I dread to think what I'll look like in old age. Can you suggest a skin cream?**

Your chemist will have several to choose from. Gentle fingertip massage, done by yourself) is worth persevering with. Remember eye strain (due to lack of proper glasses) can cause wrinkles, as can unhappy expressions.

August 31, 1958 — **My son (30) suffered acne as a youth which left pock-marks on his face. He's self-conscious and suffers from an inferiority complex. He's reluctant to meet strangers and never seeks the company of the other sex. Can anything be done?**

Modern plastic surgery, called "abrasion", can make a big difference.

— Chapter 14 —

Not To Worry You, But . . .

SOME of the ailments brought before The Doc sounded serious. Very serious.

In fact, if you had these sort of medical issues today a Channel 4 team would swiftly be in touch to make a documentary.

But, far from sending a reassuring message, at times The Doc of the 1950s appeared to quite enjoy predicting the various and terrible troubles that lay ahead for his patients.

He describes conditions such as — twisted brain, gland deficiency, slow chilling, and fatty degeneration of the heart that would give anyone pause. And heaven help you if you don't regularly change your socks.

Some of the things described sounded terrible.

Some of the other things sound unusual. Highly unusual. Indeed so unusual that they too would surely send those TV documentary-makers wild with delight.

Some of these ailments must have changed their name over the decades — or just somehow ceased to exist.

I hope!

Let's Be Serious For A Minute

February 21, 1954

MAYBE some folk won't like to read what I have to say
this week – but I think they should. It's about the
scare of cancer. Right away, let me explain this – if
you know what to guard against and live sensibly,
there's little need to worry.

"But what have we to guard against?"
you ask. Well, one thing we do know is that cancer
can be started by irritation over a long period.

Year in, year out, our body changes.
Old cells die and new cells multiply to make good the loss – in the right
proportion. But irritation can upset that proportion. As a result, a group of
cells in your body may suddenly start to grow and grow, in a completely
uncontrolled way. That, roughly, is cancer. It starts in a flash – after
possibly years of irritation.

So we come to this important guide.

Never let yourself become accustomed to an irritation, no matter where
it is or how small it is. A ragged tooth, for example, can irritate the tongue
for years. And trouble can arise that way.

Drinking tea, &c., piping hot is also foolish. The mouth and tongue can
stand heat, but the stomach and gullet may be suffering from daily abuse
without you realising it.

A mole on the neck or a wart on the hand is "dead". But constant
fingering them means irritation, and, if this goes on over the years, either
can "burst" into action.

And keep your bowels healthy. That's important. Have a clean out,
say, once every three months. Chronic constipation may or may not cause
cancer, but it certainly doesn't help.

The lower bowel is, in many ways, a key area. But don't, on any account,
unless on doctor's orders, take strong laxatives daily. Constant irritation of
the bowels is really bad.

Another thing on my black list is the harm that comes from soot, heavy
oils, possibly petrol – in fact, most products of coal. What if it's your job to
work amongst these? Well, you ought to wash oftener. A bath every night
for one thing! A walk in the fresh air as often as possible.

Don't get the idea that because you're in that group you'll take cancer.
It's just that your risk is slightly greater.

And now for this panic about smoking. Nobody can deny that smoking
irritates to some degree. We know that when a whiff gets into our eyes.

But get it right out of your head that you're bound to develop cancer because you like a cigarette or pipe. It's constant, excessive smoking that possibly does the damage.

How, then, can we minimise this irritation? First of all, cigarette smokers should ration themselves to no more than one every hour. The hour interval gives the lungs a chance to get rid of any possible ill-effects.

Another excellent idea is this. After each cigarette, take three deep breaths of fresh air if you possibly can.

Pipe smokers should allow at least three hours between each fill.

And after each smoke, a sip of water may help.

One extra tip for the pipe man – don't smoke the "dottle". If you do, the irritation is doubled!

And for all who want to cut down, I think the easiest way is to postpone the first smoke as long as possible each day.

Many workers now smoke at their jobs. I don't think this is a good thing, especially if it's in a confined space. For eight hours solid, they breathe in old smoke. And it just can't be good for the lungs. When you walk into a smoky room, the lungs revolt. But it's easy to get used to the atmosphere. And that's the danger. Don't allow yourself to get used to it!

One thing we can all do. Once you leave your work – exercise your lungs. Breathe "low" to fill the lower part of the lungs. And flatten the tummy when breathing out.

What are the signs of trouble? Well, that's difficult. Cancer in its early stages is not necessarily painful.

Still, there are two possible signs. One is a steady loss of weight when you feel you have been eating normally. The other is paleness of the face, due to bloodlessness sometimes linked with the trouble.

But for goodness sake, if you have either or both of these, don't jump to conclusions. These two symptoms are much more likely to be associated with some other less serious condition.

And anyway, even if you have the trouble in its early stages, the chances are all in favour of a cure.

THE MODERN VIEW, BY DR LYNDA

THE scare about cancer turned out to be real. Over the last 50 years, heart disease and deaths from stroke and other cardiovascular diseases have declined, but the rates of other causes of death, including cancer, are increasing.

Half of us will develop a cancer at some point in our lives, mostly because we are living longer and most cancers develop past the age of 60.

Most cancers are a disease of our genes. Our DNA and genetic make-up is continuously making new cells to replace aging and damaged ones and repair our body. But, over time, mistakes begin to appear in the DNA codes, resulting in rogue cells. These rogue cells reproduce uncontrollably and then invade normal surrounding tissue and destroy it. Why these things happen when they do, and to whom, is still mostly unknown.

The 1950s Doc was right about some things. Drinking piping hot liquids can lead to oesophageal cancer. Some chronic skin conditions and ulcers can change to malignant ones if irritated — like sun damaged cells for example.

Bowel cancer is a mix of different types of cancer, with different causes, and is associated with smoking, alcohol, a diet high in red and processed meats, obesity and also linked to conditions like Crohn's disease and colitis. Only rarely is there a genetic link.

Thank goodness there is no evidence for "a good clear out" preventing cancer. I remember the days when my mother dosed us all with syrup of figs as a precaution against . . . something. The cure was definitely worse than whatever the ailment was!

Any change to your body's normal routine or function, a new lump or prolonged cough or change in bowel habit should send you to your doctor for a check. Don't wait until you're losing weight — though it's more likely to be caused by some non-cancerous problem.

And it's not all doom and gloom. Average cancer survival rates at five years have reached over 50%, so early discovery does mean there could be a cure.

However, these 1950s ideas about smoking and lung cancer are so wide of the mark that I suspect The Doc was trying to justify his own smoking to himself.

Even in the 1920s cigarettes were recognised as a cause of lung cancer and it became almost a global epidemic in the 1940s. Cancers of the mouth, lips and throat were linked to cigarettes as early as the 18th Century.

By the 1950s it was well established as a cause.

But the influence of the tobacco industry was huge and there were examples of spurious research projects funded by tobacco companies. Huge efforts to protect their profits were made and the deception was immensely persuasive.

Sadly, the use of tobacco is still growing in much of the world.

More than 85% of lung cancers are caused by smoking and some of the rest may well be influenced by passive smoking.

The 1950s Doc was fooling himself if he thought smoking one an hour was safe, or taking gulps of fresh air and sips of water would negate the risk.

The toxins in smoke also find their way into the gullet and bowel and are linked to colorectal cancers. They are then excreted by the kidneys, causing types of kidney and bladder cancers. And all this is quite apart from the array of other diseases and cardiovascular problems smoking causes.

So for all those smoking and wishing to cut down the risk, the answer is plain. Don't "postpone the first smoke for as long as possible each day"
— JUST DON'T DO IT AT ALL!

Two Days In Bed Can Work Miracles

December 21, 1958

YOU'RE enjoying life. You're feeling fit. Then suddenly you get a dose of the shivers.

The shivers seem to come from deep inside you. Immediately you think you're starting to run a temperature.

Well, that needn't be the case. But if the skin is hot despite the shivers, your temperature is up.

Have a hot bath, take a hot drink, get to bed.

If there are no more shivers, you can be sure you'll be all right next morning.

It's a different story if the shivers persist. It's 24 hours in bed for you. A day in bed and a day indoors can save you from a bad, feverish cold.

But if the teeth chatter as well, call the doctor.

A vicious fever germ is probably attacking your lungs or kidneys. If aches and pains hit you along with the shivers, there's little doubt you're heading for flu – or, at best, a fluey cold.

The remedy is simple – at least two days in bed.

The "lucky" thing about flu is that it's self-limiting. It burns itself out in two days. It doesn't spread.

The two days (or more) in bed prevent the danger of new germs setting up complications. What the doctor can do to help is to tell you when to get up!

About this time of year you may feel cold all the time. Yet if someone touches your skin, you're surprised when they say "But you're not cold".

Should this happen to you, or anybody in the family, over a longish period, don't let it go on. There's a constant raised temperature running. It could mean unsuspected pleurisy.

Now here's a warning to mothers.

If any of the younger ones in your family are running a high temperature, shivers, and aches in the joints (not muscles), pack them off to bed at once.

There's a real risk of acute rheumatism.

This kind of fever has to be dealt with quickly, or the child's heart could be affected for the rest of his life.

But what if your hands or feet are shivery? All that means is your body is cold.

To save your innards the circulation to the extremities has been by-passed. If the small of the back feels chilled, it's more likely your temperature's going up as well.

When you suspect your temperature is up, the great thing is to conserve body heat.

So don't make these mistakes:

DON'T dose the patient with aspirins or Dovers powders.

DON'T give cold drinks to cool down the patient.

DON'T sponge him down with cold water.

Let the doctor bring down the temperature gradually.

When the sweating starts, that shows the temperature is coming back to normal.

Now here's where many folk go wrong. The doctor tells you to finish the box of tablets. But you feel a lot better – and leave the box half-finished.

It's not how you feel that matters. Unless you complete the course you're liable to a relapse. Quite a few deaths due to a relapse are caused by not completing treatment.

How, then, can we avoid the temperature going up?

Don't get chilled. And remember, a slow chilling is ten times worse than a short, sharp chilling.

You can run out into the cold to the coal cellar and come to little harm. But if you sit for a while in a cold room to watch a special TV programme, your temperature will drop and is liable to rise too high next day.

We're at our best between four o'clock in the afternoon and 7 p.m. We're at our lowest after 1 a.m.

So here's a warning to folk who are booked up for late nights in the next few weeks.

Come home with an extra wrap or scarf. No gossiping on the doorstep or street corner.

Above all, don't go to your bed cold.

Things You Shouldn't Take Without Asking

July 15, 1951

I HAD an urgent call from Mrs B. Her daughter, Mary, aged 17, had something wrong with her eyes.

I found Mary sitting with the curtains drawn. She couldn't bear strong light. Her eyes wouldn't focus. And she was preparing for an important exam, with a lot of reading to do.

Soon the whole story came out.

Mary's eyes had been a wee bit sore and inflamed. So she tried an eye bath. It was one I'd given her sister, aged three, some time ago.

That eye bath had belladonna in it. This relaxes the muscles of the eye and dilates the pupil. Since the three-year-old hadn't any reading to do, it didn't matter to her.

But when Mary used it, she got in an awful mess.

That's just one example of the daft things people do without the doc's permission.

Take the case of my friend, Jim. He had a touch of diarrhoea. So off he popped to the chemist and got a bottle of chalk mixture. He took some, and felt a bit better.

But later the trouble came back.

Then Mrs Jim and the two children went down with it. When I visited them, I diagnosed slight dysentery.

It's commoner in this country than a lot of folk think.

When Jim took chalk mixture, all he did was to hide the dysentery temporarily, and the whole family was affected.

One of my patients suffered from gland deficiency. She was stout and easy-oasy. I gave her a course of gland tablets. She lost her overweight and found a lot of new pep.

Her friend – also stout – heard about these tablets. She went looking for a box for herself.

But she wasn't suffering from gland deficiency. If anything, it was the other way round with her. Soon she got nervy and couldn't sleep. Reducing tablets which will do for one person often aren't good for another.

Here are other things you shouldn't use without seeing your doc first:-

Hair dyes – Let your doc know before you start using one. Fumes or metallic dust from your job may mix with the chemicals in your hair dye and cause a chemical reaction.

So it's important to get the right one. If you do that, there's no reason why you shouldn't use a hair dye.

Sleeping tablets – It's sheer folly to think you can take any kind of sleeping tablets. The doc will prescribe the kind that suits you. Never pass them on – particularly to someone of a different age.

Concentrated vitamin pills – ordinary vitamin pills are ok, but a lot of folk think concentrated vitamins will give them quicker benefits, and they overdose themselves.

Yes, you CAN have too many vitamins!

Cough mixtures and tonics – I had a patient who needed a tonic. I gave him one with arsenic in it (a lot of tonics have this), and told him to take it for three weeks.

When he came back some months later, I got the shock of my life. He'd been taking that tonic, intended for three weeks, for over six months!

So he'd been gradually accumulating an almost lethal dose of arsenic in his body.

Next, if you've something to take every day – like a laxative or salts – let the doc know about it before he gives you another bottle.

For instance, if you're taking a laxative already, and the doc gives you a bottle with iron in it, you may get diarrhoea.

Iron has a laxative effect.

So, please – ask the doc first about all these things. It may save him – and you – a lot of trouble.

No one
makes soup
like GRANNY'S

No one can make soup so rich, so tasty and so satisfying as Granny's Tomato Soup—and nothing is so good for you as a piping hot bowl of that wonderful soup.

Why ? Because Granny's Tomato Soup is made from the finest sun-ripened tomatoes with lots of rich, golden table butter, full cream milk, pure cane sugar and selected spices.

It's so easy to enjoy Granny's Tomato Soup. It's a real meal in itself—ready in just a few minutes. Enjoy it often.

GRANNY'S
TOMATO SOUP

Obtainable at all Grocers and Food Stores.

It's Quite Safe Till You're Forty

August 31, 1952

WE all know that worry is bad for us. But did you know it tells on us in different ways at different ages?

Excessive worry in the thirties affects the digestion.

In the forties it ruins the sleep.

In the fifties it gives heart trouble.

In the sixties, blood pressure.

So if you find you're being bothered with indigestion in your thirties, then you should take heed. Worry may be telling on you.

And if it goes on, it may tell in these other ways when you reach a later age.

This is just one example of how unhealthy habits can go on for years and then tell on the system.

Another thing that tells in time is temper. Folk suffer little harm from it until they reach 50. Then it's risky. You've simply got to control yourself, because by the time you're over 60 a quick temper can be really dangerous!

A stroke, or heart attack, can come then simply because you've been bad tempered all your life. Bad temper sets the heart pounding. It weakens blood vessels. One may collapse in the end.

Nobody under 45 need be gravely worried if they have spells of constipation. But after that age not one of us should allow it. We've simply got to keep our bowels right.

Otherwise you may have 15 years of apparently good health, and then – you're in for serious internal trouble in the sixties.

As for the person who takes too much alcohol – from 55 to 60 he's practically certain to develop fatty degeneration of the heart.

In the early sixties, the nerves will be inclined to go ragged.

Over-smoking is most serious in the late thirties and the sixties. When you're getting near 40 there's a risk of heart trouble and in the sixties, pipe smokers may find their eyesight affected.

Now here's one for father.

For goodness sake show the heavy hand if your boy's in the teens and starts smoking.

Cigarettes do affect a boy in the growing stages. They may stunt his height and certainly his physique.

What about that modern curse – overweight?

Your last chance to beat it is in the forties. If you let it go on to the fifties, the knees, legs, and heart may all cause trouble.

Now for the eyes. Normally there's little strain until you're 40. But after that 90 out of every 100 of us begin to lose the power of focusing without strain.

Reading glasses are then essential, and I don't care how good your eyesight has been.

You hear folk say, "Since I got glasses I can't do without them. Now if I take them off I can't see nearly so well".

This isn't a bad sign. Far from it. What's happening is that the strain has been eased. You're dodging headaches and very poor eyesight in later life.

Next, teeth. Look after them particularly well at two stages of life, and you're pretty well set.

The first stage is 18-21 years. The second danger time is when you are around 50 years.

The second stage is the most important for general health. Bad teeth in middle age aggravate rheumatism, indigestion and hardening of the arteries.

And last, but by no means least – the feet.

It's amazing the number of women in the fifties I see who are bad on their feet.

Think back, ladies. The damage begins at 40. But you're often so busy then you put off doing anything about it.

If you've any trouble with your feet, there's time to do something about it up to 50. After that it's often too late.

Now, here's one for the youngsters. Keep your feet clean round your teen age. Change socks regularly.

You'll bless this years and years after, for you'll escape that annoying (and common) trouble – perspiring feet.

In everything remember – you may get away with any of these abuses for years.

But there comes an age when they begin to tell.

Coughs That Can Be Dangerous

October 7, 1956

IT'S a curious thing, but nearly everybody has the wrong idea about coughs. Did you know, for instance, the most dangerous cough isn't the painful one? It's the apparently harmless cough, **the useless cough**.

You haven't a cold. There's nothing wrong with your throat. You don't bring up phlegm. Yet persistently throughout the day and every day you have short coughs, either singly or maybe three or four at once.

It may not trouble you. You may not even notice it – except in the morning.

Don't fool yourself that it's just a habit. And get the idea out of your head that a cough mixture from the chemist will cure it.

See the doctor for a check-up. This kind of cough is due to some permanent irritation in the throat, voice-box, or lungs.

The damage need not be immediate, but to let it go on is risking trouble in throat or lungs.

Above all, remember that a change in the voice, a roughness or hoarseness, should be investigated at once.

A working man in his fifties came to me not long ago, complaining of his cough.

"What do you work at?" I asked. "I'm a builder's labourer", he said. "Well, it's not a cough mixture you need – but a heart tonic", I told him.

"That cough of yours is a warning you'll have to change your job".

Yes, **the heart cough** is the second dangerous type of cough. It, too, is a short cough.

It's a sort of tickling cough that leaves you breathless for the moment. But it only comes on after doing something strenuous. If you start coughing after a dash for the bus, after a heavy lift, or after walking up steps – then it's wise to get a check-up.

Mind you, there's no need to think you are done for. Your heart need not be diseased, or even weakening. But these two possibilities would come about if you ignored that cough.

It's quite likely you're simply out of training. Perhaps you're getting too old for your manual job. Maybe all you need is a heart tonic.

But to let such a cough go on is asking for trouble.

Danger cough No. 3 is **the stomach cough**. It comes on in a bout of 20 quick coughs in, say, 30 seconds. It can last a minute, but it could go on for five.

Very often the worst bout occurs in the morning as soon as you get out of bed. Then after dinner it comes on again, but maybe not so violently.

There's no phlegm, but there could be a little froth or sourness.

This isn't a cough to "thole" either. It can go on for months without doing apparent harm.

But in the long run you're almost bound to be in for trouble. One day, you may have a tendency to vomit during the coughing. By that time it's more difficult for a doctor to cure it.

This stomach cough is a sign of irritation. If it only lasts a day or two, you're in the clear. But if you let it go on, you risk indigestion, then ulcers.

Of course, most folk escape the worst. But one thing you're unlikely to escape is a flabby stomach. What happens is that the stomach loses its power to empty itself. Call it chronic gastritis if you like, but you'll only be half fit for the rest of your life.

Cough mixtures are the last thing you should think of for these three coughs. But we doctors are all for cough bottles – when they're needed. And it's imperative to get your doctor to prescribe the mixture.

For instance, a proper cough mixture is vitally important for bronchitis.

A cough can be a good thing in a way. It's a warning of a threat to the lungs. Once the threat has been heeded, then we must ease the cough right away.

That's because needless coughing is far more harmful than you'd think. It can tear and break the tiny muscles in the throat. It can damage the membrane of the throat and bronchial tubes.

The lungs themselves suffer – the fine air cells there are strained.

But keep this always in mind about coughing – it's the quiet, seemingly harmless but persistent cough that can often carry the biggest threat. Look out for it. Get it seen to.

Will playing bagpipes spoil the shape of my face?

The DOC REPLIES

January 20, 1952 — **I have just started to play the pipes. My friends tell me it will spoil the shape of my face. Also, when finished, I get a passing faintness and headache. Is this serious?**

The shape of your face may be altered slightly, but it won't be "spoiled". The discomforts after practice will disappear in time.

September 7, 1958 — **My scalp is sore and my hair brittle and comes out if I just slide my hand through it. Can anything be done? I'm male (21).**

It sounds like ringworm of the scalp.

June 12, 1955 — **When I go to the pictures or read, I see purple patches on the screen or page. When I close my eyes a sea of purple is before me.**

See an eye specialist without delay. This suggests increased pressure inside the eyeballs, a dangerous condition if neglected.

December 29, 1957 — **My son (56) had his leg off below the knee a year ago. He is now ill again. The doctor says it's general arterio-sclerosis. Is there any hope of a cure?**

I'm afraid cure is out of the question, but skilled attention will help him.

September 19, 1954 — **I've been troubled for a few weeks with an irritating itch, mostly in arms and legs. What do you recommend?**

A visit to your doc. at once, to make sure it is not scabies. He'll put you on to the proper treatment (or to a specialist, if necessary).

January 27, 1952 — **I'm troubled with my right leg being icy cold and red and blue. But in bed it resumes its normal colour. My left leg is only red about the ankle. Is this excessive coldness?**

It should be investigated in case there is inflammation of the veins of the leg, which should not be neglected.

February 15, 1959 — **My husband was told he had sugar in the urine. He's ignored his doctor's letter. He never seems hungry but always thirsty. He's getting bad-tempered and short of breath.**

I insist he sees his doctor at once and carries out all instructions. If not, you will one day find him unconscious or in a fit.

March 9, 1952 — **What causes me to shiver from head to foot in bed, even though I'm not cold?**

I've known this to happen only when it's a sign of rising temperature due to flu or some other infectious disease.

May 31, 1959 — **In January I took the shivers and a bad cough. I went to bed for a couple of days and had stomach pains and no control over my urine. Then I started passing blood. I still have the cough and urine trouble.**
This requires full investigation, preferably in hospital.

February 3, 1957 — **I've recently been troubled with sores on my face that don't heal. I'm 60 and don't drink**
These may be spots of impetigo, surprisingly difficult to heal unless correct treatment is carried out. Remember that a "dry" ulcer or wart on the face should never be neglected at any age, but particularly after 50.

March 11, 1956 — **What's Paget's disease? Is there a cure?**
Sorry, there's no cure known. This name is usually applied to bony changes (thickenings) which are slow and don't affect the general health.

March 10, 1957 — **Seven months ago I took terrible pains in my left buttock. I still have them, but what worries me is my left leg has started to swell from thigh to toes.**
See your doc about this at once. It may be deep-seated phlebitis, requiring skilled treatment.

November 20, 1955 — **For the last year I've had very loose bowels. Is there anything I can take apart from boiled milk?**
Such a condition must be gone into thoroughly by a hospital team if it has lasted anything like as long as you say. Your doc will arrange this.

May 9, 1954 — **After washing my hair, I feel two painful lumps near the back of my ears. I bleached my hair for years. Is there any connection?**
You've probably irritated your scalp and set up a chronic infection, causing these glands to be enlarged.

September 25, 1955 — **I've a cough which keeps going almost all day. It's as if something was sticking in my breast, and I sweat a lot at work. Sometimes my forehead is wet with cold sweat.**
An X-ray is desirable, quickly. Ask your doc to refer you to a chest clinic without delay.

February 5, 1956 — **I started a new job and must wear rubber boots. Now my big toes have broken out in a rash. I wash my feet every night and change my socks often.**
See your doc at once, before this gets worse.

December 15, 1957 — **I've a nasty chest and husky voice. I've had it three years now.**
Such symptoms mustn't be neglected. Get a full examination and treatment if necessary at the nearest chest clinic.

— Chapter 15 —

The Ones We Couldn't Print

IN the 1950s (and some of these are from the 1960s) there were topics that a family newspaper just couldn't print.

It was a different era, there were different standards. But people then, as now, had personal questions, suffered embarrassing ailments and made odd observations that were sometimes of a quite delicate nature and that they found it difficult to talk about openly.

So they wrote to The Doc.

This posed a problem for Sunday Post staff of the time. Care had to be taken to approach these matters responsibly. Often, contact was made with the letter writer in an attempt to put their mind at ease, or engage outside help for them.

And the letters were then kept on file for years, just in case the medical authorities asked about them at some point in the future.

People wrote on other subjects, too. They regarded The Doc as the font of all knowledge. And sometimes not a great deal of care was taken with spelling. On occasion, the questions were so baffling that even The Doc couldn't think of an answer. Often, there was no possible answer!

This is a selection of Doc Replies letters, or parts of letters, that we wouldn't, or couldn't, print. Therefore there were no answers given.

In some cases, you'd have to wonder what on earth sort of reply could ever be made!

Dear Doc. I am at present 54 years old, and have been for the past two years.

Dear Doc. Just around Christmas my mother, who is 76, had a bad bout of influence.

Dear Doc. I haven't seen my wife unclothed for many years and she has run away to Yorkshire.

Dear Doc. I have been informed by my doctor that I may be prostrate.

Dear Doc. I (name supplied) a very good fellow, religious, well behaved, have had a few problems. In my room we had 4 beds and now we have 6 beds. Too many, I guess. Then (name supplied) pissed on me while I was sleeping. He does it on the floor and my bed when I'm not around and still when I'm sleeping he pisses on me again. What can I do? I'm asking the people if they ever had the experience such as I, please write and tell me. OK? Good. When this fellow wakes up he doesn't remember a thing. What am I to do? I don't mind an argument, but I hate like hell getting pissed on.

Dear Doc. Could you please tell me if it's only the men that drink who snore, or maybe most men do? And why. Very worried.

Dear Doc. I have one enlarged testicle which was caused by the string of my pyjamas.

Dear Doc. Would you please prescribe tablets that I could get from a chemist that would help to arrest the acid in the urine, and help me to retain it a little bit longer?

Dear Doc. Should people taking iron tablets have electric blankets on their beds?

Dear Doc. I talk like a girl. Can you get an operation to get stronger or treatment on the NHS?

Dear Doc. I saw my doctor during an attack of asthma. He told me there was a new treatment involving something up the back passage. He did not explain why, or what it would accomplish.

Dear Doc. Can you please solve my problem. Occasionally, when I sneeze several times, my nose begins to bleed quite severely. I have seen a specialist, and was informed that it was just my imagination.

Dear Doc. Can a woman lose her virginity without knowing how she lost it?

Dear Doc. Every time me and my wife have intercourse, she sneezes. What could be the cause of this?

Dear Doc. After lovemaking my husband has a bout of sneezing. His nose runs as if he has a real heavy cold. This clears after a few minutes. Can you tell me if there's a reason for this?

Dear Doc. We have recently rented a TV set, which is the first time, and have been wondering where to get the advertisements on it. And each of my ankles have swollen up a little bit.

Dear Doc. Thank you, thank you, thank you for your piece in today's paper about piles. I have just finished reading it and already I feel a different person.

Dear Doc. Before I met my husband he was bitten by an Alsatian. And a doctor told him that he couldn't produce any children. We have been going out together for a year and we would like to get married and start a family. Is there any chance of him having an operation?

Dear Doc. I have a friend who has been told by his doctor that he suffers from Perferial Neuropathy. Can this be caused by a twist to the neck I received some time ago? Can it be cured? It has left his digital fingers in both of my hands nearly paralysed.

Dear Doc. I went to an ear specialist about my hearing. He asked me about my bowels. He didn't explain at the time and it has bothered me.

Dear Doc. I will never forget this Hogmanay, as I spent it in jail, my first ever Hogmanay in jail. And I have been bothered with gout for 12 years and my own doctor couldn't give me anything to help. The prison doctor cured me in two days. I don't know if he used me as a guinea pig but if he did the stuff he gave me was magic. No wonder the jail is always full, the Christmas and New Year dinner was out of this world. It was the best I had eaten for years, the turkey was just magic.

Dear Doc. I suffer from chronic bronchitis and high blood pressure. My height is 5ft 4 in, and I am 15st, 4lb, which I know is too heavy. I asked my doctor for a diet sheet and his answer was stop eating. I said to him what if I should die and he said start eating again. My doctor should have given me a diet sheet.

Dear Doc. Every so often, my heart goes racing away. It usually comes back after two or three days. But I worry in case I have serious trouble.

Dear Doc. My wife passes wind five or six times during the night. Please, what is the cause of this? It is quite bad.

Dear Doc. I think I might have lupins.

Dear Doc. Is it possible that I am happy and quite big?

Dear Doc. Could I have a pain in my back after falling and fracturing my lumbar spine?

Dear Doc. Thank you very much for solving the problem of my organ. The organ was uplifted on Saturday afternoon.

Dear Doc. I am hoping you can help me. I suffer from premature ejaculation. Although I was a married man with seven children, I am now separated and awaiting divorce. I have had this problem since I was 16 years old and am now 35.

Dear Doc. As a contract fitter I've travelled well. Now it seems as if the East Anglian Water Board put a chemical in the water that gives the kidneys aches and pains. Nowhere else in the country do I get this trouble. However, I've gone over to spring water and milk. The beer here is the same, so I'm on to gin & tonic.

Dear Doc. Could you let me know what a hyena's hernia is, as I had something stuck in my throat which I got tablets for and they done no good.

Dear Doc. I'm a young mother and am convinced I'm a hypochondriac.

Dear Doc. Is it true that one section of every brain is kept aside for recording of an everlasting five-sense electric movie of every action each one takes to help another and is exclusive to individual memory playback at the end of each day?

Dear Doc. My wife's doctor told her to stop taking the pill because of phlebitis in her leg. So I've been taking the pill instead of her. But I've been told this will be harmful to me. I have taken one month's supply already and I have had no ill effects up to now. I would like to know if it is safe to carry on taking the pill. We have tried the sheath and other contraceptives but we don't like any of them as we don't wish to have any more family.

Dear Doc. Would you please tell me if I could put the pill in my female cat Fiona's food? Would it prevent the cat having kittens?

Dear Doc. Is it true that there is no orange in Government-issue orange juice and that it is made of ostrich eggs from South America? And it is brought to Southampton docks on battleships?

Dear Doc. My brother has one leg after the war. If he has children, will their legs be both there? He is 43 and is not married. It was shrapnel.

Dear Doc. Can you get a powder if you quietly tell the chemist that his servant girl would be better?

Dear Doc. Last year you told me to see my own doctor. I didn't go to see my own doctor and my trouble has never gone away. What can I do now?

Dear Doc. My aunt is going mad. She is also rude.

Dear Doc. My trouble started long ago, just after I was married. My husband doesn't know this happened.

Dear Doc. If I wrote to you, could you answer if I didn't tell you what is wrong with me?

Dear Doc. Is having hives anything to do with being stung by a bee?

Dear Doc. My husband works with fish gutters and still smells of fish even when he is on his holidays. We can't recognise what kind of fish he smells of.

Dear Doc. I have been married twice. When I am intimate with my husband, it is very different to the way it was before. Are there pills that can give a man more pep? My former husband died.

Dear Doc. You said that wearing high heels was bad for the legs. But my shoes and legs don't fit unless they have high heels.

Dear Doc. Can I stop my next-door-neighbour building an outhouse that will block light to my garden if I say I am ill from lack of sunlight?

Dear Doc. I often think I used to be a princess of another country. I remember being in a castle and was born in an aeroplane. Could I have been kidnapped and brought to Fife when very young? How could I go about proving this to a legal court?

Dear Doc. I don't think you were right about the legs. I have had two and this lasted for years.

Dear Doc. Can anything be done for people like my neighbour? I feel very very sorry for her and she now can't go to church. It's her head.

Dear Doc. Do "Teddy Boy" trousers make men walk dangerously?

Dear Doc. It started with a pain in my chest but the pain wasn't really in my chest. I thought it was but my wife said it wasn't in my chest. Then we went to Canada and came back. Could there be a connection?

Dear Doc. My neck has become fat. I am quite fat in the tummy as I eat a lot of pudding. But my neck is fatter than that.

Dear Doc. Are trench coats dangerous to children? My brother-in-law says they have taken children's eyes out when flapping in a strong wind.

Dear Doc. When I drink a lot my head hurts.

Dear Doc. When you drink cold milk and your head hurts, does it mean you are going to need false teeth?

Dear Doc. I'm very worried about my husband. He hasn't been home since September 1952.

Dear Doc. When I was in the Army I swallowed lots of things. What were they?

Dear Doc. Last year, my husband had a twisted bowl.

Dear Doc. If a man was bitten by a vampire bat does he have bad blood and could he be a father? It's my daughter I'm worried about as she is going to marry him no matter what we say.

Dear Doc. Do all male children get less clever the older they get?

Dear Doc. Is there some place vicars can go to meet nice women who like them?

Dear Doc. Can a woman get in the family way if she is wearing second-hand clothes?

Dear Doc. Is there any danger to my son if he touched a coffin?

Dear Doc. I have wide legs.

Dear Doc. Could you tell my doctor he is wrong about me? He is a rather difficult man, so watch out.

Dear Doc. Since my husband died I have been quite happy. Should I tell my doctor, or is it a sign of lunatic?

Dear Doc. Our son is very friendly with another boy. Would cold baths help him?

Dear Doc. How many times does the average man breathe in a minute sitting down at about 9 o'clock?

Dear Doc. Several extended areas of my wife have turned brown.

Dear Doc. Can doctors tell the truth in a court if they are paid?

Dear Doc. If they dropped the atom bomb on us, which room in my house would be the safest?

Dear Doc. I am 23 and still want to grow taller. It is important because my brother is taller.

Dear Doc. Would it be possible to stop the spread of flu at the English Channel if no one ever went there again?

Dear Doc. Is Dr Finlay on television real?

Dear Doc. Do doctors get powders that stop them getting ill? Can ordinary working folk get the powders or is it secret?

Dear Doc. You said that people who get cancer are very serious. But in Japan they have people who don't get cancer and they live for hundreds of years.

Dear Doc. My doctor's woman is very rude and tells everyone out loud what is wrong with people. I'm not going back until I die and neither is my wife.

Dear Doc. Would you be allowed to tell me what is wrong with my friend? She is my best friend.

Dear Doc. When my son walks, his heels hardly touch the ground. My husband doesn't like it so would it help if he carried an Army knapsack? It is a large-sized one and we have filled it with sand but not all the way up. It isn't really from the Army and he paid four shillings for it.

Dear Doc. Is it against the law to grow your hair long if you live in Scotland?

Dear Doc. I would like to wash one of my son's schoolfriends. Would this get him or me in trouble with his mother?

Dear Doc. I have a rash on my chest, shoulders, arms, wrists, hands, fingers, tummy, back, shoulder blades, neck and head. It is closely pointed red and inbetween normal. I have had it for four days. Is it right to be red or should I have another colour?

Dear Doc. One of my ribcages has begun to hurt quite badly.

Dear Doc. I have never had this before. My mother thinks she had it about 20 years ago and it went away. Do all women get it?

Dear Doc. If I eat cold ox's tongue will I be able to swallow it?

Dear Doc. I have never had anything wrong with me but now I do. I have just turned 30. Is this something I should see my own doctor about?

Dear Doc. Can I get an operation on the throat that would make me a better singer?

Dear Doc. My wife slapped her sister because she was excited. Now her sister says she has no feelings, but she looks all right.

Dear Doc. Very few people get coughs now and they used to. Is this a sign of better health?

Dear Doc. A lorry wheel ran over my foot. I have no complaints but cannot walk.

Dear Doc. How long does it take between gestation and evacuation of a baby if you can't remember when you started it? I have a fair idea but not sure.

Dear Doc. I am having to move to Stevenage. Can I still see my doctor by going on the train and I don't know where the station is?

Dear Doc. My wife wrote to you but has had no answer. You do not now have to answer her as she died this morning.

Dear Doc. You will probably remember I wrote to you in 1951 about my husband's lungs. I am sorry to inform you he is now dead. The minister mentioned your part in curing his illness at the funeral, which was nice.

Dear Doc. Is having six toes normal? He is aged 12 (next birthday) so could he have an operation?

Dear Doc. My husband has a gap where his bottom used to be.

Dear Doc. I went to my own doctor but could not bring myself to tell him he is a man.

Dear Doc. How much should I spend on a good pair of shoes for Sundays? They would have to be black.

Dear Doc. I have been bringing up phlegm that is bright yellow and I am quite worried about it. I have enclosed a hankie to show you the phlegm, although I notice that as it is drying it becomes more green in colour.

Dear Doc. I have a rash over my chest and upper arms. I've enclosed some of the scabs.

(Tuesday's postbag) **Dear Doc**. You have everyone to tell that the person you wrote about is not me. I have told a policeman. And other policemen who can arrest a doctor. Even Winston Churchill. Everyone is saying it is me. Do not put my name and address in your story.

(Friday's postbag) **Dear Doc**. I thought you talked about me in your story but now it isn't me. But I can see you in court if it was. So don't do it, even I wasn't in it. I am asking tomorrow and next week for a move of house.

(The following Wednesday's postbag) **Dear Doc**. I understand my mother has been writing to you, threatening the raising of a legal case. She got very, very upset when she thought you had written a story that was about her keeping a dog Brownie and cleaning it. But she didn't read it. Our sincere apologies. You do good work.

(The following Friday's postbag) **Dear Doc**. I am writing to you doctor to apologise as I wasn't in your story but the woman of downstairs said it was. You will not be arrested by policemen I didn't talk to them. My dog is every time behaved on the stairs. I am very sorry. Do not put in my name and address. It is Maria.

Praise for the Doc. Sir, you are both a gentleman and a scholar. May you live long and die a good colour.

You Might Also Like...

PASS IT ON — HOUSEHOLD TIPS FROM THE 1950S
More than 1,200 cleaning, ironing, and knitting (and many more topics) bits of wisdom, in the words of housewives of the time. How to get dents out of the carpet, how to clean behind an immovable wardrobe, how to get any kind of stain out of any fabric. The tips are clever, still useful — and strangely funny.

PASS IT ON — COOKING TIPS FROM THE 1950S
A collection of incredible, and still useful, cooking and baking tips, recipes, and oddities collected from newspapers and magazines of the 1950s — when housewives used to write in with their ingenious, tasty hints and tips. Remember when your mum used to make THAT dish you enjoyed so much?

LIFTED OVER THE TURNSTILES — SCOTTISH FOOTBALL GROUNDS IN THE BLACK & WHITE ERA.

The best book about old Scottish football grounds ever published. Almost 200 never-before-seen photos. The perfect gift for anyone who used to attend football matches in the 1940s, 50s, 60s and 70s — this was where they celebrated and despaired. It is a history of how spectators, not players or managers, experienced football.

Available from:
www.dcthomsonshop.co.uk
Or Freephone 0800 318846
(Mon-Fri 8am-6pm. Saturday 9am-5pm)